TEACHERS GUIDE
VOLUME ONE

BRIDGES IN MATHEMATICS

BRIDGES IN MATHEMATICS 2

written by
Allyn Snider
Donna Burk

illustrated by
Tyson Smith

Published by
The MATH LEARNING CENTER
Salem, Oregon

Bridges in Mathematics Grade 2 Teachers Guide Volume One

The Bridges in Mathematics Grade 2 Package consists of—

Getting Started

Bridges in Mathematics Volume One

Bridges in Mathematics Volume Two

Bridges in Mathematics Volume Three

Bridges Blacklines

Bridges Overheads

Home Connections

Technology Connections

Work Place Games & Activities

Manipulatives

Number Corner Teachers Guide

Number Corner Student Book Blacklines

Number Corner Calendar Markers

Number Corner Components

Number Corner Manipulatives

The Math Learning Center, PO Box 12929, Salem, Oregon 97309. Tel. 1 800 575–8130.
© 2007 by The Math Learning Center
All rights reserved.
Prepared for publication on Macintosh Desktop Publishing system.
Printed in the United States of America.

QP133, QP68 and QP154   B2TG-1
P0807   11152_SALBLU

Bridges in Mathematics is a standards-based K–5 curriculum that provides a unique blend of concept development and skills practice in the context of problem solving. It incorporates the *Number Corner*, a collection of daily skill-building activities for students.

The Math Learning Center is a nonprofit organization serving the education community. Our mission is to inspire and enable individuals to discover and develop their mathematical confidence and ability. We offer innovative and standards-based professional development, curriculum, materials, and resources to support learning and teaching. To find out more, visit us at www.mathlearningcenter.org.

This project was supported, in part, by the National Science Foundation. Opinions expressed are those of the authors and not necessarily those of the Foundation.

ISBN 9781886131668

acknowledgements

Book Design
Susan Schlichting

Cover Design
Susan Schlichting and Tyson Smith

Layout and Graphics
Christy Peterson, Ingrid Williams, Vaunie Maier, and Travis Waage

Illustrator
Tyson Smith

Editorial Consultants
Dr. Albert B. Bennett Jr. and Dr. Gene Maier

Production Editor
Vaunie Maier

Materials Production
Tom Schussman and Don Rasmussen

Technical Support
Kieran Downes

. . . .

We give special thanks to
Kathy Pfaendler, Linda Foreman, and Gene Maier for being our teachers and mentors over the years. Their insights and understandings have helped us grow.

Dr. Rosemary Wray for her priceless friendship and continued support in the area of student assessment.

Dr. Amy Driscoll for teaching us the difference between assessment and evaluation.

Beth Ardell, Becky Boergadine, Jill Board, Andy Clark, and Cheryl Ogburn for their unflagging devotion to teachers and children everywhere, the hours of thoughtful reflection and conversation they've shared with us, and their willingness to try new things.

Dona Beattie and Bob Nicholas for basic support in the form of food, keys, money, computers, parking permits, and faith.

Mary Baratta Lorton, Kathy Richardson, and Marilyn Burns for being original and continuing sources of inspiration.

The late Dr. Michael J. Arcidiacono for his vision, quiet spirit, sense of balance, and extraordinary teaching skill.

Scott Duyan and Lark Palma of Catlin Gabel School for their moral and financial support.

The teachers who field-tested Bridges in Mathematics, Grade 2, allowed us to observe its implementation in their classrooms, and/or permitted us to explore new ideas with their students. In particular, we thank:
Beth Ardell, St. Cecelia's, Beaverton, Oregon;
Jill Board, Riverbend Elementary, Springfield, Oregon;
Julie Brennan, Ainsworth School, Portland, Oregon;
Janet Johnstone, Russell Elementary, Portland, Oregon;
Anne Heimlich, Catlin Gabel School, Portland, Oregon;
Ingrid Gordon, Catlin Gabel School, Portland, Oregon;
Tracy Arensberg, Catlin Gabel School, Portland, Oregon;
Theresa Giffin, Union Elementary School, Montpelier, Vermont

We also wish to acknowledge the many children who have been involved with the field-testing of Bridges in Mathematics, Grade 2. As always, their enthusiasm, intelligence, and candor has taught us much and been quite influential in shaping the program.

And finally, we thank our spouses, Fred and Gary, and our families for their incredible patience, support, and encouragement.

volume One

Unit 2: Hungry Ants

Unit 3: Addition, Subtraction & Probability

Don't Forget!

Getting Started with Bridges in Mathematics, Grade 2
has lots of important information that will help you use the
Bridges program in your classroom more effectively. This
volume includes year-long planning suggestions, ideas for
setting up your classroom and organizing your materials,
and an overview of assessment and evaluation you can't
afford to miss. Be sure to read Getting Started before you
get started!

unit 1 sorting, patterning & number

UNIT ONE

What's Going to Happen in This Unit?

This unit, Sorting, Patterning & Number, introduces students to many of the materials and routines they'll use throughout the year. Each hour-long session opens with a Problems & Investigations lesson and then moves into Work Places. During the first few weeks of school, children move from creating their own inventions with Unifix cubes, frogs, buttons, pattern blocks, and other manipulatives, to sorting and patterning these items in a variety of ways. As the unit progresses, students begin using visual and number patterns to make predictions and solve problems. Homework assignments are offered each week as a way to encourage parent participation in children's learning and to strengthen bridges between home and school. These activities and worksheets can be found in the Home Connections book and are designed to be sent home after Sessions 6, 11, 16, and 21.

This unit is meant to last 5 to 6 weeks, and includes a wide variety of Problems & Investigations, blended with three rounds of Work Places. In the 23 sessions that make up Sorting, Patterning & Number, students have many opportunities to solve problems individually, in small groups, and with the entire class. Ideas, strategies, and solutions are shared as children play games, do Work Place activities, and participate in group lessons and discussions.

This unit lets you get to know your students. One of the first activities is a paper-and-pencil assessment in which children are asked to write and draw what they know about patterns. This assessment is repeated at the end of the unit and offers one way to look at children's growth. During Work Places, you'll have many opportunities to observe children's interactions with one another, as well as their work with numerous sorting and patterning tasks. Several of the sessions will produce work samples to be saved in children's math files. Also, we recommend that you conduct individual interviews with students after some of the basic routines have been set and things are running smoothly. These interviews take about 15 minutes apiece and will allow you to collect baseline information about your students' understandings of number combinations to 18 as well as place value.

The unit opens with a lesson in which children generate many different attributes about themselves. In the days that follow, teacher and students use the suggested attributes to sort the class in several different ways. Next, the students are introduced to glyphs, simple pictures or figures whose parts represent information about a given subject. Each child creates a glyph to represent him or herself.

"You can tell that I'm a girl because my beetle is long and skinny. My birthday is in August, so I put 8 dots on my beetle—1 for every month. There are 5 people living at my house, so I put 5 stripes on my beetle. And my favorite sport is soccer, so I made her hat red."

The glyphs are then sorted in several different ways and finally used to create a colorful and informative wall display. Sessions 1 through 7 also feature a round of Work Places designed to familiarize the class with basic materials and routines.

Sessions 8 through 16 extend and intensify some of the sorting activities from the previous lessons and introduce the concept of growing patterns. Some of the patterns children will encounter in problems, investigations, and Work Places are as simple as:

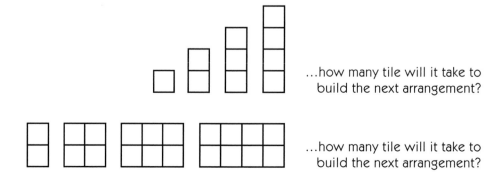

...how many tile will it take to build the next arrangement?

...how many tile will it take to build the next arrangement?

Others such as:

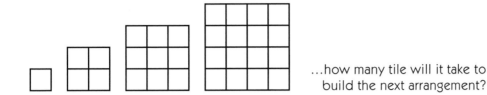

...how many tile will it take to build the next arrangement?

are more complex and challenging to extend.

In sessions 17 through 22, many of the whole group explorations from earlier lessons begin to resurface as games and activities in the Work Places. The group lessons give children a chance to investigate pattern and symmetry as they create simple quilt blocks and combine them to make a single class quilt that illustrates the power of working together. Session 23 returns to the assessment given at the beginning of the unit.

· ·

What's the Big Idea? Patterns, Functions & Algebraic Thinking

To many of us who have taught primary grades over the past twenty years or so, the idea of patterning has been largely synonymous with using Unifix cubes, pattern blocks, or other manipulatives to have children create repeating sequences: red, white, blue, red, white, blue; or hexagon, hexagon, square, hexagon, hexagon, square. Students have come out of our classrooms enthusiastic about patterns, looking for and finding them everywhere. What they understand, more than anything, is that a pattern is something that repeats. Our children know that patterns can be as simple as ABABAB, or as complex ABCDDABCDD, as long as they start over again and repeat themselves at some point. These important and powerful ideas create a foundation for considering a different kind of pattern: one that grows in some regular manner.

🚲	**2**
🚲🚲	**4**
🚲🚲🚲	**6**
🚲🚲🚲🚲	**8**

Asked to predict what comes next in the sequence shown on the previous page, many second graders will respond that it would have to be 5 bikes and 10 wheels. How do they know? "It's a pattern!" they reply. What repeats? Perhaps there's a puzzled silence for a minute or two. If the sequence doesn't start over, where *is* the repeat? Finally, someone hesitantly volunteers that there's 1 new bike in each row, and 2 new wheels.

A bit different from patterns they may have encountered before, this is a recursive, or "growing" pattern, in which each new piece grows by a certain, and predictable amount. The number of bikes determines the number of wheels, and after a bit of consideration, some second graders are able to predict that the 10th row will have 10 bikes and 20 wheels. Some are able to imagine the 100th row with 100 bikes and 200 wheels. A few are able to make the generalization that you'll always have twice the number of wheels as bikes, or Wheels = 2 × Bikes.

As students move into the realm of number, they encounter more and more patterns that grow rather than repeat. Some take the form of bike wheels or circles for snow people (1 snow person requires 3 circles, 2 require 6, 3 require 9, and so on). Others are more complex.

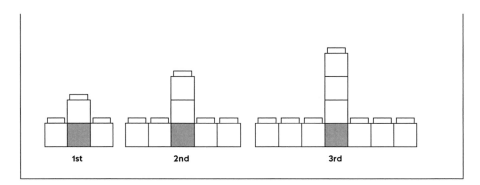

"Here are the first 3 arrangements in a growing pattern. Can you imagine what the 4th arrangement will look like? How many cubes will it take to build the 4th arrangement? What about the 10th arrangement?"

Whether patterns are simple repeats, like AABAAB..., or growing situations, like 4, 7, 10, 13, ..., you can predict what will come next and ultimately make some kind of generalization about the entire sequence if you're able to step back and analyze what has come before. You must be able to spot likenesses and differences to find relationships between the elements already present. We've found that sorting activities help sharpen children's abilities to do these very things, and have included a good many such activities in this unit alongside the patterning investigations. Children who are accustomed to searching for relationships between similar and disparate objects may notice that an extra cube is added to each "leg" of the design above with each new arrangement. They may build the 4th arrangement like this and count the cubes to find a total of 13.

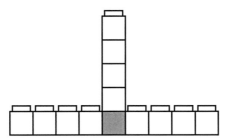

Children used to studying collections to figure out how the objects have been sorted may notice that the 4th arrangement in this sequence has 1 cube in the center of 3 legs, each leg being composed of 4 cubes. Asked to imagine or build the 10th arrangement in the sequence, many second graders will have to build all the arrangements in between. With encouragement and experience, though, some will build or even just imagine a figure with 1 cube in the middle and 3 legs of 10. A very few will have a solid enough understanding of the pattern to report that you simply triple the arrangement number and add one to determine the number of cubes needed for any term in the sequence. All are working toward making generalizations and using variables, two operations central to algebra.

How Do I Sequence My Instruction For This Unit?

There are 23 sessions in the Sorting, Patterning & Number unit. (If you use the Number Corner calendar routines in addition to the work in this unit, the time you'll be devoting to math instruction will be 1 hour and 15 minutes to 1 hour and 20 minutes a day.) Most of the sessions open with a problem or investigation posed to the entire group. Frequently, children go off to work on these challenges by themselves, with partners, or in small groups. As they finish, they get their work folders and begin Work Places. There will be occasions when an investigation will take the entire hour or more and there won't be time for Work Places. There will be other days when you'll want to use the entire session to introduce a new set of Work Places and have the children choose where to begin.

The lessons and activities in this unit are intended to be taught in sequence and we offer the planner on pages 7 and 8 as a guide. Ultimately, however, you will determine your own pacing. You may decide to repeat a lesson twice. Discussion may run 15 minutes longer in your class than it did in ours and there will be no time for Work Places. There may be days you decide to skip or postpone a whole group activity and devote the entire session to Work Places. It may take you longer than 5 or 6 weeks to get through the material, especially the first year you use the program.

Although the needs of your students will guide many of your planning decisions, it's important to bear in mind that they won't achieve "mastery" at each step. Each concept will be revisited again and again through this year and beyond. If some of your children don't understand the idea of sorting by more than one attribute or extending a Unifix cube pattern in such a way that it grows rather than repeats, they'll have many more encounters with these ideas. We urge you to watch your children carefully, but not to delay instruction as you wait for each student to "get it" each time. They will have many, many opportunities to construct understandings about pattern and function in the coming months and years.

We also urge you to supplement the sessions in this unit with the Number Corner calendar routines, even though they're not shown in the planning guide. These routines are described in the Number Corner teacher's guide and can be done before or after the unit sessions or at another time of the day completely. They change each month and have been designed to complement the lessons and activities in each unit.

The calendar pattern for the first month of school, for instance, is a growing pattern (1 red apple, 1 green apple, 1 red, 2 greens, 1 red, 3 greens, and so on). As the pattern grows day by day, many second graders are puzzled as can be. When is the pattern going to start over again? About the time they first encounter Unifix Cube and Pattern Block Growing Patterns, they realize that the pattern on the calendar is growing too. Along with the pattern of apples on the Calendar Grid, children examine the collection of cards on the Hundreds Grid for number patterns each day and practice a counting-by-5's pattern on the Bean Clock.

How many days have passed this month?

⚹September

Sunday	Monday	Tuesday	Wednesday	Thursday	Friday	Saturday
	1	2	3	4	5	6
7	8	9	10	11	12	13
14	15					

Unit 1 Planning Guide

SESSION 1	SESSION 2	SESSION 3	SESSION 4	SESSION 5
People Sorting: Alike & Different, p. 9	People Sorting: Guess My Rule, p. 14	Beetle Glyphs, p. 21	Beetle Glyph Sorting: Finding Many Ways, p. 24	Beetle Glyph Sorting: Venn Diagrams, p. 27
Assessment What is a Pattern? p. 11				
	Introduce Work Places 1	Work Places 1 ————————————————————————→		

SESSION 6	SESSION 7	SESSION 8	SESSION 9	SESSION 10
Unifix Cube Growing Patterns, p. 30	Race You to 25¢, p. 34	Introduce Work Places 2, p. 37	**Work Sample** Unifix Cube Growing Patterns: Another Look, p. 49	Growing Patterns: Making a Chart of 2's, p. 53
Work Places 1 ————————————→			**Work Places 2** ————————————→	
Home Connection 1				**Assessment** Start Individual Interviews, p. 55

SESSION 11	SESSION 12	SESSION 13	SESSION 14	SESSION 15
Work Sample Growing Patterns: What Do You Notice About the 2's Chart? p. 62	**Work Sample** Growing Patterns: Extending the 2's Chart, p. 66	Math Bucket Sorting: Finding Many Ways, p. 70	Math Bucket Sorting: Venn Diagrams, p. 73	Which One Doesn't Belong? p. 76
Work Places 2 ————————————————————————————————————→				
	Assessment Continue Individual Interviews ————————————————————→			
Home Connection 2				

SESSION 16	SESSION 17	SESSION 18	SESSION 19	SESSION 20
Pattern Block Growing Patterns, p. 79	An Hour or Bust!, p. 84	Getting Started with Work Places 3, p. 99	The Churn Dash Quilt: Describing and Making the Quilt Blocks, p. 101	The Churn Dash Quilt: Figuring the Quilt Lay-Out—How Many Different Rectangles Can You Make? p. 105
Work Places 2	**Introduce Work Places 3**		**Work Places 3** ————————————→	
Assessment Continue Individual Interviews ————————————————————————————→				
Home Connection 3				

Unit 1 Planning Guide (cont.)

SESSION 21	SESSION 22	SESSION 23		
The Churn Dash Quilt: What Do You Notice About the Finished Quilt? p. 109	**Work Sample** Tile Growing Patterns, p. 112	**Assessment** What is a Pattern? Revisited, p. 116		
Work Places 3 ⎯⎯⎯⎯⎯⎯⎯⎯⎯⎯⎯⎯⎯⎯⎯→				
Assessment Continue Individual Interviews ⎯⎯⎯⎯⎯→				
Home Connection 4				

Session 1

PROBLEMS & INVESTIGATIONS

People Sorting Alike & Different

Overview
Children generate a list of what's alike and what's different about 2 student volunteers. The teacher then chooses 1 attribute from the list by which to sort the class. After this short, opening activity, the class moves on to a paper-and-pencil assessment on pattern.

You'll need
★ chart paper
★ marking pen

Skills
★ observing and describing
★ finding likenesses and differences
★ classifying sets into 2 or more groups
★ using attributes to eliminate and select group members

Ask for two volunteers from the class to stand in front of the group. Have the group list likenesses and differences they notice. Record their ideas on a piece of chart paper:

After your students have come up with a number of ideas, have the two volunteers sit down. Then explain that you are going to sort the entire class into groups, using one of the ideas on the chart. Choose one of the listed attributes that's easy to see and have the children stand a few at a time to sort themselves accordingly.

> **Teacher** This is an interesting list. Suppose I choose one of the differences you noticed between our 2 volunteers—say, pants and dress—

Session 1 People Sorting (cont.)

and ask people with pants on to stand in the right front corner of the room and people with dresses on to stand in the left front corner of the room. Will you all know where to stand?

Children *Sure!*
Yeah!
What about me? I don't have pants or a dress. I have a skirt!
What about people with shorts?

Teacher *Let's see what happens. Raise your hand if you're sure you know where you belong. Alyssa, Briana, Jesse, and Bryce, please go to the corner in which you belong. Okay. Now, how about Andrew, Sarah, Peter, and Eloise?* (The students who have been named stand and walk to the appropriate corner.) *What's the same about all the children in the right corner?*

Children *They all have pants on!*

Teacher *And what about the children in the left corner?*

Children *They all have dresses!*

Alejandrina *What about me? I have shorts on. Where should I stand?*

Teacher *Class?*

Evan *Let's make a new group, one for people with shorts.*

Teacher *Okay. Those of you with shorts, why don't you come and stand front and center?*

Ciel *I have a skirt on. Do I get to stand in my own group?*

Alyssa *There are getting to be too many groups. Skirts are almost like dresses. Let's have children with skirts on stand with the dress group.*

Once everyone is up and sorted, take a minute to discuss the groups. What's the same about the children in each group? Why can't Alyssa join the group with dresses? Why can't Kaitlin stand in the left corner? Which group has the most today? Will it turn out the same tomorrow?

Session 1 What is a Pattern?

ASSESSMENT

What is a Pattern?

Overview

Children draw examples of patterns and write whatever they can to show what they know about patterns. On a second sheet, they extend several different picture and number patterns. This assessment will be repeated at the end of the unit and will provide one way to see some of the growth that's taken place over the course of Unit 1.

You'll need

★ Pattern Assessment sheets 1 and 2 (Blacklines 1.1–1.2, run a class set of each)

★ pencils

★ crayons

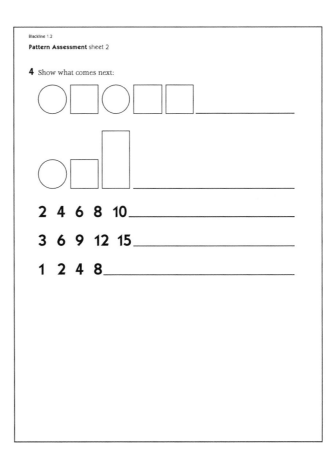

Explain to your students that you would like to see what they know about patterns so you'll be able to plan your instruction more effectively. In order to get this information, you're going to ask them to draw some patterns, extend some patterns that have already been started, and write down anything they know about patterns from kindergarten or first grade. Although there are many, many times you'll encourage children to work together on math

Session 1 What is a Pattern? (cont.)

projects, this is a time you'll want to ask them to work alone. Show them both sheets, explain anything you need to in the way of routines for getting pencils and crayons, and have them go to work.

ASSESSMENT TIPS ▶ Looking at Children's Work—Sheet 1

When the work is done, collect the sheets and take some time to look them over. Save them in children's work sample files for future reference. Although many children can draw patterns of one sort or another coming into second grade, it's quite challenging for them to write anything; some of your students will only be able to show what they know in drawings. Part of the reason we ask them to write about such an abstract concept the very first day of school is to establish a baseline. It's then doubly fascinating to see what they write and draw at the end of the unit. In looking at these assessment sheets the first time around, you might take note of the following:

• the items a child includes in her drawings. Did she include shapes, colors, pictures, numbers, and/or items that vary in size?

• the existence of a pattern in the drawing. Is there, in fact, anything that repeats?

• the complexity of the pattern(s): ABABAB or something more complex?

• the content of the writing. Does the child simply describe a pattern she might have drawn otherwise, as Eloise has done below, or is she able to make some kind of general statement about patterns, as Alejandrina has done? Is she able to write anything else about patterns? (In the last few years, we've had a few children write about patterns for making clothes or patterns for building something, "Like a blueprint.")

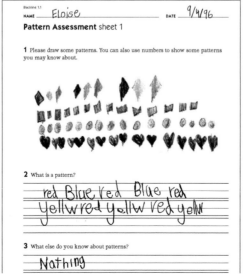

Work Sample 1   Work Sample 2

Session 1 What is a Pattern? (cont.)

Looking at Children's Work—Sheet 2

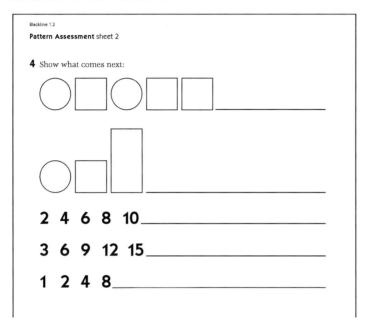

Blackline 1.2

Pattern Assessment sheet 2

4 Show what comes next:

2 4 6 8 10 _____

3 6 9 12 15 _____

1 2 4 8 _____

The second page of this assessment asks children to extend several different patterns as best they can by drawing shapes and writing numbers. This early in the school year, most second graders will extend by repeating. That is, they'll draw the sequence of shapes over and over on the top two lines, and probably write each number sequence once or twice more on the bottom three lines. These responses indicate that students understand the idea of repetition in patterning. (It's possible that some children will not be able to do this, and may either be so puzzled that they don't know what to draw or write, or will draw shapes and write numbers somewhat at random.)

You may have a few students who give you a different response, especially on the third and fourth lines. These students may write in 12, 14, 16, 18, 20 on the third line, and 18, 21, 24, 27, 30 on the fourth line. At some level, these children understand that growth is another form of repetition, and that the numbers in the third line are growing by 2's, while the numbers in the fourth line are growing by 3's. The last number sequence is a doubling pattern (1 + 1 = 2, 2 + 2 = 4, 4 + 4 = 8, and so on. It's possible to extend this pattern by repeating it: 1, 2, 4, 8; 1, 2, 4, 8, but a much more sophisticated response would be to continue to double the numbers: 1, 2, 4, 8, 16, 32, 64, 128, and so on. It would be unusual to see a student do this at the beginning of second grade. By the end of the unit, though you might expect to see more children extend these patterns by increasing the quantities rather than repeating them because the idea of "growing patterns" is a major focus of instruction.

Session 2

PROBLEMS & INVESTIGATIONS

People Sorting Guess My Rule

Overview

The teacher or a student sorts the class again, using the list of attributes generated yesterday. This time, however, the attribute by which the group is being sorted is not named, and the children work to figure out what it is by comparing likenesses among the children in each group and differences between the groups themselves. After a few rounds of People Sorting, the teacher introduces the first set of Work Places.

You'll need

★ the chart of likenesses and differences the children made yesterday

Skills

★ observing and describing

★ finding likenesses and differences

★ classifying sets into 2 or more groups

★ using attributes to eliminate and select group members

. . . .

For your information By focusing on likenesses and differences, students are beginning to think algebraically. If, for instance, you examine the pattern shown below, you'll notice that some things remain the same from arrangement to arrangement and some things change.

    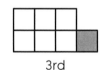 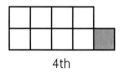

1st   2nd   3rd   4th

"You double the arrangement number each time. First there is 1 and 1, then 2 and 2, then 3 and 3, and so on. But the one gray tile at the end always stays the same."

In algebra, things that remain the same are called constants, and things that change are called variables. By engaging in this and other sorting lessons, second graders are learning to search carefully for likenesses and differences; to ferret out the things that remain the same from object to object and the things that vary.

. . . .

Now that your students have been introduced to People Sorting, you might try conducting the activity with a bit more mystery. Start by choosing an attribute from the list that's easy to see, but not too obvious. Don't tell the class which one you've selected. Put a star on the chalkboard to indicate that no one is to talk, not even the teacher, for now.

Motion for one of the students to come up. Send her to one side of the room.

Session 2 Guess My Rule (cont.)

Motion for another to come up. If she shares the selected attribute with the first student, send her to the same side of the room. If it's the opposite, send her to the other side of the room.

Continue in this fashion with 1 or 2 more students and then shrug your shoulders as you bring the fourth or fifth person up, as if to say, "Which side of the room should this student stand on? What do you think?" If you wait, children in the "audience" will begin to point in the direction they think the student should go.

Repeat 2 or 3 more times, and then erase the "silent star." Ask the group a few questions about what's going on:

- Does the way I'm sorting these children have to do with whether or not they're boys or girls?
- Does it have to do with their clothing?
- Does it have to do with something in their hair?
- Is there anyone who thinks he knows on which side of the room he belongs?

Call on a child who thinks she knows where to stand. If she is correct, agree with that child and let her take her place. If not, ask her to join the opposite group. Call another child or two to place themselves and then put the silent star back up. Continue sorting children, pausing each time to have students point to the direction they predict for each child called.

After you have about two thirds of the children placed, erase the star once again and ask a few more focus questions. If a child says he knows how you're sorting, let him share his idea. Then explain that this theory can be tested by watching where the next few children are placed. Call up 1 or 2 more children and send them in the correct direction. Do their placements seem to confirm the idea put forth? Yes? No? Does anyone have a different idea? Remind the class that it's something from the list.

Session 2 Guess My Rule (cont.)

Continue sorting until every child is standing. Ask again for ideas. How have they been sorted? What do the children in each group have in common? Once the mystery has been solved to everyone's satisfaction, repeat the activity. If you have time and your students are really engaged, you might let one of the children have a turn to be the leader. If you do, be sure to have that child whisper the attribute she has selected in your ear. Also, be prepared to repeat this activity many times over the next few weeks in spare moments, because everyone's going to want a turn to be leader at least once.

Session 2 Work Places

WORK PLACES

Introduce Work Places 1

Overview
After doing a few rounds of People Sorting, the teacher introduces the first set of Work Places and the work folders. Children help deliver the Work Place baskets to their designated spots around the room and then choose where to work. Each child uses a planning sheet on the front of his or her folder to keep track of the Work Places he or she visits during this session.

You'll need
★ work baskets 1A–1F, set up as shown below

★ a work folder for each child with a copy of the Work Places 1 Planner stapled to the front (Blackline 1.3)

Skills
★ building and inventing with a variety of materials

★ counting

★ sorting

★ patterning

. . . .

Note Be sure to read Chapter 2 of Getting Started *before you introduce the Work Places described on the next few pages. Among other things, you'll find instruction for marking your geoblocks before you mix them, which is extremely important. Also, if you are interested in using the computer-based Work Places, be sure to read the first 9 pages of the* Technology Connections *book now.*

. . . .

Work Places 1 Setup

1A Unifix Cubes

This Work Place basket will need

✓ 1,000 Unifix Cubes

1B Pattern Blocks

This Work Place basket will need

✓ 3 buckets of pattern blocks

1C Tile

This Work Place basket will need

✓ 400 1" square tile

Session 2 Work Places 1 (cont.)

1D Geoboards

This Work Place basket will need

✓ 6 geoboards

✓ 3 ziplocks of geobands for children to share

1E Geoblocks

This Work Place basket will need

✓ 5 or 6 bags of geoblocks mixed together to make 1 large set

Be sure to mark every block in each set so you can put the individual sets back together later. See *Getting Started*, page 37, for marking instructions.

1F Math Buckets

This Work Place basket will need

✓ math bucket of frogs

✓ math bucket of bugs

✓ math bucket of buttons

✓ math bucket of glass blobs

✓ math bucket of shells

The first round of Work Places is called Inventions, and when children go out to work, they will be doing exactly that. Building, counting, sorting, examining, and perhaps patterning, but basically following their own purposes. Although many of your children may have had opportunities to explore these materials in kindergarten and first grade, there are several very important reasons to allow some time for free play again in second grade:

• Children bring new skills and abilities to second grade. Their pattern block creations will probably be larger, more complex, and possibly more collaborative. At this age, more children are beginning to work together rather than side by side. Work Places provide a wonderful opportunity to begin building your classroom community.

• Some of the materials, including the shells, glass blobs, frogs, and geoblocks, may be new to them.

• When you're trying to establish the routines that will carry you through the rest of the year—Work Place setup and cleanup, care of materials, work folder procedures—it helps to have activities that are low stress and high success.

• The fact that children are free to choose their own Work Places and follow their own purposes will give you a good opportunity to watch them. Who

Session 2 Work Places 1 (cont.)

leads? Who follows? Who likes to work with other children? Who seems to prefer to work alone? What do they do with the materials? Who creates pictures with the manipulatives or uses them to tell stories? Who prefers to build 3-dimensional structures? Are any of the children sorting, counting, or patterning? (We don't see any particular need to use checklists or take notes to record this information, but watching carefully as children work helps us to get to know and understand them better.)

Introduce the six Work Places one by one. Explain that each one is set up for a maximum of six children, and that for this round of Work Places, they will be free to use the materials to build and create whatever they choose. As you show the materials, you might want to address issues of safety and sharing. Can children think of tips from other years about using the geobands and geoboards safely? What about sharing materials that everyone wants to use, like the yellow hexagonal pattern blocks? What about cleanup time? Will you want children to help others clean up when they're finished, and if so, do you want them to ask permission before they start taking someone's prized structure apart?

Once you've introduced the materials, show the work folders. Explain that each child will have a folder. These folders will provide a place for students to store their papers in future Work Place rounds, and will also provide a way to keep track of where they've been and where they still need to go. They are to visit each Work Place at least once over the next few days. After their first visit to a Work Place, they're to color in the star in the box below the picture of that Work Place on their planner. This shows they've visited that Work Place once. They can move from place to place whenever they choose as long as there's room, and move through the activities in any order. Once they've gone to all six Work Places, they are free to go back to their favorites, indicating each visit by marking one of the blank boxes.

Session 2 Work Places 1 (cont.)

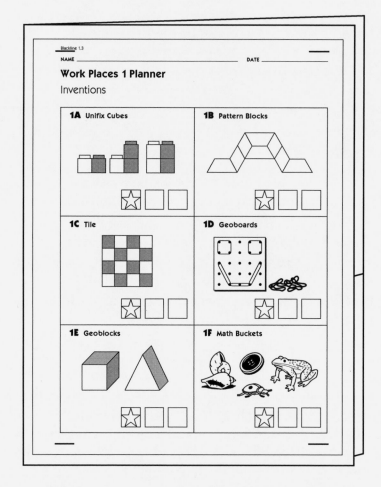

After you've introduced the materials and the folders, send your students off one by one with work folders and pencils in hand to find their Work Places. Most will choose an activity and stay with it for the remainder of the session, but some will want to move once or twice. We allow them to do so, as long as there's room at another Work Place. Although none of the Work Places in this round involve paper-and-pencil tasks, you'll want to help the children get used to carrying their work folders and marking the places they've been. The planner also serve as a menu, reminding children of what is available in this round of Work Places. Don't be surprised if you find a few folders lying around here and there. It may take a few days, or even a few weeks, before all the procedures become clear to everyone.

Near the end of the math session, you'll want to give a 3-minute warning. Something to the effect of, "In 3 minutes, when the minute hand on the clock has reached the 11, it will be time to clean up. This is the time to start finishing up or taking a look around the room at what some of your friends have done." After the materials have been cleaned up and the Work Place baskets put away, take a minute to make sure all your students have marked their planners to show where they went today. Then have them put their work folders back in the storage box you've set up. (We keep ours on the shelf right beside the Work Place baskets.)

Session 3

PROBLEMS & INVESTIGATIONS

Beetle Glyphs

Overview

Children are introduced to the idea of a glyph and the specific things represented by various parts of 2 paper beetles. Each child makes a beetle to represent himself or herself.

Skills

★ observing and describing

★ creating and interpreting glyphs

You'll need

★ Beetle Glyph Key (Blacklines 1.5–1.10, run 1 copy of each blackline on paper or cardstock. Assemble as shown on Blackline 1.4.)

★ a chart written on paper or on the board that lists all 12 months and their numbers (January—1, February—2, March—3, etc.)

★ the 2 beetle shapes run on yellow, orange, blue, and green construction paper (Blacklines 1.11–1.12, run 8 copies of each shape on each color—this will probably give you enough for this year and some for next.)

★ 2 sheets of 9″ × 12″ black construction paper cut into 1/2″ × 3″ strips

★ ten 3″ × 3″ pieces of construction paper in each of the following 4 colors: red, brown, white, and turquoise or light blue

★ crayons, pencils, scissors, glue, or gluesticks

Egyptian hieroglyphics or picture writing are the basis for a recent invention known as a glyph (rhymes with "cliff"). A glyph is a method of presenting data in picture form, and is being used by doctors, astronomers, meteorologists, geologists, and other scientists. A glyph, or simple picture or figure whose parts represent information about a given subject, is an alternative to a chart or table. According to Patricia Cartland (*Arithmetic Teacher*, Volume 2, Number 6, February 1996), "One of the original uses of this shorthand occurred in hospitals, where physicians need to interpret data on a patient quickly and efficiently." Doctors developed "human anatoglyphs" to display vital statistics that helped them track a patient's condition at a glance. Glyphs have become increasingly popular with mathematicians of all ages, partly because they're fun to make and fun to interpret, and partly because so much data can be shown at once.

Session 3 Beetle Glyphs (cont.)

In this lesson, each child will create a construction paper beetle about himself or herself that will show his or her gender, birth month, favorite season, favorite sport, and how many people he or she has living at home, using the symbols on the Beetle Glyph Key below. If the child is a boy who likes summer and soccer best, has a birthday in June and 5 people living in his house, he will make a round yellow beetle with 6 dots, 5 stripes, and a red hat. If students have access to the Key when they look at his beetle, they'll know he's a boy who likes summer best, etc. The beetles will be used for a variety of sorting activities and then displayed on the wall.

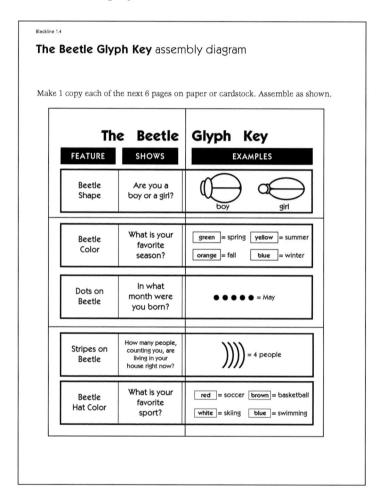

Blackline 1.4

The Beetle Glyph Key assembly diagram

Make 1 copy each of the next 6 pages on paper or cardstock. Assemble as shown.

FEATURE	SHOWS	EXAMPLES
Beetle Shape	Are you a boy or a girl?	boy girl
Beetle Color	What is your favorite season?	green = spring yellow = summer orange = fall blue = winter
Dots on Beetle	In what month were you born?	● ● ● ● ● = May
Stripes on Beetle	How many people, counting you, are living in your house right now?	))))) = 4 people
Beetle Hat Color	What is your favorite sport?	red = soccer brown = basketball white = skiing blue = swimming

To start, explain to your students that they are going to use something like hieroglyphics to present some information about themselves to their classmates. Display the Beetle Glyph Key and explain the symbols and their meanings.

You'll probably also want to go through the process of making your own beetle. Lay out the different beetle sheets so the children can see them all; pick a girl- or boy-shaped beetle in the color that shows your favorite season. Cut the beetle out and make enough large, heavily-colored dots to clearly show your birth month. Stop just short of making a hat that shows your favorite

Session 3 Beetle Glyphs (cont.)

sport or putting your stripes on because, if you do, many of the children will make exactly the same hat and put their stripes in the exact same location. Do be sure to tell them to make their dots and stripes in heavy black crayon so they can be easily seen.

Show them how to cut the $^1/_2'' \times 3''$ strips in half lengthwise to create really skinny strips for legs and antennae. Some of our children like to accordion-fold these strips for the legs. We insist that they glue 2 antennae on the head and 6 legs coming out of the thorax because real beetles have these things, and we want to be semi-realistic.

Once you've read the Beetle Glyph Key together and modeled making your own beetle, call your students up one by one to get their materials and go to work. It's easiest if the crayons, pencils, scissors, glue, and black construction paper strips are already out at the desks or tables.

 WORK PLACE NOTES

When children have finished their beetle glyphs, have them put their names on the back, set them in a safe place to dry, and get out their work folders and the Work Place baskets if time permits.

Session 4

PROBLEMS & INVESTIGATIONS

Beetle Glyph Sorting Finding Many Ways

Overview
Children generate as many ways as they can think of to sort the beetle glyphs they created during Session 3. The teacher records each description on a strip of paper. These strips will be used in future sorting activities.

You'll need
★ the children's beetle glyphs
★ the Beetle Glyph Key
★ about 30 pieces of 3″ × 9″ paper
★ marking pen

Skills
★ sorting by a variety of attributes (color, number of spots, shape, etc.)
★ thinking divergently

Gather your students into a discussion circle and have them set their beetle glyphs out in the middle of the ring. After they've had a minute to admire one another's creations, ask them to think about how the glyphs might be sorted.

. . . .

Note *If you have many more than 20 students, you might want to do this activity with half the beetle glyphs and save the other half for the Problems & Investigations activity in Session 5.*

. . . .

Let the children talk for a minute among themselves and then take suggestions. As a suggestion is made, have a couple of students sort the beetles into the appropriate groups. Then write out a label for each description on a piece of 3″ × 9″ paper. (The thing that's particularly interesting about sorting glyphs is that each method yields a new set of data about the class. Sorting by beetle

Session 4 Finding Many Ways (cont.)

color, for instance, is also a way to discover students' favorite season. You can bring this out in your discussion.)

Teacher *Which of these beetles belong together?*

Tara *We could put all the same colors together.*

Teacher *Do you remember what those colors mean?*

Michael *The colors mean the seasons that kids like the best. Mine's yellow because I like summer the best.*

Teacher *Tara and Michael, could you put the beetles into color groups?* (The teacher waits as the two children quickly sort the beetles.) *Now that the beetles have been sorted by color, what do you notice?*

Children *Way more people like summer than spring. Summer's got the most by far. Winter has a lot too. Fall only has 3. Winter has 7!*

Teacher *Before we find another way to sort these beetles, I'm going to make a label for each group of beetles. How many labels will I need for the color sort you just did?*

Anna *4—one for each color.*

Teacher *Okay. I have 4 slips of paper here. Before we go on, I'll write green, yellow, blue, and orange.*

Continue this activity until the beetles have been sorted in at least 5 different ways and you have a total of about 25 different sorting strips. Save the strips for tomorrow's session.

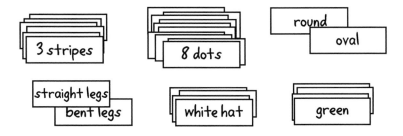

 WORK PLACE NOTES

At the conclusion of the lesson, have a child or two set out the Work Place baskets while you hand out work folders. Before you send your students out to choose Work Places, you might want to take a minute to review the routines. Remind them that they should:

Session 4 Finding Many Ways (cont.)

• Think of lots of ways to use the materials creatively. This might include sorting, counting, creating designs, pictures, or structures, and patterning. It won't be long until the Work Places are considerably more structured, so they should take advantage of this opportunity to play and explore now!

• Choose where they want to start, and move to a place where space is available as they finish.

• Get around to each Work Place before they start revisiting favorites. (This will take several days.)

• Mark their planning sheets to show where they go each time. That way they'll be able to see where they've gone and where they still need to go.

Session 5

PROBLEMS & INVESTIGATIONS

Beetle Glyph Sorting Venn Diagrams

Overview

The class chooses pairs of sorting strips from yesterday's session and uses them to sort the beetles. A 2-circle Venn diagram is used to define the sets visually.

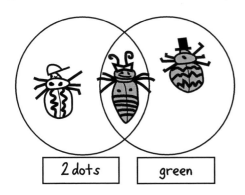

You'll need

★ the children's beetle glyphs

★ the Beetle Glyph Key

★ the beetle sorting strips from Session 4

★ 2 large yarn loops or hula hoops to define the categories

Skills

★ creating and analyzing Venn diagrams

Spread the beetle glyphs out on the floor and gather your students into a discussion circle around them. (If your class is much larger than 20, you might want to use half of the beetles for a bit, and then switch sets.)

Explain that the class will use the sorting strips from yesterday to sort the beetles in some new and interesting ways. Have two children pick sorting strips from the collection as you hold them out, face down. The two strips they pick may be related (like green and yellow), but more likely, they'll be unrelated.

Suppose they pick one strip that says "2 dots" and one strip that says "green." Set one of the strips beside one of the hula hoops or yarn loops and the other

Session 5 Venn Diagrams (cont.)

beside the other hoop or loop. Have students sort the beetles according to the strips—green beetles in one loop and 2-dot beetles in the other. There might be some beetles that are both green and 2-dot and, of course, some beetles that are neither green nor 2-dot. Have students decide where to put each of these piles. When all of the beetles have been sorted, take a minute to discuss what the children observe. Then push the beetles back together, pick up the sorting strips, shuffle the pile, and have two more children pick two different strips by which to sort the beetles. Repeat 3 or 4 times.

· ·

Important One of the Work Places in the next round gives children a chance to revisit their beetle glyphs. At some point in the next day or two, *you'll need to make a wall display of all the beetle glyphs.* It will be important to hang them low enough so that children can see and even touch them.

You'll also need to give your students time to write clue cards for their own beetles, either before they choose Work Places today, or at some other time in the next few days. These don't have to be elaborate. Just give each child a 3" × 5" index card and ask her to write 3 things about herself that would help someone else identify her beetle. (Be sure to display the Beetle Glyph Key for students to see as they write their clues, and be sure they label their cards with their names.) Here's an example:

Beetle Clue Card   Gary

1. My birthday is in April.
2. 2 people live in my house.
3. I like winter best.

"Let's see if we can find Gary's beetle by using the clue card he wrote. It will be a round beetle for a boy. He has 2 people in his house, so his beetle must have 2 stripes. It must be blue for winter and have 4 dots for April. It's the first beetle in this row!"

· ·

WORK PLACE NOTES

At the conclusion of the lesson, have a student helper set out the Work Place baskets while you hand out work folders. Before you send children out to work, let them know that they only have 3 more days, counting today, with these particular activities. If there's a Work Place they haven't yet visited, they might want to start there first.

Notes

Session 6

PROBLEMS & INVESTIGATIONS

HOME
CONNECTIONS

Unifix Cube Growing Patterns

Overview
The teacher displays 2 growing patterns at the overhead and asks children to build and discuss what they think will come next in each case.

You'll need
★ Unifix Cube Growing Patterns (Overhead 1.1)

★ Unifix cubes

★ overhead tile

★ Home Connection Blacklines HC 1.1–1.3

Skills
★ recognizing, describing, reproducing, and extending growing patterns

★ exploring functions

★ doing mental arithmetic

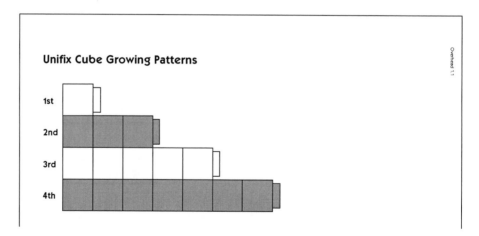

Show the first growing pattern at the overhead—the sequence that shows 1, then 3, then 5, then 7 Unifix cubes. Ask your students to copy the pattern with their Unifix cubes, creating their own trains of 1, 3, 5, and 7. Then have them tell you what they notice about the sequence. Is it, in fact, a pattern? Is there anything that repeats with each new arrangement or changes in a predictable manner? If your children are unfamiliar with the idea of growing patterns, this might throw them for a bit of a loop. Some might notice that the Unifix trains get longer each time. Others might notice that the trains grow by 2 each time.

Then ask them to use their Unifix cubes to build what they think the next arrangement, the 5th arrangement, might look like. After they've had a minute

Session 6 Unifix Cube Growing Patterns (cont.)

to build, have them share their ideas with the children sitting near them. Have a couple of children come to the overhead to demonstrate their ideas with transparent tile. Some might have built a train of 9, believing that the 5th arrangement would increase by 2, and be 7 + 2, which is 9. Some might respond with a train of 8 or 10—they may see that it's going to be bigger, but not be sure how much bigger. Others may display a train of 1, reasoning that the pattern goes 1, 3, 5, 7; 1, 3, 5, 7; and so on.

Acknowledge all ideas and theories, and take the opportunity to point out that there are different ways to extend this pattern. Then have a volunteer come up to the overhead to count and record the number of cubes in each train. Take a minute to discuss the changes from train to train. How many more have been added each time? Is it the same every time?

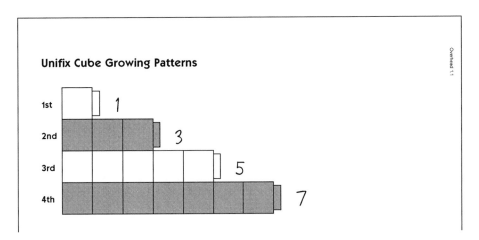

Unifix Cube Growing Patterns

1st 1
2nd 3
3rd 5
4th 7

Overhead 1.1

Amanda *It looks like big stairs. You'd have to take really big steps to climb them.*

Sarah *It's adding 2 more each time. Look—1 plus 2 is 3 and then 2 more is 5, and then 2 more is 7.*

Corina *But it can't be a pattern unless it starts over. Patterns have to repeat. The next thing would have to be 1 cube. Then it could go 1, 3, 5, 7, 1, 3, 5, 7, and keep on going and going.*

Teacher *What if I told you there was a different kind of pattern—one that never started over, but just kept growing and changing in ways we could predict?*

Andrew *I think I remember that kind from first grade. Like counting by 2's is a pattern—2, 4, 6, 8, 10—like that.*

Teacher *If it never starts over, is there anything that repeats?*

Children *No.*
But there is something the same. It keeps getting bigger and bigger each

Session 6 Unifix Cube Growing Patterns (cont.)

time.

Yes! It adds on 2 more every time. The next one would have to be 9!

It's like counting by 2's, but it lands on the odd numbers.

I don't get it!

You will probably have some children who really won't get the idea the first time around. Some may not be ready to accept the idea that a sequence can be a pattern because it grows or changes in some consistent way, no matter what you say. Don't worry about it; you'll revisit the idea many times.

After you've worked with the first pattern for a bit, move on to the second. Have the children take a minute to copy it with their own cubes, and then ask them to share any observations they have, first with their neighbors and then with the group. What do they notice; what do they see going on here? After a bit of discussion, have them use their cubes to build what they think the 4th arrangement will look like and why. If interest remains high, you might have them build the 5th and 6th arrangements as well. Encourage volunteers to show their thinking at the overhead with tile, and discuss.

Although it's very challenging, you might conclude the lesson by asking your students if anyone can imagine what the 10th arrangement would look like. Some may want to build it; a few might be able to describe it without building it. Take time to draw out any ideas children might have. Is there any connection they can find between the arrangement number (1st, 2nd, 3rd, etc.) and the number of cubes in either the top or bottom row? (This may already have come up in discussion. Some students will notice that the 1st arrangement has 1 on top and 2 on the bottom. The 2nd arrangement has 2 on top and 4 on the bottom; the 3rd arrangement has 3 on top and 6 on the bottom. A few children may reason that the 10th arrangement will probably have 10 on top and 20 on the bottom.)

Session 6 Unifix Cube Growing Patterns (cont.)

Encourage any theories and generalizations about this pattern that arise. Again, some students may have the whole idea put together, while others will be in the dark. If you can bring yourself to create just a little disequilibrium, children will continue to puzzle, stretching their own brains to grapple with the concept over the coming weeks. Assure them that they'll have many more opportunities to work with growing patterns this year.

WORK PLACE NOTES

When the lesson is finished, send your students out to the Work Places with their work folders. Remind them that this is the next-to-last day with these materials; almost the last chance to visit something they haven't yet tried, or to revisit a favorite.

HOME CONNECTION 1

Activity Coin Sorting (Blacklines HC 1.1–1.2, pp. 1–2)
Worksheet Counting Coins (Blackline HC 1.3, p. 3)

Remember to send the first activity and worksheet home with children after this session. You'll find the blacklines for these in the Home Connections book.

Blackline HC 1.1 Use after Unit 1, Session 6. Run back-to-back with HC 1.2

NAME _____   DATE _____

Home Connection 1 ★ Activity

NOTE TO FAMILIES

The activity on this sheet is designed for you and your child to do together. It will help you understand what we've been learning in math this past week, and help your child extend his or her sorting skills. All you'll need is a pocketful of change and some time to relax and have fun together.

. . . .

Coin Sorting

Find a penny and a nickel. After looking at them very carefully, list as many differences and likenesses as you can.

Here's how our penny and our nickel are *alike*:

_____
_____
_____
_____
_____
_____
_____
_____
_____
_____

Here's how our penny and our nickel are *different*:

_____
_____
_____
_____
_____
_____
_____
_____
_____
_____

(Continued on back.)

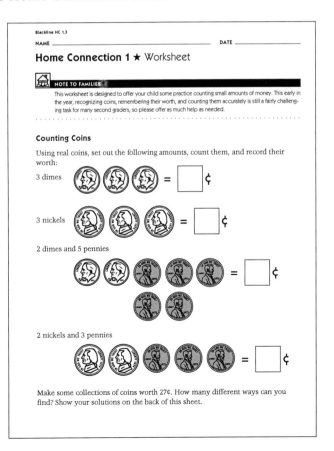

Blackline HC 1.3

NAME _____   DATE _____

Home Connection 1 ★ Worksheet

NOTE TO FAMILIES

This worksheet is designed to offer your child some practice counting small amounts of money. This early in the year, recognizing coins, remembering their worth, and counting them accurately is still a fairly challenging task for many second graders, so please offer as much help as needed.

. . . .

Counting Coins

Using real coins, set out the following amounts, count them, and record their worth:

3 dimes

3 nickels

2 dimes and 5 pennies

2 nickels and 3 pennies

Make some collections of coins worth 27¢. How many different ways can you find? Show your solutions on the back of this sheet.

Session 7

PROBLEMS & INVESTIGATIONS

Race You to 25¢

Overview

The teacher introduces a game in which pennies are traded for nickels and nickels are traded for quarters. This game reinforces the 5's counting pattern and will be included in slightly more complex form with the next round of Work Places.

You'll need

★ Race You to 25¢ (Overhead 1.2)

★ overhead coins—pennies, nickels, and quarters

Skills

★ counting by 5's and 1's

★ recognizing coins and their worth

★ regrouping by 5's and 25's

★ mental arithmetic—adding and comparing quantities to 25

Pull the children into a comfortable group around the overhead. Explain that you have a new game to teach them; one that they'll see again in the next set of Work Places. It's called Race You to 25¢, and you'll be playing against all of them. Show Overhead 1.2 and give students a minute or two to talk to each other about what they notice.

> **Children** *It has lots of pennies and nickels.*
> *5 pennies and 5 more—10 in all.*
> *10 nickels too. Let's see, that's 5, 10, 15, 20, 25, 30, 35, 40, 45, 50.*
> *There are only 2 quarters.*
> *Hey! 5 nickels—that's the same as a quarter.*
> *There's a spinner in the middle.*

Then explain that you'll take turns spinning and collecting the number of pennies the spinner designates each time. Whenever you have 5 pennies you can trade them in for a nickel, 5 nickels can be traded for a quarter, and the first players to reach a quarter win. You'll place overhead coins right over the drawings of coins on the gameboard so everyone can easily see what's happening. Start the game and let students take turns spinning and setting overhead coins on the board each time it's their turn. If you set out the coins when it is your turn, it keeps the pace more lively.

Session 7 Race You to 25¢ (cont.)

Although this lesson is designed to introduce an upcoming Work Place activity, you'll find many opportunities to pose problems and reinforce counting patterns as you play. Be sure to have students count their money at every turn and take time to compare their total to yours as frequently as possible. You can also ask them how much more money they'll need to get to a quarter several times during the game.

> *Teacher* My goodness! You had 2 nickels and 4 pennies on your side of the board. Now that you've just spun another 4, how much will you have in all?

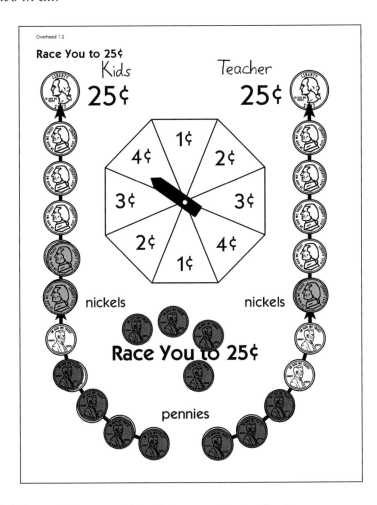

> *Children* We can add 1 of the pennies to the 4.
> We can get a new nickel—take those 5 pennies off and trade them for a nickel!
> Then we'll have 3 nickels and 3 pennies.
> That's 5, 10, 15, 16, 17, 18!

> *Teacher* How much more money do you need to get to a quarter?

Session 7 Race You to 25¢ (cont.)

Children *18, 19, 20, 21, 22, 23, 24, 25. We need 7 more pennies.*
We could get that in only 2 more spins if we get a 3 and a 4.
I don't get it. On the board it shows we still need 2 pennies and 2 nickels.
But when we get 2 more pennies, we can trade them in for a nickel,
and then we'll only need 1 more nickel after that.
I still don't get it.

Although many children will become familiar with the mechanics of the game during this lesson, not all of them will understand the underlying mathematics at the same level. For some, this will be an opportunity to learn the names and worth of pennies, nickels, and quarters. For others, it will be a good chance to practice counting by 5's and 1's, and gain some experience with regrouping. For still others, your questions and challenges will provide good mental math and problem-solving opportunities. It's essential to interact with your students in such a way that every child has some point of access.

 WORK PLACE NOTES

Remind students that this is the last day with Work Places 1. Tomorrow they'll begin a new set, which will include the game you just played.

Session 8

WORK PLACES

Introduce Work Places 2

Overview
The teacher introduces a new set of Work Places, many of which build on previous lessons. After the activities have been introduced, the children go out to try them.

You'll need
★ work baskets 2A–2F set up as shown below
★ a work folder for each child with a copy of the Work Place 2 Planner stapled to the front (Blackline 1.13)

Work Places 2 Setup

2A Unifix Cube Growing Patterns

This Work Place basket will need
✓ Unifix cubes
✓ Unifix Cube Growing Pattern Cards

2B Race You to 50¢

This Work Place basket will need
✓ 6 Race You to 50¢ gameboards
✓ 3 containers, each holding 40 pennies, 10 nickels, and 4 quarters

2C Match the Beetle Game

This Work Place basket will need
✓ a wall display of the beetle glyphs the children made, along with the beetle glyph key
✓ beetle glyph clue cards (children make these also)
✓ Match the Beetle record sheets (Blackline 1.14, run 30 copies and place in a folder)

2D Geoboards & Records 7-Band Challenge

This Work Place basket will need
✓ 8 geoboards
✓ geobands
✓ Geoboard record sheets (Blackline 1.15, run 30 copies and place in a folder)
✓ 6 clear rulers

Session 8 Work Places 2 (cont.)

2E Geoblocks

This Work Place basket will need

✓ 5 or 6 bags of geoblocks mixed together to make one large set

Be sure to mark every block in each set so you can put the individual sets back together later. See *Getting Started*, page 37, for marking instructions.

2F Count & Compare 5's

This Work Place basket will need

✓ 3 Count & Compare 5's gameboards

✓ 3 sets of Count & Compare 5's cards

This session opens with an introduction to Work Places 2. Two of the Work Places—Geoblocks and Geoboards & Records—have fundamentally remained the same as they were in the last round of Work Places. Three are new, but build on the Problems & Investigations lessons you've been doing. The sixth, Count & Compare 5's, takes its lead from some of the August/September calendar routines featured in the Number Corner. Your goal for this session is to introduce the Work Places and give students a bit of time to get started with them if possible.

In preparation for this session, you'll want to read through the descriptions of the Work Places on the next few pages. Each description explains how to play the game or do the activity, and includes some "instructional considerations" for you to bear in mind as you introduce the Work Places and use them with your students over the coming days. You'll also need to set up your Work Place baskets as shown on pages 35 and 36, and staple the new Work Place planners to children's work folders.

As you begin this session, gather your students in a discussion circle and explain that you have some new Work Places to introduce. Then show them the

Session 8 Work Places 2 (cont.)

materials in each Work Place basket as you explain the activity. When you've modeled all six Work Places, show the children their work folders with the new planners attached. Explain that two of the Work Places involve record sheets, which the students will store in their folders as they work their way through the activities. Have children designate one pocket for finished papers and one for unfinished so they can see at a glance where they need to start if they haven't had a chance to complete an activity the day before.

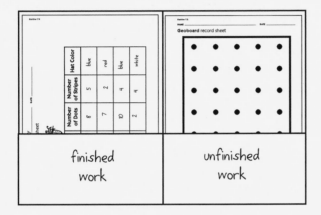

Student I finished my beetle sheet yesterday, but we had to clean up just as I was starting the geoboard Work Place. That's where I'm going to start today.

As with the first round of Work Places, the work folders will also provide students a way to keep track of where they've been and where they still need to go. They are to visit each Work Place at least once over the next few days. After their first visit to a Work Place, they're to color in the star in the box below the picture of that Work Place on their planner. This shows they've visited that Work Place once. They can move from place to place when they choose, as long as there's room, and move through the activities in any order. Once they've gone to all six Work Places, they are free to go back to their favorites, indicating each visit by marking one of the blank boxes on their planner. (Coloring in the star under an activity on the planning sheet indicates a first visit. There are two other blank boxes after the star to be marked on subsequent visits.)

After you've introduced the materials and new planners, send your students off one at a time with work folders and pencils in hand to find their Work Places. Most will choose an activity and stay with it for the remainder of the session, but some will move once or twice as they complete record sheets or finish playing games. You will probably still need to remind some of your students to take their folders with them from one Work Place to another, and also to mark their progress on the planners.

Session 8 Work Places 2 (cont.)

. . . .

Note *The Work Place descriptions on the next few pages are for your benefit. Although you could run copies and place them in the Work Place baskets, we intended that you would read them and then model the games and activities for your students, rather than expecting children to read the instructions themselves.*

. . . .

 WORK PLACE 2A

Unifix Cube Growing Patterns

This Work Place basket will need
★ Unifix cubes
★ Unifix Cube Growing Pattern Cards

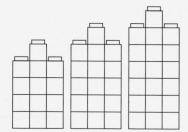

Skills
★ copying and extending growing patterns
★ exploring functions

To Work

1. Take one of the Unifix Cube Growing Pattern Cards. Copy what's on the card with Unifix cubes.

2. Use your cubes to build the next 2 or 3 arrangements in the sequence. Can you explain what's going on with this pattern to someone else?

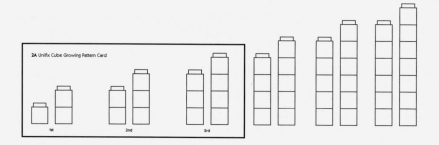

Student 1 *It goes 1, 2; then 2, 3; then 3, 4; so I figured it had to get bigger every time.*

Student 2 *It's kind of like counting, so I built 4, 5; then 5, 6; then 6, 7.*

3. See if you can build or imagine what the 10th arrangement in the sequence would look like and tell someone else.

Session 8 Work Places 2 (cont.)

> **Student 2** *The 10th one? I'm not sure, but I could keep going until I got to the 10th. Hey, maybe it would have 10 and 11. I'll build it and see.*

4. Repeat the process with a different card. You can do as many as you like, but you need to try at least 2 or 3 different cards.

Instructional Considerations for Unifix Cube Growing Patterns

We have found in our own classrooms that we've needed to spend more time at this Work Place than some of the others, talking with children about what they're doing and offering challenges as needed. You'll probably want to have them explain to you why they have built the 4th, 5th, and 6th arrangements as they have, understanding that their extensions might not match what you would have done.

Depending on the child and the level of interest, you might also ask what the 10th arrangement of a particular sequence would look like. A few of your students may be able to make generalizations well enough to tell you without actually building the arrangement. Others won't be able to, but may be interested enough to actually build out the 7th, 8th, 9th, and 10th.

In looking at their work, see if you can help them spot trends. What seems to be going on each time? Is there any relationship between the design and its arrangement number? One possible way to look at the pattern below is that if the 1st arrangement goes 1, 2, 1; the 2nd goes 2, 3, 2; and the 3rd goes 3, 4, 3, the 4th might go 4, 5, 4. If this were the case, what would the 5th and 6th arrangements look like? Sometimes if you help children verbalize what they see in each arrangement, they can come to some sort of generalization more easily.

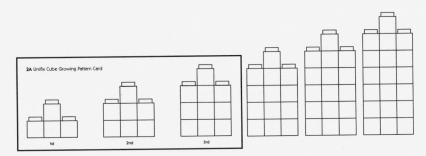

> **Student** It goes 1, 2, 1; 2, 3, 2; 3, 4, 3 on the card. Every time, it does the number, and then one up, and then back down—1, 2, 1, see? So the 4th one has to be 4, 5, 4. The 5th one is 5, 6, 5. The 6th one would be 6, 7, 6. The 10th one would probably 10, 11, 10. I'd have to build up that far to be sure. (Even when they've made a solid generalization, many second graders like to "build it out, just to be sure.")

Session 8 Work Places 2 (cont.)

WORK PLACE 2B

Race You to 50¢

This Work Place basket will need

★ 6 Race You to 50¢ gameboards

★ 3 containers, each holding 40 pennies, 10 nickels, and 4 quarters

Skills

★ counting by 5's and 1's

★ recognizing coins and their worth

★ regrouping by 5's and 25's

To Work

1. Get a partner, two gameboards, and a container of coins to share.

2. Take turns spinning and setting the appropriate number of pennies on your board.

3. Each time you have 5 or more pennies, you can trade 5 for a nickel. When you collect 5 nickels, you can trade them in for a quarter.

4. The first person to get 2 quarters wins the game. It's okay to have a few pennies over 50¢.

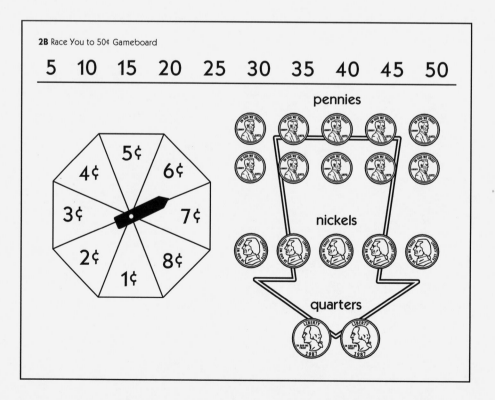

2B Race You to 50¢ Gameboard

5   10   15   20   25   30   35   40   45   50

pennies

nickels

quarters

Session 8 Work Places 2 (cont.)

Instructional Considerations for Race You to 50¢

Because children will have just played a whole-group version of this game in Session 7, you probably won't need to do any extensive modeling. We do find it helpful to take two gameboards out of the Work Place basket, along with a container of coins and play through the first few spins with one of our students while the others watch. This is enough to get some youngsters started, and often they'll be able to help the children who aren't quite sure what to do when they go out to Work Places.

▮ WORK PLACE 2C

Match the Beetle Game

This Work Place basket will need

★ a wall display made up of the beetle glyphs children made and the Beetle Glyph Key

★ beetle glyph clue cards made by children (see page 28)

★ Match the Beetle record sheets (Blackline 1.14, run 30 copies and store in a folder)

Beetle Clue Card   Amy

1. There are 5 people at my house.
2. My birthday is in August.
3. I like summer.

Skills

★ reading and interpreting glyphs

★ using attributes to eliminate and se-lect items

- -

Note   Unless you have a very small class, you might want to display only half the beetle glyphs at a time, simply because it's very difficult to consider more than 10–15 at once. If you decide to do this, put the corresponding clue cards in the Work Place basket and save the others for later when you change the beetles on display. Another advantage of displaying only half the beetles is that a new collection midway through this round of Work Places may lure some children to come back and try the activity again.

- -

To Work

1. Choose a clue card from the Work Place basket. Read it carefully and then take it over to the beetles on the wall. Can you find the beetle that matches all three clues? (Actually, you have four clues because the name on the clue card tells you whether the person who made the beetle is a boy or a girl.)

Session 8 Work Places 2 (cont.)

Beetle Clue Card   Jason

1. I love summer.
2. My birthday is in January.
3. There are 3 people in my house.

Student Let's see. Jason made this card, so the beetle has to be round for a boy. It has to be yellow for summer, and have one dot for a birthday in January. I already know which beetle it is! It's the one in the middle!

2. When you think you have matched a beetle with its clue card, write a description of the beetle, along with the name of the person who made it on a Match the Beetle record sheet. (There is an example already done for you on the sheet, and room for you to do three more of your own.)

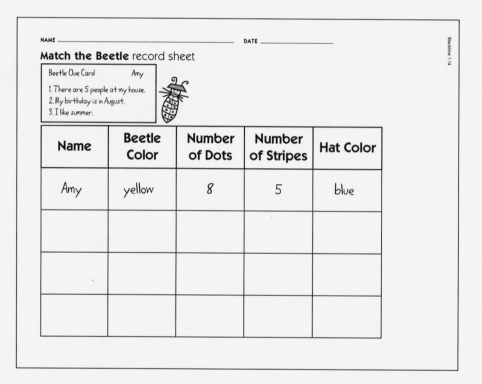

3. Be sure to return the clue cards to the Work Place basket as you finish with them; other children will need them.

4. Store your completed sheet in your work folder.

Instructional Considerations for Match the Beetle Game
This Work Place is challenging but entertaining; many children are thrilled to see their own beetle glyphs up on the wall and enjoy matching clue cards with beetles to discover who made the other beetles. You'll want to model the

Session 8 Work Places 2 (cont.)

recording step carefully; in fact, it might be worth identifying and recording at least two beetles before moving on. If you find that children are having trouble matching the beetles and clue cards as they work on their own, reduce the number of beetles on display and the number of corresponding clue cards in the Work Place basket.

 WORK PLACE 2D

Geoboards & Records The 7-Band Challenge

This Work Place basket will need

★ 8 geoboards

★ geobands

★ Geoboard record sheets (Blackline 1.15, run 30 copies and place in a folder)

★ 6 clear rulers

Skills

★ using shapes to create pictures

★ recording visual information

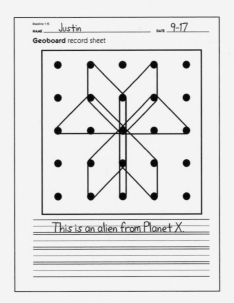

Note Normally, we set up Work Places for 6 children. Geoboards are so popular, however, that things go more smoothly if we have enough materials to accommodate 8 children.

To Work

1. Using just 7 rubber bands, create a picture on your geoboard. The challenge here is to come up with something that looks like a picture rather than an abstract design!

2. Once your picture is made, use a ruler to help record it as accurately as possible on a Geoboard record sheet.

3. Decide on a name for your picture and write it at the bottom of the sheet. Don't forget to put your name at the top of your paper too! Store your completed sheet in your work folder.

Session 8 Work Places 2 (cont.)

WORK PLACE 2E

Geoblocks

This Work Place Basket will need

★ 5 or 6 bags of geoblocks mixed together to make one large set

Skills

★ exploring the properties of 3-dimensional figures

★ exploring the relationships between 3-dimensional figures

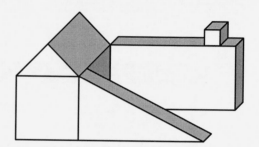

. . . .

Note Mark your geoblocks as shown in Getting Started, *page 37, before you mix the sets.*

. . . .

To Work

1. Take a batch of the geoblocks. What can you build with them? What do you notice about the blocks as you are building?

2. Are the other children creating things that are the same as or different than yours? Talk to each other about the things you are building; it may be that you decide to work together to build something really special.

Instructional Considerations for Geoblocks

Each set of geoblocks contains a wealth of cubes and prisms in varying sizes; 5 or 6 sets combined are a real treasure trove. These blocks are a fabulous tool for exploring many geometrical concepts, but at this point in the year, children simply need time to build with them. One of the reasons the blocks are so satisfying to build with is that they relate well to each other—2 rectangular prisms fit together to make a cube; 2 triangular prisms fit together to make a rectangular prism; there are 3 or 4 different sized cubes. These relationships make it possible to build structures of striking balance and symmetry.

As they work, children may discover some of the properties of these blocks, even if only intuitively. The more time they can spend with the blocks now, the more productive your geometry lessons will be later. You might even consider leaving the geoblocks out for continued free play after this set of Work Places has been put away; they will not resurface in a more formal way until Unit 4.

Session 8 Work Places 2 (cont.)

WORK PLACE 2F

Count & Compare 5's

This Work Place basket will need

★ 3 Count & Compare 5's gameboards

★ 3 sets of Count & Compare 5's cards

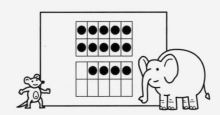

To Work

1. Find a partner.

2. Get a gameboard and a set of cards from the Work Place basket. Shuffle the cards and place them face down between you and your partner.

3. Draw 1 card from the top of the pile and have your partner do the same.

4. Read the number on your card or count by 5's (or 5's and 1's) to determine the worth of your card.

5. Place your cards where they belong on the gameboard—1 card in the "more" box, the other in the "less" box. (If the 2 cards are equal, put them both back into the stack and draw again.)

6. Spin the spinner at the bottom of the gameboard to determine who gets to take both cards. If it lands on "more," the person who had the card that was worth more gets to take both the cards. If it lands on "less," the person who drew the card that was worth less gets both cards.

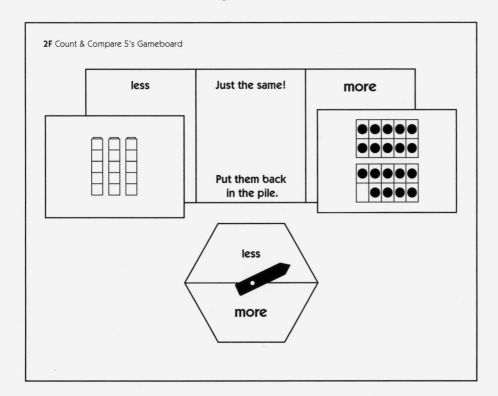

Session 8 Work Places 2 (cont.)

Child *Your card is 19 and mine is 15. You have more, but look! The spinner landed on less. That means I get to take both cards this time.*

7. Take turns drawing cards, counting and then comparing the quantities shown, and spinning until you are out of cards. The winner is the one with the most cards at the end. (Or, if you like, you can let the spinner determine the overall winner of the game. If it lands on "less," the person with fewer cards wins. If it lands on "more," the person with more cards wins.)

Instructional Considerations for Count & Compare 5's

This game provides practice counting by 5's and 1's using several different models, including nickels and pennies, stacks of 5 Unifix cubes, and the ten-frames, which you have introduced during the Number Corner. Even with careful modeling, you'll probably find some of your students counting the dots and squares one by one to determine the quantities on the cards; while many of them may know how to count by 5's, counting by 5's and 1's is more difficult. You can help by emphasizing the Daily Number Chart during Number Corner and also by nestling in during Work Places and helping some of your students individually as they play this game.

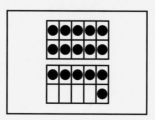

Teacher *It's true that you can count one by one to find out how many dots are on this card. Can you think of a different way?*

Child *By 5's?*

Teacher *Let's try it. 5, 10, 15...now what?*

Child *We can't keep going by 5's. There is only 1 dot left.*

Teacher *What comes right after 15 if you're counting by 1's, then?*

Child *16.*

Teacher *Okay—here we go...5, 10, 15, 16. That's it!*

Session 9

PROBLEMS & INVESTIGATIONS

Unifix Cube Growing Patterns Another Look

WORK SAMPLE

Overview
This lesson revisits Unifix cube growing patterns and gives children another chance to consider the idea of patterns that grow rather than repeat. In this version of the lesson, the teacher shows 2 patterns at the overhead, which the children build, extend, and discuss as a whole group. Then students go off to work individually or in partners to figure the 4th, 5th, and 10th configurations of a new Unifix cube pattern. Their record sheets may be saved as work samples.

You'll need
★ More Unifix Cube Growing Patterns (Overhead 1.3)

★ A Unifix Cube Growing Pattern Problem (Overhead 1.4)

★ pencils

★ A Unifix Cube Growing Pattern Problem (Blackline 1.16, run a class set)

★ Unifix cubes

Skills
★ recognizing, describing, reproducing, and extending growing patterns

★ making generalizations and predictions

★ doing mental arithmetic

Remind your students about the day you did the growing Unifix cube patterns together at the overhead, and tell them that you have some new growing pattern problems to pose today. With the children working at their desks or at the rug, show the first Unifix cube growing pattern on the overhead.

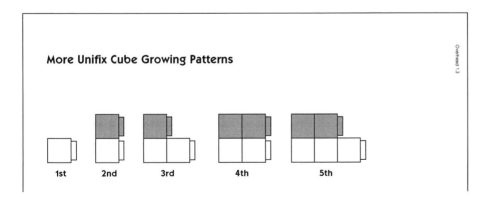

Have them look at the first 5 arrangements. What do they notice? (Welcome all observations and speculations. You may be surprised at some of the things your students tell you.) Next, ask children to use their Unifix cubes to build what they think the 6th arrangement will look like. (Some children will enjoy building the first 5 arrangements and then building the 6th; others are ready to jump in and just build the 6th. Either way is fine.)

Session 9 Unifix Cube Growing Patterns (cont.)

After they've had a few minutes to work, have them share their ideas with their neighbors. Then ask for a volunteer to show his 6th arrangement to the entire class and explain his reasoning.

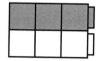

Joey I think the 6th arrangement will look like this because the pattern goes 1, 2, 3, 4, 5. There will be 6 in the 6th one.

Alejandrina I made mine like that too. On the 3rd and 5th ones, 1 of the cubes doesn't have a partner. On the 2nd, 4th, and 6th, every cube has one to go with it.

Solicit other ideas and explanations and then challenge your students to build the 7th arrangement. Is there any connection between the arrangement number and the number of cubes it takes to build each arrangement? Can they imagine what the 8th one will look like? What about the 10th, 15th, 20th? How are they figuring these things out? Jumping from the 6th or 7th arrangement to the 10th and beyond may be too much for many of your children, but see what happens if you pose the question—can anyone respond?

Repeat the same procedure with the second pattern on the transparency, and then explain that you want to pose one more problem with Unifix cubes. Distribute copies of A Unifix Cube Growing Pattern Problem, and display Overhead 1.4, which shows the same sheet.

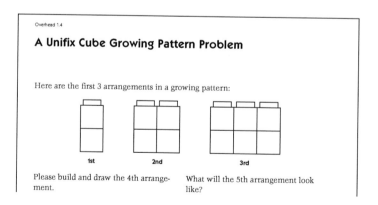

Overhead 1.4

A Unifix Cube Growing Pattern Problem

Here are the first 3 arrangements in a growing pattern:

1st   2nd   3rd

Please build and draw the 4th arrangement.

What will the 5th arrangement look like?

Do the first part of this sheet together—you at the overhead and your students at their seats or on the rug. Can anyone figure out what the 4th and 5th arrangements of this pattern will look like? Have them work together to build and draw the 4th and 5th arrangements on their sheets and to record anything they notice about the pattern so far. (Don't despair if some of your students can't write much in the way of observations. Most will be able to build and draw the 4th and 5th arrangements by working together, but some won't have the words to express what they're doing yet.)

Session 9 Unifix Cube Growing Patterns (cont.)

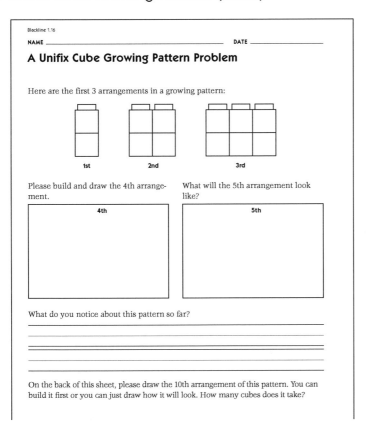

Finally, challenge your students to work the last part of the sheet, which involves building and drawing the 10th arrangement in the sequence, on their own. Some children will need to pool their Unifix cubes with neighbors to build the 6th, 7th, 8th, 9th, and finally the 10th arrangements. Others may have spotted a pattern that will help them take a shortcut straight to the 10th. Still others may need to have the problem cut down a bit. Perhaps for them, it will be enough to figure out what the 7th arrangement looks like, and you can certainly individualize as you watch your students work. Children who are very quick to figure the 10th arrangement and record their solutions may enjoy sketching or writing about a larger arrangement. You can choose something for them, or let them think of their own.

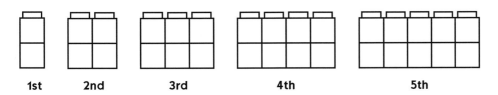

Child I think I see what's going on here. On the 1st arrangement there's 1 cube on the bottom and 1 on the top. On the 2nd one, it's 2 on the bottom, 2 on the top. On the 3rd one it's 3 on the bottom and 3 on the top. It just keeps going that way. The 10th one will just have 10 on the bottom and 10 on the top! That's 20 cubes. I bet I could figure out a bigger one!

Session 9 Unifix Cube Growing Patterns (cont.)

If only 1 or 2 students make a generalization that enables them to quickly imagine the 10th, 20th, or even 100th, it's worth having them share with the class. Even if they don't see it for themselves, some children can listen to others' ideas and extend them as they begin to understand them. What we're doing in this lesson is trying to help students see that once they've figured out a pattern—figured out "what's going on"—they can use it to help make predictions about arrangements that are much bigger than the original set. Ultimately, we're hoping to develop their skills at making and applying generalizations.

WORK PLACE NOTES

If there's time as children finish their sheets, have them get their work folders and pull out a Work Place basket or two. We often have children who finish early do Work Places at the rug until enough children have finished to move the baskets to their regular areas around the room.

ASSESSMENT TIPS ▶ Looking at Children's Work

If you're planning to keep files of children's work this year, you may want to save the sheets your students just completed. We usually date work samples and have a look before we file them away. Looking over the entire set gives us a sense of the group's response to the problem, and we're also able to make notes on some individual's papers if it seems warranted. Here are some things to consider:

1. How is this group of children doing with the idea of growing patterns? Are most of the children beginning to understand that a pattern is something that grows or changes in a predictable manner?

2. Were most of the children able to build and draw the 4th and 5th arrangements of the pattern on this sheet successfully, or were some youngsters really at a loss?

3. How did students go about figuring and recording the 10th arrangement? Did they need to build all the arrangements up through the 10th (which is very typical at this stage), or did some of them have ideas that led them to the 10th arrangement without building everything in between?

4. Were there any students who were able to come up with some sort of generalization about this pattern that enabled them to figure arrangements beyond the 10th easily? Were they able to explain their thinking to others?

Session 10

PROBLEMS & INVESTIGATIONS

Growing Patterns Making a Chart of 2's

Overview

Children brainstorm a list of things that come in 2's. They select one of the ideas—eyes, for instance—by class vote. Then each student draws a picture of the selected idea and mounts it on a class chart.

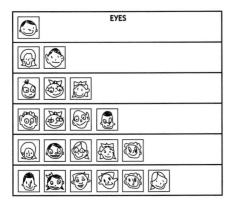

You'll need

★ chart paper and marking pen *or* chalkboard and chalk

★ 30 or more 5" × 5" white construction paper squares

★ a piece of butcher paper about 36" × 48", folded into 6, 7, or 8 rows, depending on the size of your class (A class of 21 or fewer will need 6 rows; between 21 and 28 will need 7 rows; over 28 will need 8 rows.)

★ crayons, pencils, glue, or gluesticks

Skills

★ making mathematical connections— what comes in 2's in the world around us?

Start by having your students brainstorm a list of things that come in 2's. Record all their ideas on a piece of chart paper or on the blackboard. (We've seen groups generate such ideas as eyes, hands, feet, twins, bike wheels, shoes, wings, rabbit ears, and many more.) After they've come up with a sizable list, ask them to vote for the one they'd most like to have on a class chart. When the group has decided, have each student make his or her drawing on a piece of 5" × 5" paper and glue it onto the chart, as shown above. This chart will be used to promote discussion and speculation about number patterns during Sessions 11 and 12.

WORK PLACE NOTES

Once children have finished their drawings and glued them onto the chart, have them get their work folders and choose Work Places for the remainder of the session. As you circulate, you might pay particular attention to how things are going at each of the Work Places. When you visit the Match the Beetle Game, for example, are students able to use the clue cards to find the correct beetles and then describe them on their record sheets without too

Session 10 Making a Chart of 2's (cont.)

much trouble? If things aren't going as smoothly as you'd like, try taking down a few of the beetles and removing the corresponding clue cards from the Work Place basket to reduce the challenge a bit. You might also model the recording process again.

When you nestle in beside children who are playing Count & Compare 5's, are they counting by 5's and 1's to determine the quantities on their cards? If not, you might work with a few of them on the spot. (Work Places provide wonderful opportunities to do some individualized instruction.)

> **Teacher** *David, you are doing a great job of counting those spots by 1's. Do you or Ben notice anything about the arrangement of spots on this card that might help you count them even faster?*

> **David** *We could count by 2's.*

> **Teacher** *That's true. Have you noticed how many spots are in each column?*

> **Ben** *There are 5. Oh! We can count by 5's on these cards! Let's see...5, 10, 15, 20, 25, 30! Is it 30?*

> **Teacher** *Let's look again. We have 5, 10, 15—but then there aren't any more columns of 5.*

> **David** *So it would be 5, 10, 15, 16, 17, 18 right?*

> **Ben** *That's faster, but I'm not too good at it sometimes.*

Even though you won't be able to get around to each Work Place every day, your interactions with children as they work—your questions, encouragement, and teaching, can greatly enhance the learning that's taking place.

Session 10 Individual Interviews

ASSESSMENT

Individual Interviews Addition & Subtraction, Place Value

Overview

Starting today, or very soon, the teacher conducts individual interviews with children to get a sense of their strategies for solving addition and subtraction combinations and their understanding of place value. Interviews take about 15 minutes each and may be conducted during Work Places or at another time of the day over a 2–3 week period.

You'll need

★ Individual Interview: Addition & Subtraction, Place Value (Blackline 1.17, run a class set)

★ 20 buttons, or other small counting objects

★ a pencil and some slips of paper

Blackline 1.17

NAME _____ DATE _____

Individual Interview Addition & Subtraction, Place Value

Addition and Subtraction Strategies

5	7	2	5	6
+ 0	+ 1	+ 6	+ 5	+ 5

10	9	8	9	13
+ 3	+ 6	+ 5	+ 9	+ 4

6	9	8	9	10
− 0	− 1	− 2	− 9	− 5

8	8	16	16	17
− 4	− 5	− 10	− 9	− 7

Place Value

☐ Can read the number 14 _____

☐ Can count out 14 objects accurately _____

☐ Checks counting accuracy by _____

☐ Shows the 4 in 14 with 4 objects _____

☐ Shows the 1 in 14 with 10 objects _____

In addition to giving paper-and-pencil assessments, collecting work samples, and observing children at work, many teachers like to conduct individual interviews. In our own classrooms, we are able to learn a great deal about our students by watching them at work, listening to them explain their thinking

Session 10 Individual Interviews (cont.)

in small and large group settings, and by holding informal conversations with them during Work Places. We also like to conduct a set of interviews with all of our students early in the fall to collect baseline information about their understandings in three key areas—addition, subtraction, and place value. Later in the year, these tests and others reappear in paper-and-pencil form, but this early in the year, it pays to talk with children.

These individual interviews take about 15 minutes per child and consist of two sets of questions. One set revolves around students' strategies for solving addition and subtraction combinations. The other looks at children's grasp of place value. If you decide to conduct these interviews, you'll want to run a copy of the interview sheet for each of your students (Blackline 1.17), label sheets with students' names, collect some small counting objects, and read through the interview instructions carefully. Plan to pull children aside one by one during Work Places, or at another time of day when your class is able to work or play independently. Depending on your class size, it may take several weeks to get to all your students. Though this requires extra effort, the information gained is very useful, and the opportunity to interact with each child individually is invaluable.

Looking at Addition & Subtraction Strategies

The top portion of the interview sheet shows 10 addition and 10 subtraction combinations. These problems will allow you see how each child adds and subtracts 0's, 1's, 2's, 10's (10 + 3, 16 − 10, and 17 − 7), and 9's (9 + 6 or 16 − 9). You'll also be able to see how they deal with adding and subtracting doubles (5 + 5 or 8 − 4) and neighbor numbers (6 + 5 or 8 − 7).

As you point to each addition and subtraction combination, have the child read it aloud and tell you the answer. (If she reads a combination incorrectly, help her read it again.) If she reads the combination and gives the correct answer immediately, just circle the fact. If she answers incorrectly or takes more than a second or two to come up with the answer, don't correct her or advise her to speed up. Just ask her how she got the answer and jot notes right on the interview sheet. Watch for her strategies—her ways of figuring things out.

$$
\begin{array}{ccccc}
5 & 7 & 2 & 5 & 6 \\
+\,0 & +\,1 & +\,6 & +\,5 & +\,5 \\
\hline
\end{array}
$$

Teacher *Let's look at the addition and subtraction facts on this page. Please read the first one and tell me the answer.*

Session 10 Individual Interviews (cont.)

Child *What if I don't know the answers to all of them?*

Teacher *That's okay. I'm eager to see how you figure out some of the things you don't know already.*

Child *5 + 0—easy! It's 5.*

Teacher *What about the next one?*

Child *7 + 1. That's 8.*

Teacher *Okay.*

Child *2 + 6...ummmm...8.*

Teacher *Great! How did you figure that one out?*

Child *I went 6—7, 8.*

Teacher *What about the next one?*

Child *5 + 5, that's 10.*

Teacher *And the next?*

Child *6 + 5.* (Child is silent a moment, figuring.) *11.*

Teacher *How do you know?*

Child *Well, if 5 and 5 is 10, 6 is 1 more, so the answer has to be 11.*

$$\left(\begin{array}{c} 5 \\ + 0 \\ \hline \end{array}\right) \quad \left(\begin{array}{c} 7 \\ + 1 \\ \hline \end{array}\right) \quad \begin{array}{c} 2 \\ + 6 \\ \hline \end{array} \quad \left(\begin{array}{c} 5 \\ + 5 \\ \hline \end{array}\right) \quad \begin{array}{c} 6 \\ + 5 \\ \hline \end{array}$$

counted on from 6   worked from 5 + 5

Child *What are you doing on that paper?*

Teacher *I'm marking your answers. If you know a fact very quickly, I circle it. If you take awhile to figure it out, I write down how you do it. I'm very interested in seeing what you do to figure out the facts you don't already know.*

Continue in this fashion until you've worked your way through all the facts on the sheet. At this point, we can see that the child above probably knows about adding 0's, 1's, and at least some of the doubles. She also has some efficient ways to work with facts she doesn't know immediately.

Session 10 Individual Interviews (cont.)

Checking Place Value Understandings

> **Teacher** (Write the number 14 on a slip of paper.) *What number is this?*

> **Child** *14.* (If the child can't read the number, make a note of it and read it to him.)

> **Teacher** *Please take 14 buttons out of the basket and put them here on the table.* (Child counts out 14 buttons.)

> **Teacher** *How can you be sure you really have 14?* (Watch how the child checks himself. Does he re-count them by 1's or by 2's? Does he group them in some fashion to show that he has 14? What does he say or do? Make a note of it on the interview sheet.)

> **Teacher** (Show the child the number 14 on the slip of paper and circle the 4.) *Please show me with your buttons what this part of the number means.*

> **Child** (Pulls aside 4 buttons to show.) *4.* (Important: If the child only says 4 and doesn't use the buttons to show, be sure to remind him to do so.)

> **Teacher** (Show the child the number 14 on the slip of paper again and circle the 1 this time.) *Please show me with your buttons what this part of the number means.*

At this point in the year, most children will pull aside 1 button. A few older or very advanced children may show you 10. Either way, you want to explore just a bit further. Let's look at what to do with the children who show you 1 button.

Session 10 Individual Interviews (cont.)

Teacher *So you are showing me that this part of the number* (point to the 4 in the number 14) *means 4, and this part of the number* (point to the 1 in the number 14) *means 1.* (Child nods happily.) *I'm wondering about all these extra buttons here in the middle. What about them?*

Child *Oh, they don't really matter. I'm not sure what they're for.*

This early in the fall, most second graders will be unconcerned about the remaining 9 buttons. A few will count them and puzzle, but not for long. Every so often, a student may push the 9 and the 1 together and say, "Hey, wait a minute! That doesn't mean 1—it really means 10!" These children are the fence-sitters, just beginning to understand the nature of our place value system. You'll find more on the fence by midyear.

Now let's look at what to do with the children who show you 10 buttons in the first place.

Teacher *So you are showing me that this part of the number* (point to the 4 in the number 14) *means 4, and this part of the number* (point to the 1 in the number 14) *means 10. But this number* (point again to the 1 in the number 14) *says 1! Why are you showing me 10?*

Child *Because the 1 doesn't mean 1 when it's there. It means 10. It means 1 group of 10 and 4 more!*

Session 10 Individual Interviews (cont.)

Most children who show you 10 in the first place aren't going to be pushed out of their convictions easily. By the end of this year, most, if not all of your children should be at this level.

ASSESSMENT TIPS ▶ Looking at Interview Results

What should you do with these interviews? What can you learn about students as individuals and as a group, and how should that information impact your instruction?

First of all, take a good look at each interview sheet and then save them in children's work sample files for later. You will conduct similar tests later in the year and will find this baseline information very useful. No matter what the results of the first round, you will see growth in the months to come. This early in the fall, most of your students will demonstrate lots of counting behavior when they add and subtract. A few children may know some or all of the facts immediately, and many will be quick at adding and subtracting 0's and 1's. Some of your students will set up the problems on their fingers and count by 1's. Others may count on (6 + 5 is *6—7, 8, 9, 10, 11*) or backwards (8 − 5 is *8—7, 6, 5, 4, 3*).

You may also see the beginnings of more sophisticated strategies. A few children may report that 8 − 4 is 4 because 4 + 4 is 8. Some may tell you that 9 + 6 is 15 because 10 + 6 is 16, and 9 is 1 less than 10. The Number Corner activities, whole group lessons, and Work Places will help students move from counting behaviors so typical of primary children to more efficient methods as the year progresses.

A few students may be confused about subtraction. It's not unusual for children to misread subtraction as addition, or to add the numbers instead of subtracting them, even if they read the combination correctly. Sometimes they'll add the two quantities and then subtract one of them, so the answer to 6 − 4 will be 6 (6 + 4 = 10 − 4 = 6). If you encounter students who seem confused about the process of subtraction, you might want to explore a little further. Try posing a subtraction problem in the form of a story—*I had 5 goldfish and 3 of them died. How many were left?* Most second graders will make sense of this situation and correctly answer 2.

Few students will have solid place value foundations yet. Although most will be able to read the number 14 and count out 14 buttons accurately, few will comprehend the complexities of our number system. The idea that the numeral 1 can mean 1, 10, 100, or 1,000 depending on its placement is quite abstract. This is the year most children will move from counting by 1's to thinking and working in multiples of 5's, 10's, and 100's. Given many opportunities to make sense of numbers, most students will be well on their way to understanding place value by the end of second grade.

Session 10 Individual Interviews (cont.)

How should this information impact your instruction? You've probably discovered that your children are working at many different levels. What should you do for the few who seem quite confused or obviously advanced? We find that the information we derive from individual interviews tends to heavily impact the interactions we have with children during Work Places. As we nestle in with individuals, we are able to pitch our questions and challenges with greater accuracy and to individualize instruction as we move around the room. As our lessons change from patterning and sorting to whole number operations later in the fall, we have the information we need to help us meet individual needs. A spinner addition game can be used to help children understand the process of addition, or gain proficiency with a set of facts or strategies, or study probability. This knowledge will also help us ask more appropriate questions in our Problems & Investigations lessons whether those lessons involve sorting, patterning, number, geometry or data analysis. While the individual interviews may not alter the main course of your instruction, they can help you fine-tune your interactions with individuals.

Session 11

PROBLEMS & INVESTIGATIONS

WORK SAMPLE   HOME CONNECTIONS

Growing Patterns   What Do You Notice About The 2's Chart?

Overview

Students label the 2's chart they made yesterday and discuss the things they notice. Then each child notes some of his or her observations and predictions on a record sheet. These sheets may be saved as work samples.

You'll need

★ the 2's chart your students made yesterday

★ a black, wide-tip marking pen

★ 2's Chart record sheet (Blackline 1.18, run a class set)

★ Home Connections Blacklines HC 2.1–2.3

Skills

★ counting by 2's

★ describing and extending a growing pattern

★ making generalizations and predictions

★ exploring functions

★ doing mental arithmetic

Post the 2's chart that your class made yesterday. Take a minute to look at each row with the children and record how many eyes, feet, or whatever it was they chose to draw, there are in each row.

Then have your students tell you what they notice about the chart. Their comments will probably range all the way from remarks about specific pictures to visual and number patterns they're able to see. As the discussion proceeds, be sure to extend children's thinking just a little bit beyond what they can see by posing such questions as:

• How many (eyes) would you see in the row after the last one on our chart? How do you know?

• If I was looking at a row with 16 (eyes) which row would I be looking at? How did you figure it out?

• How many (eyes) do you think there would be in the 10th row? How did you figure it out?

• What about the 20th row? What about the 100th row? (This sounds a little farfetched, we know, but you may have a few children who are able to make the generalization that with a growing pattern of 2's, the number of (eyes) is

Session 11 What Do You Notice... (cont.)

always double the row number. This kind of generalization is what you're hoping for in the end, but it's a long road.)

After some discussion, send your children out to write some of their observations on a 2's Chart record sheet.

Blackline 1.18

NAME _____ DATE _____

2's Chart record sheet

Please write down 3 things that you notice about our 2's chart.

1 _____

2 _____

As children finish writing their observations, you might want to have them share their papers with at least one other student before they turn them in. Then have them get their work folders and go out to Work Places if there's time.

. . . .

Note If you want to make your class 2's Chart even more informative and eye-catching, post some of the children's comments. We usually select a comment from every student's paper as we read through the sheets, type them up on the computer in standard spelling using a size 36 font or larger, print them out, cut them apart, and glue them to the chart (or post nearby). The children love rereading their own observations and those of their friends, and if you post the chart out in the hall, you're also likely to see parents, teachers, and students from other classes taking time to read what your children have written.

. . . .

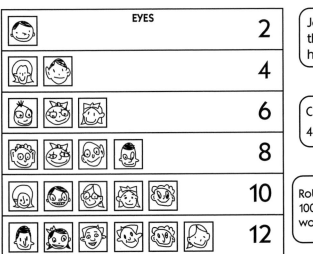

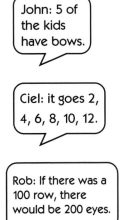

John: 5 of the kids have bows.

Ciel: it goes 2, 4, 6, 8, 10, 12.

Rob: If there was a 100 row, there would be 200 eyes.

Session 11 What Do You Notice… (cont.)

ASSESSMENT TIPS ▶ Looking at Children's Work

This is another set of papers you may want to save in the children's work sample files. They will be asked to make observations about a chart for 3's later in the year, and it's both fascinating and valuable to be able to compare and contrast the two sets of work.

Even after group discussion, the task of writing observations about the chart will not be easy for some of your students. This early in the year, many children will write about the pictures themselves rather than the numbers or the patterns. You will see comments such as, "Three kids have bows"; or "Two kids have blonde hair"; or "Lots of kids have black hair." But even these comments are mathematical in the sense that they involve counting and sorting. Here are some other things to look for as you examine each child's paper before filing it:

• Has he or she made any observations about the counting pattern? (e.g., "It goes 2, 4, 6, 8, 10, 12"; or "It is made out of 2's"; or "The numbers count by 2's.")

• Has he or she made any observations about the arrangement of the pictures? (e.g., "It looks like a staircase"; or "It looks like a half pyramid"; or "The pictures go 1, 2, 3, 4, 5, 6.")

• Has he or she been able to make any generalizations or predictions? (e.g., "If there were 7 rows, there would be 14 eyes"; or "In the 10th row there will be 20 eyes"; or "The number of eyes is just double the number of faces"; or "The number of eyes is always even." Although you can elicit remarks like these in discussion, it's rare to see them in writing at this point in the year. As children continue to work with growing patterns through the year, however, these observations will become more typical.)

Here are two work samples from one of our second grade classes. These children voted on twins for their 2's chart.

Blackline 1.18
NAME _____Briana_____ DATE _____
2's Chart record sheet

Please write down 3 things that you notice about our 2's chart.

1 On row 1 and 2 there are
   Preple Shrt and pants.

2 they go by two's

3 Some have Black hair and
   Brown hair.

Blackline 1.18
NAME _____Rod_____ DATE _____
2's Chart record sheet

Please write down 3 things that you notice about our 2's chart.

1 it LUKS LiKe A
   HAF PerUMid

2 iFTeHr WUS A loo roe
   ther wiL bee 200 Heds

3 it MAd OWt
   oF 2

Session 11 What Do You Notice... (cont.)

 HOME CONNECTION 2

Activity Searching for Pairs (Blacklines HC 2.1–2.2, pp. 5–6)
Worksheet 2's to the Rescue! (Blackline HC 2.3, p. 7)

It's time to send another activity and worksheet home with children. This week, both are designed to reinforce the work you're doing with multiples of 2.

Blackline HC 2.1 Use after Unit 1, Session 11. Run back-to-back with HC 2.2.

NAME _____ DATE _____

Home Connection 2 ★ Activity

NOTE TO FAMILIES

During the past couple of weeks, we've been working hard on counting patterns. The ability to think and work in 2's, 5's, 10's, and 100's is very useful in solving all kinds of arithmetic problems. These patterns also help children make the kinds of generalizations so often seen in algebra. If you know that 1 bike has 2 wheels and 2 bikes have 4 wheels, and 3 bikes have 6, you can figure out how many wheels 100 bikes have. It's not far from there to the generalization that any number of bikes has twice the number of wheels, or 2B = W. To practice the 2's counting pattern and just have a little fun, I'm asking you to work with your child to find and list some of the many things around your house that come in pairs.

Searching for Pairs

Search your home for things that come in pairs—shoes, mittens, what else can you find? List some of your discoveries below:

Blackline HC 2.3

NAME _____ DATE _____

Home Connection 2 ★ Worksheet

NOTE TO FAMILIES

Here's a worksheet designed to give your child more practice thinking and working in 2's.

2's to the Rescue!

Write the numbers from 1 to 30 in the grid below. Then color in the count-by-2 numbers, starting with 2 (2, 4, 6, 8, and so on).

Now try these number combinations and problems. Use the grid to help if you want.

4 + 2 = ____	14 + 2 = ____	24 + 2 = ____	8 + 2 = ____
18 + 2 = ____	28 + 2 = ____	16 – 2 = ____	26 – 2 = ____
10 – 2 = ____	20 – 2 = ____	30 – 2 = ____	

4 2-spotted ladybugs

10 honey bees

6 2-spotted ladybugs

20 honey bees

How many spots in all? _____

How many wings in all? _____

How many spots in all? _____

How many wings in all? _____

The challenge! 16 wings—how many honey bees? _____ (Hint: Draw a picture on the back to help.)

Session 12

PROBLEMS & INVESTIGATIONS

WORK
SAMPLE

Growing Patterns Extending the 2's Chart

Overview

Children work from the class 2's chart to circle all the multiples of 2 on a hundreds grid. Then they write observations about the resulting patterns. These sheets may be saved in their work sample files.

Skills

★ counting by 2's

★ reading numbers to 100

★ using patterns to solve problems

★ describing and extending a pattern

★ making generalizations and predictions

You'll need

★ the 2's chart your students made

★ Finding 2's on the Hundreds Grid (Overhead 1.5)

★ Patterns & Problems with 2's (Overhead 1.6)

★ Finding 2's On the Hundreds Grid (Blackline 1.19, run a class set)

★ Patterns & Problems with 2's (Blackline 1.20, run a class set)

★ pencils and crayons

Distribute pencils and copies of the Finding 2's on the Hundreds Grid sheets. Explain that you will work together to circle all the numbers that show up on the class 2's chart and then extend the pattern even further. While students work on their papers and you work at the overhead using Overhead 1.5, pose the following questions:

• How many eyes in the first row of our chart? 2? Let's circle that number on our sheets. Please circle your numbers in pencil.

Session 12 Extending the 2's Chart (cont.)

• How many eyes in the second row of our chart? 4? Let's circle that number on our sheets.

• What numbers will we circle next? 6, 8, 10, 12? We're out of numbers on the class 2's chart. Now what? It'll be 14? How do you know? Now what? 16? What makes you so sure? Do you notice any patterns so far?

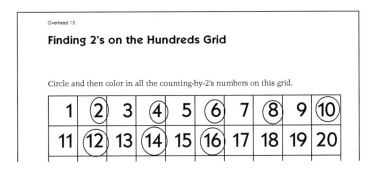

When you've worked up to 14 or 16 together, explain that you'd like them to keep working on their own to circle all the multiples of 2 on their sheets—all the numbers that count by 2's. Ask the children to circle their numbers in pencil first and then color them in. Before they go off to work on their own, it's fun to ask whether or not they think the 100 will wind up being circled and find out why they think so.

As children begin to finish this task, gather them together for a minute to show Overhead 1.6.

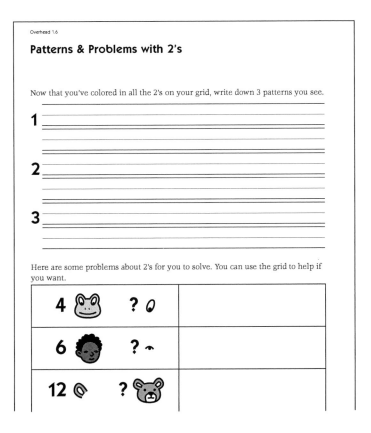

Session 12 Extending the 2's Chart (cont.)

Take a minute to discuss some of the patterns they've discovered now that they've colored in the multiples of 2, from 2 to 100. (Did 100 get colored in? Why? If you saw 100 [eyes], how many [faces] would you be looking at? What makes you think so?) Again, you're asking them to record some of their observations about the patterns that have emerged on the grid. At the bottom of the sheet, you're also asking them to solve some problems about 2's. Read the first one together—4 frogs, how many eyes? Some children may pop out with the answer, while others won't be so sure. How could one go about solving this problem? Then read the third problem together—12 ears, how many teddy bear heads? This and the fourth problem (not shown) are a bit different from the first two. Solicit ideas and strategies for dealing with these problems and then send them back to work.

As they finish both papers, you may want to have them share their work with at least one other student. If they didn't get the same answers for the four problems at the bottom of the page, ask them to work together until they've found answers that agree. This kind of collaboration and sharing will go better for some children than others, but we think it's reasonable to ask that they try. As the year goes along, their reasoning abilities will improve, and students will get used to checking with one another rather than always turning to the teacher to see if they're correct.

WORK PLACE NOTES

Most of your students will probably need the entire session to do the two record sheets discussed on the preceding pages. Some may need even more time than you've allotted. If you do have students who finish early, however, they can get their work folders and use the Work Places at the rug or in some other area that doesn't interfere with the rest of the class.

One thing you might consider, too, is using tomorrow's math session to focus exclusively on the Work Places instead of moving ahead with Session 13. An occasional "Work Places Only Day" gives you a chance to review any Work Places that aren't going as smoothly as you'd like, give children who need more time a chance to finish up work from the day before, and let students have a long uninterrupted session with the Work Places. Given the fact that many second graders learn as much, if not more, by participating in Work Place activities than in whole group problems and investigations, it's important to keep a balance between the two.

ASSESSMENT TIPS ▶ Looking at Children's Work

· With the completion of the two sets of papers in the session, your work with 2's
· is finished. Children will do similar work with 3's later in the year. We have
· found it very useful to save all three papers (one from yesterday, two from to-
· day) in each child's work sample file for purposes of comparison later on.

Session 12 Extending the 2's Chart (cont.)

While most children will find it relatively easy to circle and color the multiples of 2 on the hundreds grid, and many will see a variety of patterns, some of your students may find it difficult to write about what they see. It's typical for early second graders to represent the patterns they see with pictures or diagrams, rather than writing about them. They may notice that one column of numbers isn't colored and the next is. It's an ABAB pattern—no stripe, stripe, no stripe, stripe, but it's difficult to express what they're seeing so perhaps they'll write

or, "no circles, circles, no circles, circles."

Here's another pattern children often notice on the grid: "1, 11, 21, 31, 41, 51, 61, 71, 81, 91" or "2, 22, 32, 42, 52, 62, 72, 82, 92" and so on.

Although some of your students will be able to write statements about the patterns rather than representing them with pictures or numbers alone, the latter has to be acceptable and even celebrated. Finding a pattern and inventing some way to represent it on paper is quite significant.

Here are some other things to look for:

• the types of patterns children discover. Most will spot the vertical stripes immediately. Does any one notice diagonal patterns, or see patterns in the numbers? (Many will be intrigued with the fact that the numbers in the first column all end with a 1, the numbers in the second column all end with a 2, and so on.)

• very unusual observations. A boy in one of our second grades who had exceptionally high spatial intelligence wrote, "If you fan-fold the chart and look on one side, you can only see one color." Children's observations so often provide insights into their ways of thinking.

• the fact that some children are able to write about the patterns they see: "Some of the numbers aren't colored in"; or "Every number in the 2's line and the 4's line is colored in"; or "There's a blank column and a circled column."

• the fact that a few students may be able to make more sweeping mathematical statements, such as, "The numbers that we circled are going by 2's," or "Odd numbers are not circled"; or "Every 10 is colored"; or "Only even numbers are circled."

Session 13

PROBLEMS & INVESTIGATIONS

Math Bucket Sorting Finding Many Ways

Overview
Children work in small groups to sort collections of objects in as many ways as they can think of.

Skills
★ sorting objects in a variety of ways

You'll need
★ *The Button Box* by Margarette Reid (optional)

★ the math buckets—buttons, shells, frogs, bugs, and glass blobs (Every 3 or 4 children in your class will need a collection of objects. You may want to divide the items from a couple of the buckets so you have 3 sets of buttons, 3 sets of shells, 2 sets of frogs, and so on.)

★ Unifix cubes

Introduce this activity by reading *The Button Box* by Margarette Reid, if you have it. It's a nice way to reinforce and validate all the sorting you've been doing in the past 2 weeks, and also a nice way to talk just a bit about sorting in our daily lives. Can your children think of any way they use sorting at home or other places they go?

If you don't have the book, you still might want to start out with a short discussion about sorting in our daily lives. From there, take out the button bucket and explain that you want to introduce an activity that will help children get even better at sorting things and really stretch their brains.

Sitting in a circle on the rug with everyone watching, have the two students beside you be part of your "team" for now. Take a small handful of buttons out of the button bucket and ask the class how you might sort them. Ideas will probably fly for a minute—by color: red, green, blue, yellow, silver; by size; by number of holes; and so on. Ask your two teammates which idea they want to try first, and work together to sort the handful of buttons in that way.

4 holes

2 holes

no holes (shanks)

Session 13 Finding Many Ways (cont.)

Explain to the rest of your students that they'll be working in teams in just a few minutes, and that in order to get credit for each sorting idea, they'll need to decide what to call each subset, raise their hands as a team, and name each subset as you come around and point to it.

Model this procedure with your team, push the buttons back together, and go through the whole process once or twice more, using a different attribute—one suggested by the children—each time. When you think most of your students have the idea, send them out in teams of three or four, each with their own collection of math bucket items, to start sorting. As they get to their tables, remind them that they should be working with a small handful of items—no more than 30 pieces—rather than the entire collection.

Watch for the hands to go up, taking the opportunity to reinforce the idea that everyone in the team has to be ready, has to have his hand up, before you'll came to the group. If you insist that they all name the subsets each time, they'll work together better and there will be less likelihood that one or two children will take over. We usually reward each round of sorting a team does with a Unifix cube; children seem to like that concrete acknowledgment. The more competitive youngsters seem to be looking over their shoulders often to see how many cubes the other groups are getting but, for the most part, the cubes seem to help focus efforts and keep children really stretching for new ideas.

You may have to do a bit of teaching right on the spot, as some groups may come up with sorting methods that involve unrelated categories ("See our shells? We have the big ones here, the brown ones over here, the pretty ones here, and the broken ones here.") Take the opportunity to demonstrate and explain related categories quickly. ("This is great! I wonder if you could sort all your shells by color next time. You already have the brown ones here. What would you call this shell? White? Great! How about putting all the white ones in another pile, and all the gray ones here. That way, all your shells will be sorted by color.") You may have to repeat this sort of instruction several times with some of your groups. If it looks like an overwhelming majority of them don't get it, you might pull your students back quickly and do more whole-group modeling; more than likely, some of them will already know what to do. Remember there will be more opportunities to sort items later.

Session 13 Finding Many Ways (cont.)

At the end of the activity, collect all the cubes from around the tables, snap them together, and ask children to estimate and count how many sorting methods the entire group came up with. This acknowledges everyone's incredible work and effort, without making it seem like it was a contest all along.

 WORK PLACE NOTES

If there's time at the end of the session, send your students out to Work Places with the reminder that they have about four more days, counting today, to get around to each activity. Are they remembering to mark where they've been each time on their planners and to store their finished papers on one side of their folders, with unfinished work on the other side?

Session 14

PROBLEMS & INVESTIGATIONS

Math Bucket Sorting Venn Diagrams

Overview

Students use sorting cards to sort collections of items from the math buckets in much the same way as they sorted beetle glyphs during Session 5. Because they'll be sorting by unrelated categories sometimes, such as "large" and "4 holes," they will use a 2-circle Venn diagram to define their sets visually.

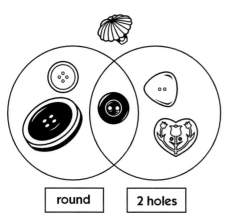

round   2 holes

You'll need

★ the math buckets—buttons, shells, frogs, and bugs (Every 3–4 children in your class will need a collection of objects. You may want to divide the items from each bucket into 2 ziplocks for this activity. You won't be able to use the glass blobs for this lesson, as there aren't any sorting cards for them.)

★ Venn Diagram Sorting Mats (Blackline 1.21, 1 copy for each group of 3–4 children)

★ Math Bucket Sorting cards

★ Unifix cubes

Skills

★ creating and analyzing Venn diagrams

★ sorting objects by related and unrelated categories

Gather your students in a discussion circle. Explain that they're going to start in the same groups they were in yesterday, and that they'll be using the math buckets to do a different kind of sorting activity today. With two children as your volunteer "team," demonstrate the following:

1. Get the button bucket and the corresponding set of sorting cards. With the two children helping you, lay the cards out on the floor one by one, reading them as you go.

2. Open the button bucket and take out a small handful of buttons—*no more than 30.*

3. Shuffle the button sorting cards thoroughly and then turn them face down. Let each of your two volunteers pick one. Have these children read their cards to the group and then lay each card beside one of the sorting circles on your mat.

4. Work with your two volunteer teammates to sort the handful of buttons according to the two cards. Your students may or may not remember this activity

Session 14 Venn Diagrams (cont.)

from two weeks ago when you did it with their beetle glyphs, but it's exactly the same idea. As with the beetles, you'll probably end up with four groups of buttons—one group inside each circle, one group that shares both attributes, and a fourth group that has neither.

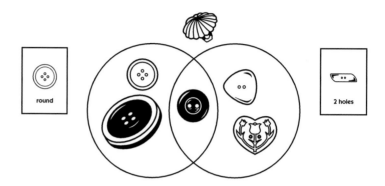

Explain to the children that once their group has gotten this far, they need to raise their hands. When they do, you'll come around to look at what they've done, award them a Unifix cube for their work, and ask them to push their objects back together, pick two more sorting cards, and repeat the process.

After demonstrating the process once or twice, send your students out to work in the same groups they did yesterday. You might even want to have them start with the same math buckets they used yesterday, and then after 5 or 10 minutes, trade buckets and cards with another group. Remind them that they're to *shuffle the cards thoroughly and pick two at random each time they sort*. Also, they're not to use any more than 30 items from their math buckets. Be aware, too, that even though they've seen this kind of sorting demonstrated with the beetle glyphs and now with the buttons, some children might have trouble with the idea of intersecting sets. You might have do a little more teaching as you circulate, showing them that sometimes objects fit into both categories and can be placed on the mat in the spot where the two circles come together, and sometimes some of the objects don't fit in either category and have to be left off the mat entirely.

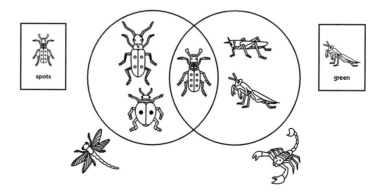

After another 10 minutes or so with new buckets, you might want to end the activity by having the groups leave their final sorts arranged carefully on the

Session 14 Venn Diagrams (cont.)

mats. The two sorting cards they used for this final sort should be laid face-down next to the correct circles. The remaining cards should be put away inside the math buckets so they don't confuse anyone. Children can then circulate singly or in pairs to guess how each group has sorted its objects. When they think they have it, they can peek at the sorting cards to check. This step is optional, but it's lots of fun and really requires some good thinking.

WORK PLACE NOTES

If there's time at the end of this activity, send your students out to Work Places with their folders. There are two more sessions after this one before the Work Places change again, which should give the children enough time to finish the games and activities in this set. If you think your students haven't had enough time with the set, you might want to schedule an extra day just for Work Places.

Another thing you might want to do at this point is go through the children's work folders and check the papers they've done so far. If you find papers that still need to be finished or discover that some of the children haven't yet done all of the Work Places, you may want to circle those activities on their planning sheets as a reminder.

Session 15

PROBLEMS & INVESTIGATIONS

Which One Doesn't Belong?

Overview
Children examine 4 pictures at a time and decide which one doesn't belong with the rest of the set.

You'll need
★ Which One Doesn't Belong? (Overhead 1.7)

Skills
★ finding likenesses and differences

★ using attributes to eliminate and select group members

Show the first half of this transparency to your students and explain that one of the four pictures doesn't belong with the others. Ask them to think about it for a minute and share their ideas with someone sitting next to them. Do they both agree? Ask them to discuss reasons with their neighbors as to why the one picture does not belong. Even if they agree on the one that does not belong, do they have the same reasons for thinking it should be eliminated?

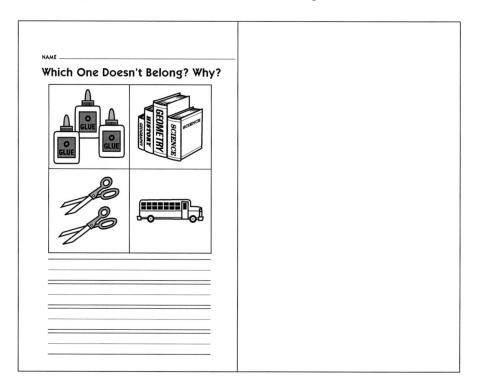

Now ask children to share their reasons with the group. Solicit a number of different ideas and explanations.

John   *I think the bus doesn't belong because it's the only one with wheels.*

Session 15 Which One Doesn't Belong (cont.)

Brianna I think the bus doesn't belong because in all the other pictures there's more than one thing.

Evan I think the books should be crossed out because they're the only ones with long words.

Alexandra The scissors are the only ones with handles—cross them out.

It is always interesting to hear what children have to say, and many youngsters will be quite motivated to listen to each other because there are so many different ideas. Some groups have found it possible to justify eliminating any one of the four pictures, all with good reason.

Acknowledge everyone's good thinking and pick one child's idea to record. Have that child come up to the overhead and cross out the item she believes does not belong. Record her reason for eliminating the item on the lines below the four pictures as she dictates. Then show the other half of the transparency and repeat the process.

DATE _____

Overhead 1.7

Which One Doesn't Belong? Why?

9	**6**
2	**14**

Again, you'll find that your children may be able to come up with reasons to eliminate any of the four numbers from the collection.

Corey Get rid of the 14 because it's the only one with 2 numbers. It's the only teen number.

Joey Rose I think we should cross out the 9 because it's the only odd number. You can't get to it when you count by 2's.

Session 15 Which One Doesn't Belong (cont.)

Kaitlin I think the 14 should go because it's the only one made out of all straight lines—the other numbers all have curves in them.

David 2 is the lowest number. All the rest are higher, so get rid of the 2.

Gary 6 is kind of in the middle. I think we should get rid of the 6.

When you're finished with both sets of pictures, explain to the children that this activity, along with many of the others you've done over the past week or so, will show up as a new Work Place in a couple of days.

 WORK PLACE NOTES

Which One Doesn't Belong? is a fairly short activity, and your students will probably have plenty of time to go out to Work Places today. Remind children again that they have today and tomorrow to get around to all the games and activities in the set. If you circled certain pictures on their planners to indicate which Work Places they still need to do, you'll probably want to explain your marking system.

Session 16

PROBLEMS & INVESTIGATIONS

Pattern Block Growing Patterns

Overview

The teacher displays 2 growing patterns at the overhead and asks children to build and discuss what they think will come next in each case.

You'll need

★ Pattern Block Growing Patterns (Overhead 1.8)

★ pattern blocks

★ overhead pattern blocks

★ Home Connection Blacklines HC 3.1–3.5

Skills

★ recognizing, describing, reproducing, and extending patterns

★ exploring functions

HOME CONNECTIONS

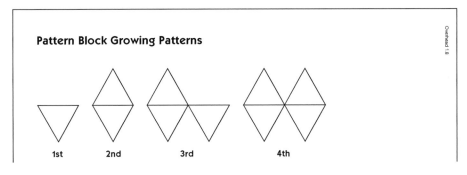

Pattern Block Growing Patterns

Overhead 1.8

1st   2nd   3rd   4th

Show the first growing pattern at the overhead—the sequence that shows 1, 2, 3, and then 4 triangular pattern blocks. Ask your students to work in groups of 2 or 3 to copy the pattern with their pattern blocks. (They'll have to pool their green triangles in order to do this.) Then have them tell you what they notice about the sequence. Is there, in fact, a pattern? Is there anything that changes in a predictable way with each new arrangement? Many will probably notice that the arrangements have 1 new triangle each time.

Session 16 Pattern Block Growing Patterns (cont.)

Then ask them to use their pattern blocks to build what they think the next arrangement, the 5th arrangement, might look like. After they've had a minute to build, have them share their ideas with one another. Many will probably build a design with 5 green triangles. Perhaps it will be similar to the arrangements shown so far, or perhaps they'll decide to place the 5th green triangle somewhere else, as shown in Possibility 3 and Possibility 4.

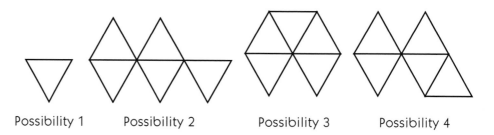

Possibility 1   Possibility 2   Possibility 3   Possibility 4

A few might respond with a single triangle, reasoning that the pattern goes 1, 2, 3, 4; 1, 2, 3, 4; and so on.

Acknowledge all ideas and theories, and then have a volunteer come up to the overhead to count and record the number of triangles in each arrangement. Take a minute to discuss the changes from arrangement to arrangement. How many more triangles have been added each time? As the discussion proceeds and children begin to present ideas about the 5th and 6th arrangements, you may want to have them build their ideas at the overhead with transparent pattern blocks.

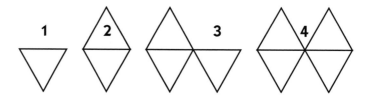

Colby *Hey, look! It's 1 triangle on the 1st arrangement; then 2 on the 2nd, 3 on the 3rd, and 4 on the 4th. The 5th arrangement has to have 5 triangles.*

Joseph *That was my idea!*

Eloise *Every time you have an even number like 2 and 4, the 2 triangles get pushed together to make a diamond. So on the 5th one, there should be a triangle hanging off the end, and on the 6th arrangement, there will be 3 diamonds.*

Sherwin *I don't get it.*

Eloise *Here—I'll show you. See?*

Session 16 Pattern Block Growing Patterns (cont.)

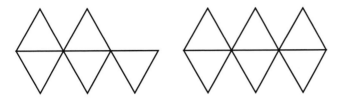

Sherwin I get it now. It's kind of like that pattern we had with Unifix cubes where it went 1, 2, 3, 4, 5, 6, and the even numbers had partners.

Teacher So if we went along with Eloise's idea, what would the 7th arrangement look like?

Rob It would have 1 triangle hanging off the end, like this:

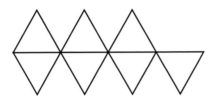

Even with children as persuasive as Colby, Rob, and Eloise, you won't have consensus on this pattern. Many children will see the connection between the arrangement number and the number of pattern blocks, and will agree with the idea that the 5th arrangement should have 5 triangles, the 6th should have 6, the 7th should have 7, and so on. But, there may not be agreement on how to arrange these triangles, and, in fact, there is no "right" answer. Many ideas can be presented and defended. The point is to reach for a generalization of some sort if the children can go that far, with whatever pattern they decide to pursue.

Teacher So, if we follow Eloise's and Rob's line of thinking, what will the 8th arrangement look like?

Corey It would be 4 and 4—4 triangles on the top and 4 on the bottom.

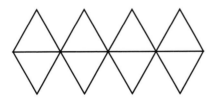

Alejandrina Hey! 8 triangles make 4 diamonds.

Teacher So 10 triangles would make...

Sarah 5 diamonds!

Teacher And 100 triangles would make...

Session 16 Pattern Block Growing Patterns (cont.)

Children *50 diamonds! That would be a long line of diamonds. We don't have that many green triangles, I bet. This is kind of like the 2's chart, remember?*

After you've worked with the first pattern on the transparency for a while, move on to the second pattern. Again, have the children take a minute to copy it with their own pattern blocks, and then ask them to share any observations they have, first with their neighbors and then with the group. What do they notice; what do they see going on here? After a bit of discussion, have them use their blocks to build what they think the 6th arrangement will look like and why. If interest remains high, you might have them build the 7th and 8th arrangements as well. Discuss.

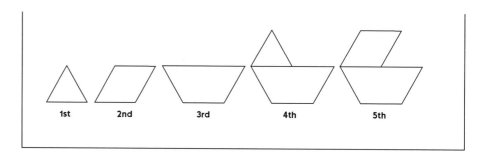

This is a particularly interesting pattern. Like the first one, it adds a green triangle, or the equivalent of a green triangle each time, but the addition is not nearly as obvious. As with the first pattern, there are many logical extensions. Again, draw out the discussion for as long as seems reasonable. Some children will be far more ready to make generalizations than others, but even the observation that the pattern grows each time is significant; the realization that it is growing by a standard amount—a green triangle—each time, is profound.

 WORK PLACE NOTES

Unless you feel that your students need an extra day with the Work Places, this is the last day with this set. Children need to finish their work here and mark the planners on their folders to indicate what they've completed. Given that not all the Work Places involve record sheets, accountability won't be perfect. It will be possible for children to mark themselves as having gone to the Geoblocks when, in fact, they haven't. In our experience, though, this isn't very likely to happen. If you feel it's been a problem with your group, you might try initialing the games and activities that don't involve record sheets as children complete them in Work Places 3 (see Session 17). One way or another, children will become more and more aware that you expect them to go to each Work Place at least once, and become increasingly accountable for their own work.

Session 16 Pattern Block Growing Patterns (cont.)

In preparation for the next round of Work Places, remove the planner from the front of each work folder and staple it at the front of any record sheets the child has completed. We usually mark each sheet in some way—with a star, a happy face, or a comment of some sort—so children and parents will know how much we value the work. Then we send these packets home with our students.

HOME CONNECTION 3

Activity Count & Compare 5's (Blacklines HC 3.1–3.4, pp. 9–12)
Worksheet 5's to the Rescue! (Blackline HC 3.5, p. 13)

It's time to send another activity and worksheet home with children. The activity is a home version of Count & Compare 5's, and the worksheet gives students a chance to do some computation with 5's.

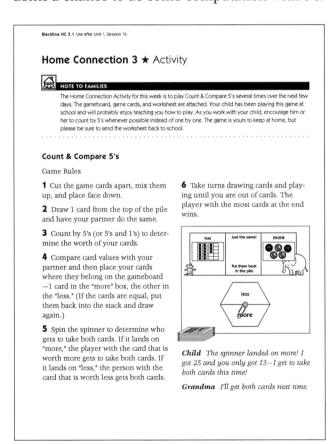

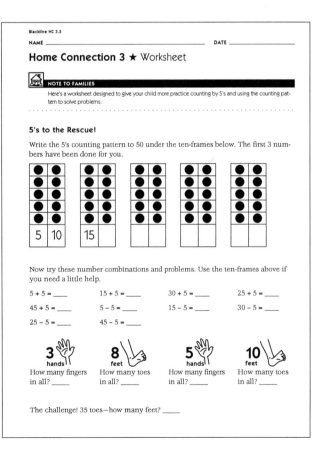

Session 17

PROBLEMS & INVESTIGATIONS

An Hour or Bust!

Overview

An Hour or Bust! is the last of the new games and activities to teach your class before introducing Work Places 3. Although children will play this game in partners during Work Places, you'll teach it as a team game—students against the teacher—in this lesson. The object of the game is to come closest to coloring in an entire clock face—60 minutes—without going over. After you've played it through with your group once or twice, you'll quickly review the other games and activities in new set of Work Places and send students out to work.

You'll need

★ An Hour or Bust! gameboard (Over-head 1.9)

★ overhead pens in several different colors

Skills

★ counting by 5's

★ reading a clock face

To start this activity, show students the gameboard transparency and discuss it for a moment.

> *Teacher* *We're going to learn one more game together before we get out the new set of Work Places. It's called An Hour or Bust!, and here's the gameboard. What do you notice about it?*

> *Children* *It has 2 clocks on it.*
> *They look like the clock in the Number Corner.*
> *They're the same—they have beans just like the big bean clock.*
> *There's a spinner on the board too, and the numbers go by 5's.*

> *Teacher* *Good observations! All of you are going to play against me, and we're going to race to see who can come closest to coloring in a whole clock face without going over. You can take up to 4 spins, but you don't have to use all of them.*

After your students have had a chance to examine the gameboard and you've explained the object of the game, decide who will start first. If it's the children, have a volunteer come up to spin the spinner, color in the requisite number of minutes, and record that number in the first box below their clock. Emphasize the need to start counting and coloring from the 12.

Session 17 An Hour or Bust! (cont.)

Teacher Let's see. Bryce came up and spun for your team. The spinner landed on 20, so he colored in 20 minutes on your clock face and wrote a 20 in your first box. Now it's my turn. The arrow landed on 15, so I'll color in 15 minutes on my clock face and write the number in the box below. Who's ahead so far?

Children We are!
We're ahead by 5 minutes!

Teacher How many more minutes do you need to fill in your entire clock face?

Children There are 60 minutes in an hour and we have 20.
It'll take 40—we have to get 40 more minutes.

Continue taking turns back and forth, coloring and recording as you go. Teams should be careful to mark each new spin on their clock face with a different color marker, and to write the number of minutes in one of the boxes below. A team may decide to stop after the first 2 spins or take as many as 4.

Teacher Oh boy. This is going to be a hard decision. You have 45 minutes on your clock. I have 50 minutes on mine and one more spin if I choose to take it. Should I stop now and take a chance that you'll get closer to 60 minutes than me, or should I take one more spin and risk getting a number that's more than 10?

Children Stay! Stay! Don't take any more spins.
No, spin! If he spins, he'll probably get 15 or 20 and go over 60 minutes, and then we'll win!

Teacher I think I'll just stay put with 50. It's your turn.

Session 17 An Hour or Bust! (cont.)

Children *We got 10!*
Now we'll be up to 55! We got closer to 60!
We won!

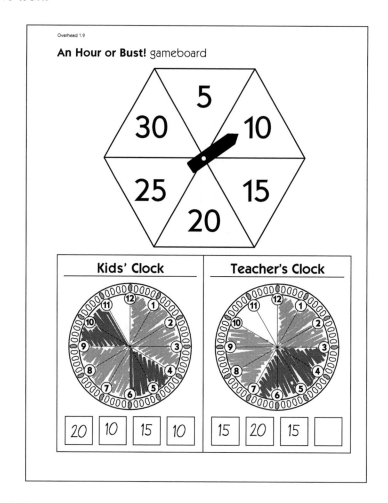

If you feel that you have enough time, erase the overhead and go through the game one more time with your class before introducing the rest of the new Work Places.

Session 17 Work Places 3

WORK PLACES

Introduce Work Places 3

Overview

Now that you've played An Hour or Bust! together, take some time to introduce the rest of the new Work Places. Children will have seen all of them in one form or another, so most of what you're showing will be review. If there's enough time at the end of the session, send them out to work.

You'll Need

★ work baskets 3A–3F set up as shown below

★ a work folder for each child with a copy of the Work Place 3 Planner stapled to the front (Blackline 1.22)

Work Places 3 Setup

3A Pattern Block Growing Patterns

This Work Place basket will need

✓ Pattern Blocks

✓ Pattern Block Growing Pattern Cards

3B An Hour or Bust!

This Work Place basket will need

✓ 3 An Hour or Bust! spinners

✓ An Hour or Bust! record sheets (Blackline 1.23, run 30 copies and place in a folder)

✓ crayons

3C Math Bucket Mystery Patterns

This Work Place basket will need

✓ the math buckets—buttons, frogs, bugs, and shells

✓ a set of sorting cards for each math bucket

3D Which One Doesn't Belong?

This Work Place basket will need

✓ Which One Doesn't Belong? record sheets (Blacklines 1.24–1.29, run 10 copies of each sheet and place in pocket folders)

Session 17 Work Places 3 (cont.)

3E Which One Doesn't Belong? Invent a Sheet

This Work Place basket will need
✓ Which One Doesn't Belong? Invention Sheets (Blackline 1.30, run 30 copies and place in a folder)
✓ Which One Doesn't Belong? Clip Art (Blacklines 1.31–1.33, run 6 copies of each sheet and place in folders)
✓ scissors, gluesticks

3F Count & Compare 2's

This Work Place basket will need
✓ 3 Count & Compare 2's gameboards
✓ 3 sets of Count & Compare 2's cards
✓ 3 Count & Compare 2's Counting Guides

Now that you've played An Hour or Bust!, take some time to introduce the other five Work Places in this new set. Students have seen all of them in one form or another over the past week or two, so you probably won't need to devote too much time to these introductions. In preparation for this part of the session, though, you'll want to read through the descriptions of the Work Places on the next few pages. Each description explains how to play the game or do the activity, and includes some "instructional considerations" for you to bear in mind as you introduce the Work Places and use them with your students over the coming days. Set up your Work Place baskets as shown on the previous page. Staple the new Work Place planners to the children's work folders.

As you begin this session, gather your students in a discussion circle and explain that you have some new Work Places to introduce. Then show them the materials in each Work Place basket as you explain the activity. When you've modeled all six Work Places, show the children their work folders with the new planners attached. Explain that three of the Work Places involve record sheets, which the students will store in their folders as they work their way through the activities. Encourage children who haven't done so already to mark their pockets "finished work" and "unfinished work" so they can see at a glance where they need to start if they haven't had a chance to complete an activity the day before.

Session 17 Work Places 3 (cont.)

finished work

unfinished work

Student I finished playing An Hour or Bust! yesterday, but we had to clean up just as I was starting Which One Doesn't Belong? That's where I'm going to start today. I'm going to do all the sheets—they're so fun!

As with Work Places 1 and 2, the work folders will also provide students a way to keep track of where they've been and where they still need to go. They are to visit each Work Place at least once over the next few days. After their first visit to a Work Place, they're to color in the star in the box below the picture of that Work Place on their planner. They can move from place to place when they choose as long as there's room, and move through the activities in any order. Once they've gone to all six Work Places, they are free to go back to their favorites, indicating each visit by marking one of the blank boxes.

If there's still enough time after you've introduced the materials and new planners, send your students off one by one with their work folders and pencils to choose their Work Places.

 WORK PLACE 3A

Pattern Block Growing Patterns

This Work Place basket will need
★ pattern blocks
★ Pattern Block Growing Pattern Cards

Skills
★ copying and extending patterns
★ exploring functions

To Work

1. Take one of the Pattern Block Growing Pattern Cards. Copy what's on the card with pattern blocks.

2. Use your blocks to build the next 2 or 3 arrangements in the sequence. Can you explain your thinking to someone else?

Session 17 Work Places 3 (cont.)

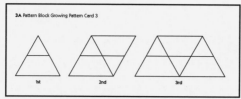 

Student Every time, it adds a big triangle—see how a red block and a green block fit together to make a big triangle? So the 1st arrangement has 1 big triangle, the 2nd has 2, the 3rd has 3, the 4th has 4, and I'm putting the 5th together right now.

3. See if you can build or imagine what the 10th arrangement in the sequence would look like and tell someone else: "The 10th one? I'm pretty sure it would have 10 of those big triangles."

4. Repeat the process with a different card. You can do as many as you like, but you need to try at least 2 or 3 different cards.

Instructional Considerations for Pattern Block Growing Patterns

We have found in our own classrooms that we've needed to spend more time at this Work Place than some of the others, talking with children about what they're doing and offering challenges or support as needed. You'll probably want to have them explain why they have built the 4th, 5th, and 6th arrangements as they have, understanding that their extensions might not match what you would have in mind.

Depending on the child and the level of interest, you might also ask what the 10th arrangement of a particular sequence would look like. A few of your students may be able to make generalizations well enough to tell you without actually building the arrangement. Others may not know, but may be interested enough to build the 7th, 8th, 9th, and 10th. In looking at their work, see if you can help them spot trends. What seems to be going on each time? Is there any relationship between the design and its arrangement number?

WORK PLACE 3B

An Hour or Bust!

This Work Place basket will need

★ 3 An Hour or Bust! spinners

★ An Hour or Bust! record sheets (Blackline 1.23, run 30 copies and place in a folder)

★ crayons

Skills

★ counting by 5's

★ reading a clock face

Session 17 Work Places 3 (cont.)

To Work

1. Get a partner, a spinner, one record sheet, and some crayons (4 different colors each). Put your name on one side of the record sheet and have your partner write her name on the other side. *You will both use the same record sheet.*

2. Decide who gets to spin first. Take your first spin, color in the number of minutes you spun starting from the 12 on your clock face. Write that number in the first box below your clock. Have your partner take a turn.

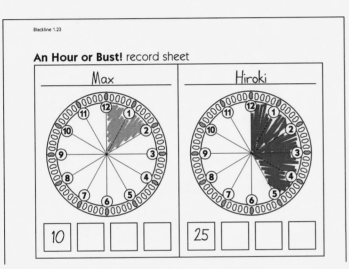
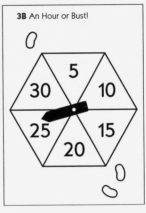

3. Take turns spinning and coloring until each of you has had 2, 3, or 4 turns. *Be sure to record each new spin with a different color crayon.* You can stop taking new turns whenever you'd like. You don't want to color in more than 60 minutes. For instance, if you spin 25 minutes on your first turn and 20 minutes on your second turn, you'll have to think hard about whether you want to stay put on your third and fourth turns or take a chance of going over 60 minutes.

4. The player closest to coloring in an hour *without going over* wins.

5. If one player goes "bust," mark an X over the number on his record sheet that caused him to go over 60 minutes.

6. Circle the winning player's clock and begin again. There is room to play 2 games on the same sheet.

7. Be sure, either now or at a later time, to play the game again so that both you and your partner will have a record sheet to put in your work folder.

Instructional Considerations for An Hour or Bust!

This is a fairly complex game, and it's possible that some of your children won't quite know what to do when they get around to it. Consider playing An Hour or Bust! again with your whole group as you get started with Work Places next session. You might also try playing the game against small groups of three or four children during Work Places in much the same manner as you played against

Session 17 Work Places 3 (cont.)

the whole group. Playing in the context of a small group may be just the step some children need in order to be able to handle the game more independently.

 WORK PLACE 3C

Math Bucket Mystery Patterns

This Work Place Basket will need

★ the math buckets—buttons, frogs, bugs, and shells

★ a set of sorting cards for each math bucket

Skills

★ sorting and patterning objects in a variety of ways

★ analyzing likenesses and differences

★ making generalizations

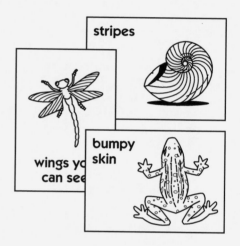

To Work

1. Take a handful of items from one of the math buckets. Find a way to sort them other than by color, and then line them up in a pattern. You can either think of your own way to sort the items or use the sorting cards for that bucket to help. Here's an example. These buttons have been sorted by the number of holes and then patterned accordingly.

4 holes 4 holes 2 holes shank 4 holes 4 holes 2 holes shank

Teacher This arrangement does not look much like a pattern unless you really study it carefully, and that's what you want to create—something tricky.

2. After you've made a mystery pattern, find a friend to come figure it out.

Instructional Considerations for Math Bucket Mystery Patterns
Following the Math Bucket Sorting lessons presented in Sessions 13 and 14, this Work Place encourages students to combine their sorting and patterning skills. The idea is to set up a pattern that isn't obvious at first glance using items from one of the buckets. If you sort by attributes other than color, size, or shape, this is quite possible to do. Here's an example:

Session 17 Work Places 3 (cont.)

In order to decipher the pattern, you have to figure out what's alike and what's different from button to button. (This pattern is ridged, non-ridged, ridged, non-ridged, and so on.)

Second graders really seem to delight in the idea of making patterns that are "mysterious" enough to stump their teachers and friends. They will often persevere at this Work Place for quite a long time, setting up pattern after pattern, each a little trickier than the one before.

We demonstrate the activity by taking a handful of items from one of the buckets, sorting carefully for the ones that match in color, setting up an absolutely obvious pattern, and telling them that if they were a year or two younger, we'd think such a pattern was a brilliant creation. Then we look through the sorting cards for the collection with which we're working. When we hit on a card or two that helps us sort in a less obvious way (say, shanks and ridges for the buttons), we use the idea to create a pattern that doesn't look much like a pattern unless carefully analyzed. This brief demonstration is enough to get most students started. Those who don't understand at first often "catch on" by watching their classmates for a bit.

WORK PLACE 3D

Which One Doesn't Belong?

This Work Place basket will need

★ Which One Doesn't Belong? record sheets (Blacklines 1.24–1.29, run 10 copies of each sheet and place in pocket folders)

Skills

★ finding likenesses and differences

★ using attributes to eliminate and select group members

To Work

1. Choose one of the sheets. Study the first group of 4 items carefully. Decide which one of the 4 you think doesn't belong and cross it out. Then write an explanation of why you crossed out that particular item on the lines below the 4 pictures.

Session 17 Work Places 3 (cont.)

2. Repeat with the other set of 4 items on the page.

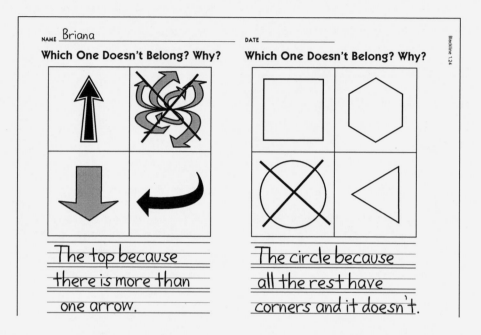

Instructional Considerations for Which One Doesn't Belong?

This Work Place is an independent version of the activity you did with your class in Session 15 and you probably won't need to do a lot of modeling. You may want to establish a minimum number of pages to be completed with each visit to this Work Place—we ask our students to do 2 sheets (4 problems) each time.

 WORK PLACE 3E

Which One Doesn't Belong? Invent a Sheet

This Work Place Basket will need

★ Which One Doesn't Belong? Invention Sheets (Blackline 1.30, run 30 copies and place in a folder)

★ Which One Doesn't Belong? Clip Art (Blacklines 1.31–1.33, run 6 copies of each sheet and place in folders)

★ scissors, glue sticks

Skills

★ finding likenesses and differences

★ using attributes to eliminate and select certain items

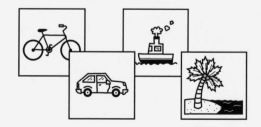

Session 17 Work Places 3 (cont.)

To Work

1. Get a Which One Doesn't Belong? Invention Sheet, a pair of scissors, a glue stick, and a sheet of clip art.

2. Look through the clip art pictures carefully and choose 4 to create a challenge for someone else in class.

3. Cut out the 4 pictures you've selected and glue them into the boxes on your invention sheet. Find 4 more for the second set of blank boxes. When you're finished, show your sheet to several classmates and see if they can solve your puzzles. Fill in the answers and explanations on the lines below each puzzle after you've had a few friends guess.

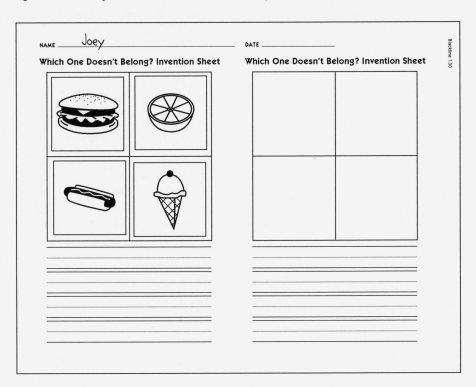

Student I chose the hamburger, the hot dog, the ice cream cone, and the orange for my first puzzle. You know why? It's because my mom says they're all junk food except for the orange!

Instructional Considerations for Which One Doesn't Belong? Invent a Sheet
You may want to introduce this Work Place a couple days after the others so children have a little time to work with the premade puzzles before they create their own. To do this, just leave one of the Work Places from the last round in Basket 3E and explain to the children that you'll introduce the new activity soon.

Session 17 Work Places 3 (cont.)

In our own classrooms, we found that the children tended to create very obvious puzzles for the first week or so; things like 3 vehicles and 1 food item, or 3 alphabet letters and a truck. Their work became a little more thoughtful on return visits and also as we encouraged them to "test" their puzzles on a friend or two before pasting the pictures down. Second graders really do enjoy challenging one another and will try hard to come up with good puzzles once they've had some experience. Remind your students to fill in the answers and explanations for their puzzles after they've shared them with a few classmates.

WORK PLACE 3F

Count and Compare 2's

This Work Place basket will need

★ 3 Count & Compare 2's gameboards

★ 3 sets of Count & Compare 2's cards

★ 3 Count & Compare 2's Counting Guides

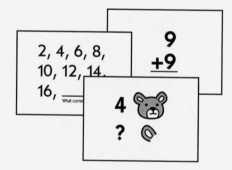

To Work

1. Find a partner.

2. Get a gameboard, a set of cards, and a counting guide from the Work Place basket. Shuffle the cards and place them face down between you and your partner.

3. Draw one card from the top of the pile and have your partner do the same.

4. Count by 2's, add the two numbers, or solve the problem to determine the worth of your card. (Some of the problem cards, like "13 boys, how many eyes?" are challenging. If you need help, use a Counting Guide.)

5. Place your cards where they belong on the gameboard—one card will be placed in the "more" box, the other in the "less" box. (If the two cards are equal, put them both back into the stack and draw again.)

6. Spin the spinner at the bottom of the gameboard to determine who gets to take both cards. If it lands on "more," the person who had the card that was worth more gets to take both the cards. If it lands on "less," the person who drew the card that was worth less gets both cards.

7. Take turns drawing cards, determining and comparing the quantities shown, and spinning until you are out of cards. The winner is the one with

Session 17 Work Places 3 (cont.)

the most cards at the end. (Or, if you like, you can let the spinner determine the overall winner of the game. If it lands on "less," the person with fewer cards wins. If it lands on "more," the person with more cards wins.)

Instructional Considerations for Count & Compare 2's

This game provides practice counting by 2's using several different prompts: dots on the ten-frames, counting sequence cards, addition facts and picture problems similar to the ones children encountered in Session 12. Even with careful modeling, you'll probably find some of your students counting the dots on the ten-frames one by one to determine the quantities on the cards. Some may also have difficulty with the picture problems, even though they've encountered similar challenges earlier in the month. We found that the counting guide helped some of our students work more effectively; be sure to model its use when you demonstrate the game the first time through.

Child *I'm not sure how to do this card.*

Teacher *What does it say?*

Child *I think it means 4 bears—how many ears? It's like one of those problems we got when we were doing 2's on the hundreds grid. But I don't remember the answer.*

Teacher *Try looking at the counting guide.*

Child *Oh, I see. If I count 4 frogs, then I can go back and count how many eyes they have.*

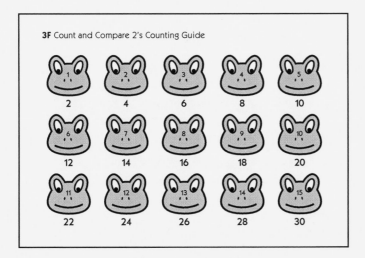

Notes

Session 18

WORK PLACES

Getting Started with Work Places 3

Overview
The teacher reviews Work Places 3 and sends children out for a long work period.

You'll need
★ work baskets 3A–3F set up for Work Places 3

★ a work folder for each child with a copy of the Work Place 3 Planner stapled to the front (Blackline 1.22)

Now that the Work Places are becoming a little more complex and demanding, it's worth devoting an entire session to their use before going on with additional group instruction, especially if children didn't have time to start work yesterday. Open today's session with the briefest of reviews, or, if your students did get out to the Work Places yesterday, take a few minutes to revisit any of the activities they seemed unsure of.

Remind students that they need to get around to each Work Place at least once in the next few days, marking their planning sheets as they go.

These are routines you will need to continue to reinforce for weeks to come, although it's interesting to look at students' responses right now. Which of your children remember to carry their folders with them from Work Place to Work Place? Which of them mark their planners carefully and keep their papers organized in their folders? Are you starting to hear remarks like, "I've gone to two of the Work Places in this round already. Four more to go, and then I can go back to An Hour or Bust! That's still my favorite!"? If you have students who have particular difficulty keeping track of their folders, organiz-

Session 18 (cont.)

ing their work, or making responsible choices, you may need to give them extra help or have them buddy up with more capable children. Your attention to these details now will make the year go more smoothly and help build the work skills your students will need throughout their careers.

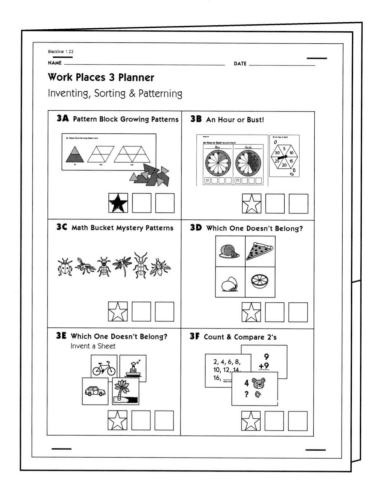

Student See? I've gone to the pattern block patterns so far today. Every time I go to one of the Work Places, I'm going to color the star blue! I'm going to make my own stars in the empty boxes when I start going back to some of the Work Places for my second time.

Session 19

PROBLEMS & INVESTIGATIONS

The Churn Dash Quilt Describing & Making the Quilt Blocks

Overview

Now that the new set of Work Places is up and running, it's time for a change of pace. Traditional patchwork quilts are so rich in pattern, geometry, and number, so beautiful to display, and so rewarding to make that they enhance any math program. The Churn Dash quilt, which students will make out of paper rather than cloth, is a nice starting point. The individual block, shown here, is relatively simple, but the finished quilt is quite complex. In today's session, children describe and then make their own Churn Dash blocks with paper. The blocks are joined to create a class quilt in Session 20. Students who finish early take their folders out to Work Places.

Skills

★ recognizing and describing patterns

★ exploring the properties of common shapes

★ investigating some of the relationships among squares, triangles, and rectangles

★ developing the concept of halves

You'll need

★ (optional) a book that emphasizes the relationship between quilting and community—*Sam Johnson and the Blue Ribbon Quilt* by Lisa Campbell Ernst or *The Patchwork Quilt* by Valerie Flourney are both nice

★ the Churn Dash Quilt Block (Blackline 1.34, run a class set)

★ 2" × 2" squares of construction paper and/or gift wrap in 3 different colors

• Color 1, 2 squares per child

• Color 2 (possibly a gift wrap print), 2 squares per child

• Color 3, 5 squares per child

★ glue or glue sticks, scissors

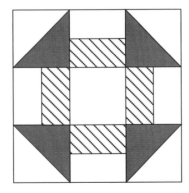

Start by reading the quilt book you've chosen. This is an optional step, but it's a nice way to set the scene for the lessons today and tomorrow. You might also choose to read this book at a different time of day, rather than using your math session.

Session 19 Describing & Making... (cont.)

Next, explain that you're going to start making a class quilt today. Instead of fabric, you'll be using paper to produce a traditional patchwork design. Distribute copies of the Churn Dash Quilt Block and ask children to share anything they notice about the block, first with one another and then with the group. Their observations may be quite rudimentary at first, but if you keep the discussion going for a few minutes, your students may surprise you with the comments they make about the patterns, shapes, and numbers they see.

After they've had a good look at the quilt block, explain that everyone will have to glue the same colors of paper into the same places on their blacklines to make the quilt come together properly. Demonstrate which construction paper pieces need to be pasted into the white, dark, and striped shapes on the quilt block blackline. You may even want to make and post a small chart to help your students remember.

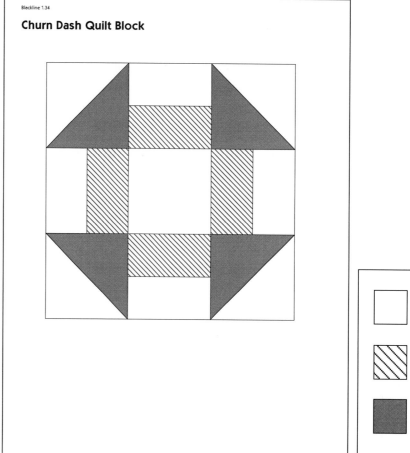

Blackline 1.34

Churn Dash Quilt Block

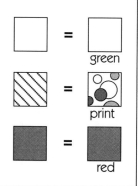

Teacher *If you forget which colors to paste where on your quilt block, this little chart may help. It's almost like our secret code. Can you tell what it means?*

Session 19 Describing & Making... (cont.)

Children *Sure! All the white squares on our sheet get covered with green colored paper squares.*
And every time you see a dark place on the sheet, you cover it with red.
And the stripey places all get covered with print paper.

The other thing you'll want to discuss before the children make their own blocks is how to cut the required shapes. You've cut squares for the children—how are they going to make the triangles and rectangles for their quilt blocks?

Joseph *I know how to cut one of those triangles. Just cut a square in half from corner to corner.*

Teacher *Can you show us what you mean, Joseph?*

Joseph *Sure. Just take a square and cut in half like this. It's easy!*

Alyssa *I know a way to cut the line so it doesn't go crooked. Just fold the square in half first, and then cut it. See?*

Teacher *Folding first would make it easier to see where to cut. Quilters are very careful about how they cut their patches because they want their blocks to look very neat and tidy. What about the rectangles? Can you use the squares to make rectangles?*

Kevin *Sure! Just fold one of the squares in half!*

Teacher *But that's how we made the triangles! How can we make rectangles the same way?*

Kaitlin *Fold one of the squares in half the other way—the across way! Can I show?*

Teacher *Sure.*

Kaitlin *Just fold a square in half like this and then cut on the line. See? You get 2 rectangles!*

Session 19 Describing & Making... (cont.)

Once students understand the color coding system and have a sense of how to create the 3 different shapes they'll need, send them out to create 1 block each. Have them set the blocks in a designated spot to dry as they finish. Be sure to let them know that you'll take care of trimming their blocks when they dry—otherwise you may end up with some pretty crooked trim jobs.

 WORK PLACE NOTES

Send your students out to Work Places with their folders as they finish their quilt blocks.

Session 20

PROBLEMS & INVESTIGATIONS

The Churn Dash Quilt Figuring the Quilt Layout— How Many Different Rectangles Can You Make?

Overview

Now that the blocks are finished, children discuss the layout of their class quilt. What shape will the completed quilt be? How big will it be? How many blocks will fit in each row? Students use 1" square tile in place of full-size quilt blocks to explore some of these questions.

Skills

★ relating form and function

★ exploring ways to combine squares to form various rectangles

★ exploring factoring through rectangular arrays

. . . .

Note Even if you have to make a few extra, be sure that the number of blocks you have can be factored in 3 or more ways. 20, 24, 28, 30, 32, and 36 are great. The other numbers between 20 and 36 don't work well.

. . . .

You'll need

★ the quilt blocks children created yesterday

★ 1" square tile in ceramic, wood, or plastic (You'll need at least 30 tile in a single color for every 2 children. Consider borrowing from other classrooms if necessary, or having children work in groups of 3 or 4 instead of 2.)

★ 3" × 3" sticky notes

★ pencils

★ glue

★ (optional) Quilt Layout Problem sheets (Blackline 1.35) and Centimeter Square Graph Paper (Blackline 1.36)

★ butcher paper (You'll probably need about a yard of 36" wide butcher paper, but the exact dimensions will depend on how many quilt blocks your class made and how the children decide to arrange them.)

Today the children are going to gather into a discussion circle to decide how to lay out their class quilt. You might start by explaining that once quilters get their blocks ready, they usually stitch them all together to form the top layer of the quilt. Because your quilt is made of paper, you'll work by gluing instead of stitching, but the class will need to figure out how many blocks should go in each row. Before they can do that, however, they'll need to decide what shape to make their quilt.

> **Children** The quilt in my bedroom is a rectangle shape.
> Mine too!
> Mine is so big I can't tell what shape it is.
> I've seen a square quilt before.

Session 20 Figuring the Quilt Layout... (cont.)

Teacher *Why do you suppose so many quilts are shaped like rectangles?*

Children *That's just how people make them.*
It's a good shape!
It fits on a bed.
Beds are shaped like rectangles, so quilts have to be that shape too.
They have to be in a shape that fits over us when we lie down!

Teacher *It sounds like most of you think our quilt should be rectangular.*

Children *Let's put it together.*

The next thing the children will need to figure out is whether their blocks can be combined to make a rectangle. Distribute 1″ square tile and have pairs of children count out enough to represent the number of blocks the class made (e.g., if your class made 24 paper quilt blocks, each pair of children will need 24 tile). Then have them see if there is any way to push their tile together to make a rectangle without any gaps or holes.

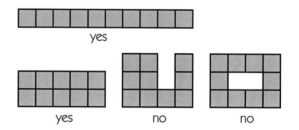

Teacher *If you were working with 10 tile, you could make a long, skinny rectangle, or one that was 2 tile high by 5 tile long. Neither of these has any gaps. You wouldn't want to make the 2 arrangements on the right because there is a gap in one and a hole in the other. If they were quilts, your arms or your tummy might freeze! Of course, you have more than 10 to work with here, so your job is pretty challenging.*

If children are all working together on the rug, they can see each other's ideas as they investigate the possibilities. They may begin to realize that there is more than one possible rectangle. In fact, given enough time, they

Session 20 Figuring the Quilt Layout... (cont.)

may discover that they can make several different rectangles with the same number. As they work, record their discoveries on the board. If you've been using magnetic tile in Number Corner work, the children may already know how to label rectangles by their outer dimensions. If not, you may be introducing this terminology for the first time.

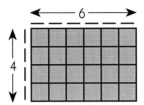

Teacher This is called a 4 by 6 rectangle because you can measure 4 tile-sides up and 6 tile-sides over. Those are its dimensions.

Sketch and label all the possibilities the children have found and then ask them to vote on the one they think will be best for the class quilt. An easy way to do this is to distribute 3″ × 3″ sticky notes. Ask children to put their names, the dimensions of the rectangle they think will work the best, and a brief rationale on their notes. When all have finished preparing their notes, have them post their stickies under the drawings on the board to form a kind of graph.

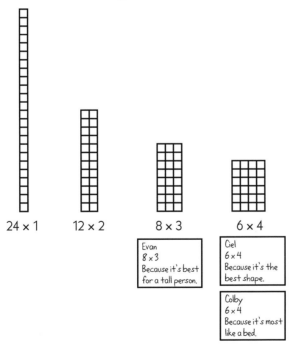

Later, you can glue the actual quilt blocks down on a butcher paper backing according to the class plan. (Taking the hypothetical number of 24 blocks, we're betting that a class might vote to arrange them in a 4 × 6 rectangle.)

Session 20 Figuring the Quilt Layout... (cont.)

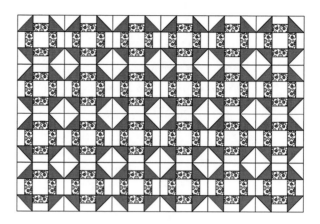

. . . .

Note As an alternative to having children work together at the rug, you can have them meet in pairs at their tables and record their own findings. In this variation, each pair of students takes the needed number of tile and works with them until they've discovered a rectangle. Then they record that rectangle by cutting a replica out of centimeter square graph paper to glue on their Quilt Layout Problem sheet.

. . . .

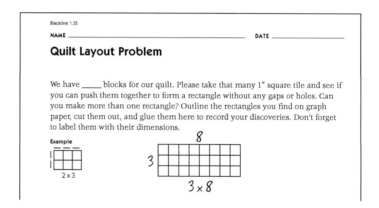

Have children continue to work until they've discovered and recorded several different rectangles. At the bottom of these sheets, each child is asked to select her favorite of the rectangles she's discovered with her partner. It's easy enough after that to go through the papers and determine which rectangle most of the children favor. This method is more challenging, but it's tempting to use if you have students who seem to do better working independently than in whole-group settings. You might also want to consider sending some of your students out to work independently while keeping others on the rug to work together.

 WORK PLACE NOTES

More than likely, children won't have time to go to Work Places today. Tomorrow's session features a discussion of the finished quilt and plenty of time for Work Places, however.

Session 21

PROBLEMS & INVESTIGATIONS

The Churn Dash Quilt What Do You Notice About the Finished Quilt?

Overview
Children discuss the completed class quilt.

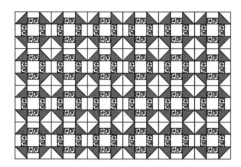

You'll need
★ the completed Churn Dash quilt
★ writing paper and pencils (optional)
★ a yardstick or pointer of some sort
★ Home Connection Blacklines
  HC 4.1–4.4

Skills
★ recognizing and describing patterns

Once the children have determined the quilt layout and the blocks have been glued together on a butcher-paper backing, display the finished quilt for all to see. You can either pin it to a wall or lay it out on the floor, where the children can gather around for a clear view. Ask them to take a good look at the completed quilt and discuss it with their neighbors for a minute. Then ask students to share their observations with the group. (We ask children to point out with a yardstick what they're talking about as they share. This helps students focus on the discussion more effectively.)

> **Teacher** *What do you notice about our finished quilt?*
>
> **Alyssa** *There are lots of green diamonds now.*
>
> **Jake** *There are lots of little green squares too.*
>
> **Eloise** *There are 5 big green diamonds in every row.*
>
> **John** *There is a small green triangle in all 4 corners of the quilt.*

If you allow this discussion to continue for more than a couple of minutes, you may be surprised at some of the things your students notice. You may also hear children beginning to piggyback on one another's ideas.

> **Gavin** *Now that it's all put together, there are some new shapes.*
>
> **Kaitlin** *I see some triangles along the edges of the quilt that weren't there when we made our own quilt blocks.*

Session 21 What Do You Notice... (cont.)

> *Peter* There's a pattern along the edge—look! Big triangle, little rectangle, big triangle, little rectangle, and it just keeps going.

This quilt will make a particularly effective wall display if you pin it up with some of the children's observations. You might record some of their remarks as they're talking, type them out on a computer (font size 36 bold), cut them into "conversation bubbles" and display them with your quilt. Or, you might have each child write a comment about the quilt after your discussion. Either way, adding children's comments to your quilt display will alert parents, teachers, and other students to the fact that this art project is very rich in mathematics.

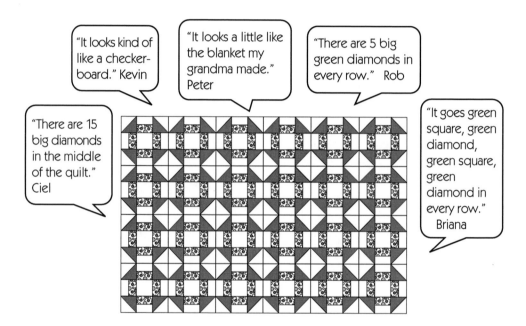

"It looks kind of like a checkerboard." Kevin

"It looks a little like the blanket my grandma made." Peter

"There are 5 big green diamonds in every row." Rob

"There are 15 big diamonds in the middle of the quilt." Ciel

"It goes green square, green diamond, green square, green diamond in every row." Briana

WORK PLACE NOTES

Once the quilt discussion is over, take a few minutes to review any of the Work Places that might still need clarification. If you feel you're not seeing quality work from some of the activities, you might model them again with an eye to inspiring some higher-level thinking.

> *Teacher* I've noticed that a lot of you are very interested in the Math Bucket Mystery Patterns. I've seen some great patterns there, and some that are very tricky. Here is one that I saw the other day. Can you figure out what would come next?

> *Children* Wow! that one really is hard!

Session 21 What Do You Notice... (cont.)

I bet I could make one that's harder!
There are 2 ladybugs and 2 green ones.
It's something with wings, I bet.
Oh! I've got it—it's no wings, wings, no wings, wings.
But ladybugs have wings. They can fly.
I know! It's spots, wings you can see, spots, wings you can see!
Yep! That one works the whole way!

Teacher *Nice job. I really had to study this one to figure it out too. The key to making them tricky is to think hard about how you're sorting the items you've chosen. Don't forget that you can use the sorting cards to help think of ideas.*

Children *I've got a really great idea for the bugs now.*
Me too. I want to start there today.
Not me. I'm going back to that one where you get to make up your own puzzle. I'm going to make a really tricky one.

HOME CONNECTION 4

Activity Race You to 50¢ (Blacklines HC 4.1–4.2, pp. 15–16)
Worksheet Counting & Comparing Coins (Blacklines HC 4.3–4.4, pp. 17–18)

The activity and worksheet to be sent home after this session give children a chance to share a favorite game with parents (Race You to 50¢), as well as an opportunity to practice counting and comparing sums of money.

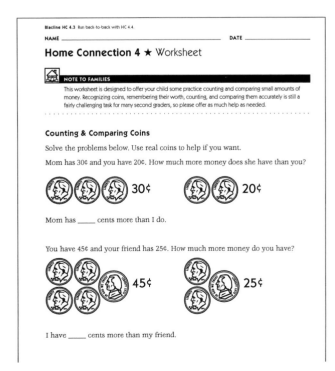

Blackline HC 4.1 Use after Unit 1, Session 21.

Home Connection 4 ★ Activity

NOTE TO FAMILIES

The Home Connection Activity this week is to play Race You to 50¢ several times. This is a game that involves counting and comparing money. It also gets at the idea of "regrouping"—you can trade 5 pennies in for a nickel and 5 nickels for a quarter. The first person to "earn" 50¢ wins. Your child has been playing this game at school and will probably enjoy teaching you how to play.

Race You to 50¢

To play this game, you'll need the 2 gameboards and also 30 pennies, 10 nickels, and 4 quarters.

Game Rules

1 Take turns spinning and setting the appropriate number of pennies on your board.

2 Each time you have 5 or more pennies, you can trade 5 for a nickel. When you finally collect 5 nickels, you can trade them in for a quarter.

3 The first person to get 2 quarters wins the game. It's okay to have a few pennies over 50¢.

4 Challenge! After you've played the game a couple of times, try playing it backwards. Have each player start with 2 quarters and take money off with each spin, making trades from quarters back to nickels and nickels back to pennies as needed. First player back to 0 wins.

Blacline HC 4.3 Run back-to-back with HC 4.4.

NAME _____   DATE _____

Home Connection 4 ★ Worksheet

NOTE TO FAMILIES

This worksheet is designed to offer your child some practice counting and comparing small amounts of money. Recognizing coins, remembering their worth, counting, and comparing them accurately is still a fairly challenging task for many second graders, so please offer as much help as needed.

Counting & Comparing Coins

Solve the problems below. Use real coins to help if you want.

Mom has 30¢ and you have 20¢. How much more money does she have than you?

30¢   20¢

Mom has _____ cents more than I do.

You have 45¢ and your friend has 25¢. How much more money do you have?

45¢   25¢

I have _____ cents more than my friend.

Session 22

PROBLEMS & INVESTIGATIONS

WORK SAMPLE

Tile Growing Patterns

Overview
This lesson gives children yet another chance to consider the idea of patterns that grow. In this version of the lesson, the teacher shows 2 patterns at the overhead, which the children build, extend, and discuss as a whole group. Then students go off to work individually or in pairs to figure the 4th, 5th and 10th configurations of a new tile pattern. In the blacklines, you'll also find an optional challenge sheet for students who are ready to extend their thinking about this sort of problem. Both record sheets may be saved as work samples.

You'll need
★ Tile Growing Patterns (Overhead 1.10)

★ A Tile Growing Pattern Problem (Overhead 1.11)

★ pencils

★ A Tile Growing Pattern Problem (Blackline 1.37, run a class set)

★ (optional) A Tile Growing Pattern: challenge sheet (Blackline 1.38, run a few copies)

★ 1" square tile

★ overhead tile

Skills
★ recognizing, describing, reproducing, and extending patterns

★ making generalizations and predictions

With the children working at their desks or at the rug, use the transparency to show the first growing pattern on Overhead 1.10.

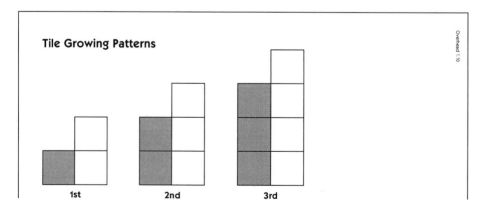

Have them look at the first 3 arrangements. What do they notice? Welcome all observations and speculations. Next, ask children to use their tile to build what they think the 4th and 5th arrangements will look like. (Some children enjoy building the first 3 arrangements and then building the 4th and 5th; others are ready to jump in and build beyond what they can see. Either way is fine.)

Session 22 Tile Growing Patterns (cont.)

After they've had a minute to work, have them share their ideas with their neighbors. Then ask for a volunteer to build her 4th and 5th arrangements on the overhead and explain her reasoning.

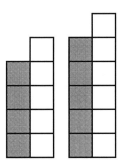

> *McCall* I think the 4th and 5th ones will look like this because the 1st one goes 1, 2. The 2nd one goes 2, 3. The 3rd one goes 3, 4. So the 4th one will have to go 4, 5, and the 5th one will have to go 5, 6.

> *Peter* I made mine like that too. Every time, it says its own number and then it's 1 more.

Solicit other ideas and explanations and then challenge your students to build the 6th and 7th arrangements. Is there any connection between the arrangement number and the number of tile it takes to build each arrangement? Can they imagine what the 8th one would look like? What about the 10th, 15th, 20th? How are they figuring these things out? Given the fact that they've already worked with Unifix cubes and pattern blocks to make growing patterns, some of your students may be ready to make the jump from what they can build to what can be imagined.

Repeat the same procedure with the second pattern on the transparency, and then explain that you want to pose one more problem with tile today. Distribute copies of A Tile Growing Pattern Problem, and display Overhead 1.11.

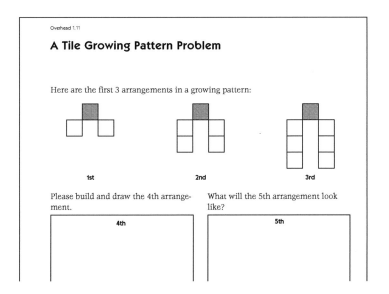

Session 22 Tile Growing Patterns (cont.)

Go over the instructions on the sheet together and then send children off to work alone or in pairs. Most will be able to build and draw the 4th and 5th arrangements by working together, but may not yet have very many words to express what they're doing. Some children will need to pool their tile with neighbors to build the 6th, 7th, 8th, 9th, and finally the 10th arrangements. Others may have spotted a pattern that will help them take a shortcut straight to the 10th. Children who are very quick to figure the 10th arrangement and record their solutions may enjoy sketching or writing about a larger arrangement. You can choose something for them, or let them think of their own.

Joey Rose I think I see what's going on here. These designs are like little robots. They have a head every time and their legs keep getting longer and longer.

Jake I see! On the 1st one, their legs are 1 tile long. On the 2nd one, they're 2 tile long. On the 3rd one, their legs are 3 tile long. The 10th one is just going to have a head and 2 long legs; 10 tile for each leg!

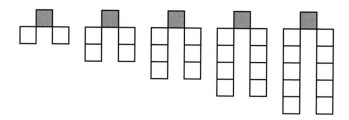

Alexandra The 100th one will have really long legs. It would take 201 tile to make that one—100 for each leg and 1 for the head.

If some of your students are able to make generalizations that help them imagine the 10th, 20th, or even 100th arrangements, it's worth having them share with the class. You might pull children together at the end of the session for some discussion, or have students present some of their solutions and strategies at the beginning of tomorrow's session.

. . . .

Note If you have students who are making generalizations about this pattern with ease and seem to need more of a challenge, there is an additional sheet—A Tile Growing Pattern Problem challenge sheet (Blackline 1.37, see following page)—you can offer them. This sheet is optional, and definitely not for everyone, but it will provide a nice extension for some of the youngsters in your class. We usually run a few and keep them on hand during this session, just in case.

. . . .

Session 22 Tile Growing Patterns (cont.)

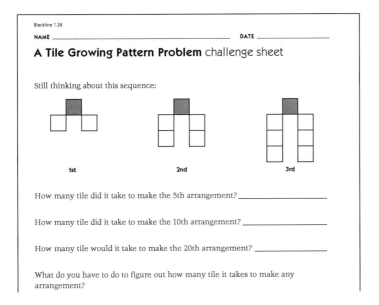

Blackline 1.38

NAME _____ DATE _____

A Tile Growing Pattern Problem challenge sheet

Still thinking about this sequence:

1st   2nd   3rd

How many tile did it take to make the 5th arrangement? _____

How many tile did it take to make the 10th arrangement? _____

How many tile would it take to make the 20th arrangement? _____

What do you have to do to figure out how many tile it takes to make any arrangement?

WORK PLACE NOTES

If there's time as children finish their sheets, have them get their work folders and pull out a Work Place basket or two. We often have children who finish early do Work Places at the rug until enough children have finished to move the baskets to their regular areas around the room.

Looking at Children's Work

To get a sense of how your instruction is going, take some time to scan this collection of student work.

1. How are children doing with the idea of growing patterns now? Are more of your students beginning to understand that sequences that grow in a predictable manner but never start over are patterns?

2. Were most of the children able to build and draw the 4th and 5th arrangements of the pattern this time around, or were some still at a loss?

3. How did students go about figuring and recording the 10th arrangement? Did they need to build all the arrangements up through the 10th (which is still quite typical at this stage), or did more of them have ideas that led to the 10th arrangement without building everything in between?

4. Were more students able to come up with some sort of generalization about this pattern that enabled them to figure arrangements beyond the 10th easily? Were they able to explain their thinking to others?

You may want to add these sheets to children's work files. Over time, they will serve as still one more piece in examining year-long growth.

◀ ASSESSMENT TIPS

Session 23

ASSESSMENT

What is a Pattern? Revisited

Overview

Children revisit the pattern assessment from Session 1, drawing and writing whatever they can to show what they know about patterns now, and working to extend the same picture and number patterns they did at the beginning of the unit. The 2 sets of sheets can be compared as one way to ascertain what's been learned over the past 5 to 6 weeks.

You'll need

★ Pattern Assessment, sheets 1 and 2 (Blacklines 1.1–1.2, run a class set of each)

★ pencils

★ crayons

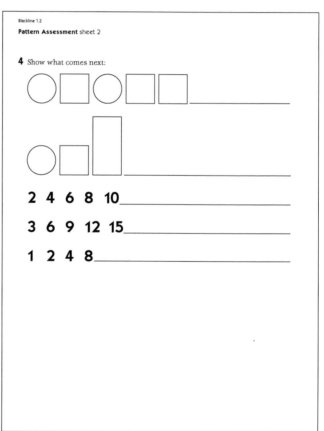

Tell children that you'd like them to show what they know about patterns by drawing and writing, just like they did at the beginning of this unit. Explain that they've done these two sheets before, but you know there will be changes. By comparing the two sets of work, you'll be able to tell some of the things they've learned over the past 5 to 6 weeks. Distribute the papers and send students out to work.

Session 23 What is a Pattern? (cont.)

WORK PLACE NOTES

As children finish their pattern assessment sheets, have them get their folders and go out to Work Places. This is the last session in Unit 1, but there's no need to have children finish at the Work Places today. There are no new Work Places introduced during Unit 2, and we suggest that you continue to use Work Places 3 throughout the second unit.

Looking at Children's Work

◀ ASSESSMENT TIPS

It is interesting to compare children's papers from the beginning of the unit with the sheets they just completed. Five or six weeks is a relatively short period of time in terms of children's mathematical growth and development, however, and you probably won't see any enormous changes. In some cases, you'll see little change at all. It's important to remember that these two sets of work reflect only part of what's been learned.

In our own classrooms, we tend to see differences in the complexity of the patterns children draw. Simple AB, AB, AB repeats change to ABCC, ABCC. Children who drew one or two patterns the first time around may draw three or four this time. Students like Andrew, who drew only repeating patterns at the beginning of the unit, may draw growing patterns now.

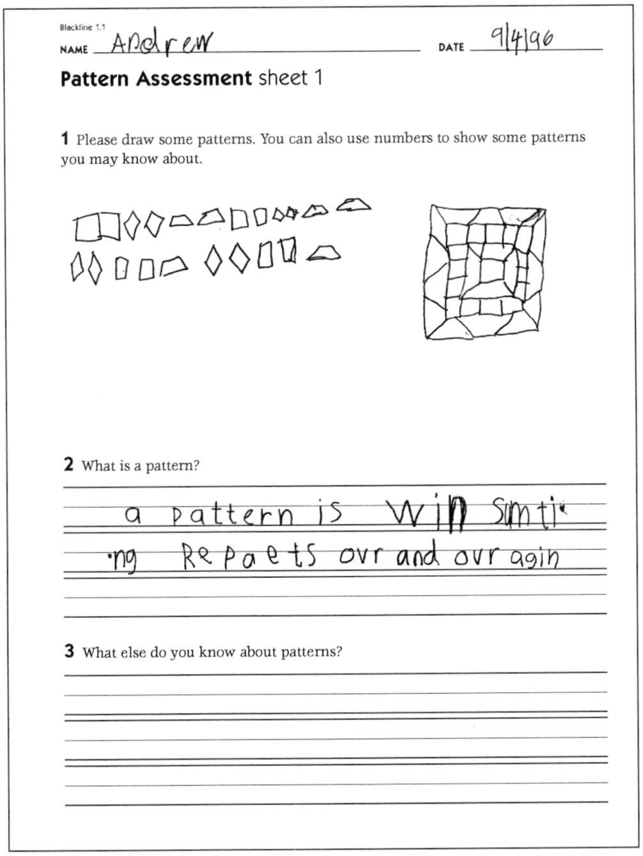
Blackline 1.1

NAME Andrew DATE 9/4/96

Pattern Assessment sheet 1

1 Please draw some patterns. You can also use numbers to show some patterns you may know about.

2 What is a pattern?

a pattern is win smti ng Repaets ovr and ovr agin

3 What else do you know about patterns?

Figure 1

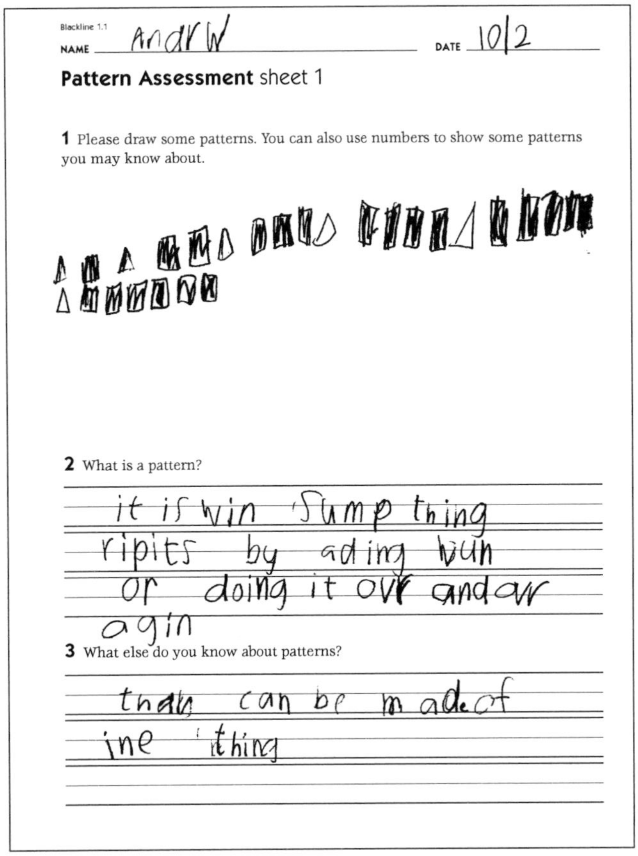
Blackline 1.1

NAME AndrW DATE 10/2

Pattern Assessment sheet 1

1 Please draw some patterns. You can also use numbers to show some patterns you may know about.

2 What is a pattern?

it is win sump thing ripits by ading wun or doing it ovr and ovr agin

3 What else do you know about patterns?

than can be mad of ine thing

Figure 2

Session 23 What is a Pattern? (cont.)

· Children like Eloise who weren't able to make general statements about pattern
  at the beginning of the unit may do so now.

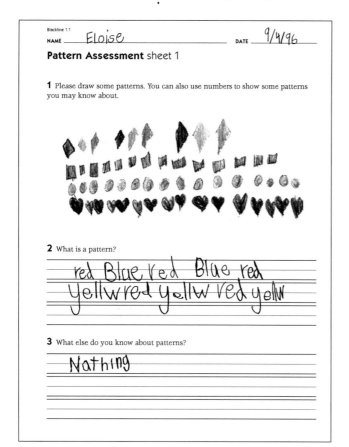

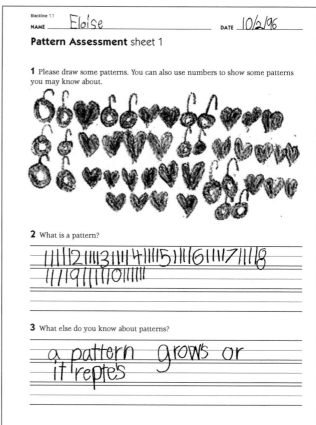

Figure 1

Figure 2

Although we might hope to see students write more sweeping generalizations
at the end of the unit ("Patterns can help you make predictions"; "You can
use patterns to solve problems.") most of their comments continue to be very
specific and personal.

> *They are neat and you can do tons of them.*
> *They can be by color or number.*
> *They can go up and down.*
> *They can be made out of anything.*
> *A pattern is something that can repeat over and over again.*
> *Patterns can get longer.*
> *They can grow.*
> *Patterns are very tricky sometimes.*

The second part of the assessment, shown on the next page, is not as open-
ended as the first, but still yields very interesting information. Even after 5 to
6 weeks of work with growing patterns, many of your second graders will
probably extend the picture and number patterns on this sheet by repeating

Session 23 What is a Pattern? (cont.)

the sequences over and over, especially on the first two lines. Others may increase the quantities on all lines, showing 1 circle and 3 squares, then 1 circle and 4 squares on the top line, developing some way to make the pattern on the second line grow, continuing to count by 2's on the third line, and 3's on the fourth line. Generally, children who understand the idea of growing patterns will respond in this way, at least in part. The last line is a true challenge, and may be too much of a puzzle for many, if not most, second graders. Some will leave it blank and others will repeat the number sequence over and over. Some, however, will grapple with the growth idea, coming up with their own extensions, while a few will realize that the numbers double each time. Children who are less willing to take risks or who may not yet fully understand the concept of growing patterns will respond with repeating patterns throughout. For a few, this in itself may be a major step.

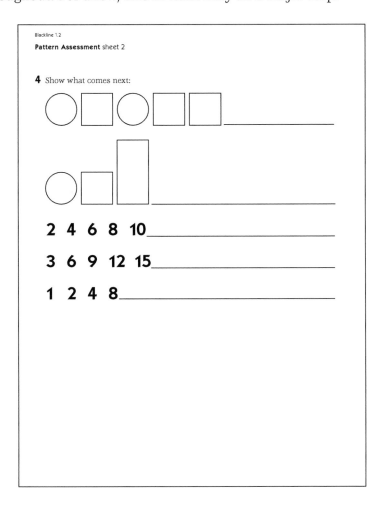

Notes

unit 2
hungry
ants

. . . .

What's Going to Happen in This Unit?

Hungry Ants is the first of two applied mathematics units for second grade. In this set of lessons, children move from collecting and sorting facts about ants to writing story problems using some of the information they've gained. The charming and funny book, *One Hundred Hungry Ants* by Elinor Pinczes, is used to introduce the topic. Students listen to the story and work the division problems presented in the text. From there they take a brief trip out to the schoolyard to observe ants in action and list the things they already know and the things they wonder about ants. The knowledge they already possess, along with their questions, form a scaffold for doing additional research in Sessions 3, 4, and 5.

. . . .

Important Note *You will need to gather some resource books about ants in order to teach this unit. We have included two fact-filled poems and four songs in the blacklines to help children gather some of the information they'll need to write their story problems. These poems and songs have been carefully and accurately illustrated and appear both in small print to be copied for individual students, and in large print to be made into classroom wall charts. You will also need to find at least one book, video, film, or filmstrip on ants to supplement the poems. Your school or local library may already have some books on ants. If not, they may have some books on insects, with good subsections on ants. We have listed some of the best children's books and other classroom "ant resources" we've been able to find.*

Read-Alouds

* *Thinking About Ants*, by Barbara Brenner. Copyright 1973 and 1997, Mondo Publishing Company, Greenvale, N.Y. (The 1997 version of this book is illustrated by Carol Schwartz, and is absolutely beautiful.)

* *Those Amazing Ants*, by Patricia Brennan Demuth. Copyright 1994, Macmillan Publishing Company, New York, N.Y.

* *Very First Things to Know About Ants*, by Patricia Grossman. Copyright 1997, Workman Publishing Company and the American Museum of Natural History, New York, N.Y.

Resource Books

The Fascinating World of Ants, by Angels Julivert. Copyright 1991, Barron's Educational Series, Inc., Hauppauge, N.Y. (This book has wonderful illustrations and is filled with facts, but it's a little too long and detailed to make a very effective read-aloud.)

Other Classroom Resources

If you have access to the Internet, there is an insect web site for children packed with information and pictures. You can find information about almost any insect and your students can also send specific questions to experts around the world using the "Ask the Experts" button. The site address is http://www.insect-world.com.

. . . .

By Session 6, students are introduced to a visual model for posing and solving story problems—quite literally, a picture of ants in their nest.

Asked for observations about the picture, children refer to some of things they've just learned about ants, correctly noting that some of these harvesters are bringing seeds into their nest, while others are in a lower chamber, presumably caring for eggs or doing other tasks required of workers. As they continue to describe what they see, some students begin to take note of numbers: 4 ants are carrying seeds, while 1 supervises, 3 ants are in the lower chamber, 2 are going off in search of food. There are 10 ants in all. There are 8 seeds in the pile already and 4 more arriving. Observations such as these become the basis for posing problems:

- How many ants in the whole picture?
- How many more ants in the nest than on the rock?
- How many seeds in all?
- How many antennae in all do the ants in this picture possess?
- Will every ant in the picture be able to have 1 seed?

In the session that follows, the teacher poses story problems in picture form, which the children solve on paper using sketches and numbers. Strategies range from one-by-one counting to more sophisticated methods. In response to the picture problem shown below, most of the children draw 22 antennae and circle groups of 2. Then they recount their groups to discover that the answer is 11. A few children may know almost intuitively that they need to find half of 22 to arrive at the answer. These same students may know that 22 divided by 2 is 11, or may take the number apart, first determining that half of 20 is 10, and half of 2 is 1, finally adding the 10 and the 1 to get 11. When most of the students have arrived at a solution, they share their strategies with each other. Nearly every child has access to the problem at some level, and all have opportunities to learn from one another as ideas are shared and sometimes debated.

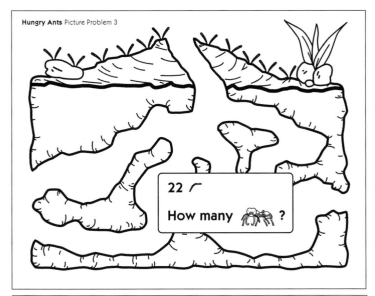

Hungry Ants Picture Problem 3

22

How many 🐜 ?

The army ants are on the move again! They've left their temporary nest in search of food. We can see 22 antennae marching down the trail—how many ants?

By Sessions 8 and 9, children are using some of the facts they've collected about ants to create their own story problems, first in picture form and then in writing. The focus is to develop problems that are factual, interesting, and challenging. In Sessions 10, 11, and 12, students solve each others' story problems, using pictures, numbers, and words to show their thinking on paper clearly enough so that their classmates will understand their strategies.

The final session is devoted to looking back at the written solutions. Given a collection of responses to the problems they have written, students are asked to consider some of the things that make for effective written communication in mathematics. Which papers are easy to understand? Which are not? How does it feel to get papers back that have no names, are messy, hold only the answer without any explanation, or are incomplete in one way or another? What makes some responses more clear than others? Children's thoughts will be revisited and refined throughout the year as they continue to solve problems and share strategies, both orally and in writing. They will have extensive opportunities to pose and solve story problems again in Units 5 and 7.

. . . .

What's the Big Idea? Problem Solving, Communication, and Connections

Although Unit 1 provided children with opportunities to count by 2's and 5's, to analyze and extend a variety of number patterns, and to do some computation, Unit 2 is the first major foray into basic operations this year. The activities in this unit give students a chance to consolidate and extend their understandings of addition and subtraction before they begin to deal with "the basic facts" in Unit 3. Children are reacquainted with the processes of addition and subtraction as they figure out how many ants are hiding in the lower chamber or total the number of soldier ants available for guard duty. The symbols 9 + 4 or 8 – 5 become shorthand ways to record transactions that are taking place in and out of the ant nest. A child who is still a bit confused about subtraction may tell you that the answer to 9 – 6 is 9 ("First I get 9. Then I add 6. Then I take the 6 away and I have 9 left!"), but is unlikely to report that there are still 9 seeds left after the ants have carried 6 of them away.

In addition to lending depth and meaning to the basic operations, this unit provides children with opportunities to solve problems, communicate mathematically, and find connections between mathematics and other endeavors. In Hungry Ants, sorting is used as a tool to organize information. Numbers are used to describe the things that can be seen in an ant's nest, and operations are used to model daily transactions in the burrows and chambers. Counting, adding, and subtracting are pressed into service as children grapple with problems like "16 ants—how many antennae?" or "15 seeds shared evenly among 5 ants—how many for each ant?" Symbols such as tally marks, quick sketches of ants' heads, numerals, addition, subtraction, multiplication, division, and equals signs are invented, remembered, traded, and relearned as children attempt to communicate their thinking on paper.

Students are also given multiple opportunities to develop visual thinking, which requires both the ability to extract and use information from pictures, and the ability to put verbal or numerical information into picture form. Looking at a picture of 3 ants on the rocks, 5 storing seeds in the middle chamber, and 4 in the lower chamber caring for the queen, and using the information to pose and solve problems is not that different from tasks children will be assigned in the years to come. The intermediate grades may bring story problems such as the one below:

> Each morning a math teacher runs a total distance of 42 city blocks and always chooses a rectangular running path. This morning her rectangular path is twice as long as it is wide. Figure the length and width of her path.

Students who are able to picture such problems and draw pertinent information from their own sketches will have a very powerful tool at their disposal.

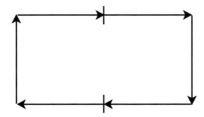

Student The total length of the path is 42 blocks. The length is twice the width, so I've made the length 2 arrows long and the width 1 arrow long. Altogether there are 6 arrows, so in order to find the length of one of them, all I have to do it divide 42 by 6. That's 7, so the length of the path must be twice 7, or 14 city blocks, and the width must be 7 city blocks.

. . . .

How Do I Sequence My Instruction For This Unit?

There are 13 sessions in the Hungry Ants unit, or $2^{1}/_{2}$ to 3 weeks' worth of work. (The time you'll be devoting to math instruction will be 1 hour and 15 minutes to an hour and 20 minutes, including the Number Corner.) Most of the sessions in this unit begin with a presentation to the entire class and then break out into small group or individual work. There are several lessons, however, in which the entire class works together for most of the math period. Hopefully, the pacing will be lively enough to engage your students. If it isn't, though, you may need to split a few of the lessons into two shorter sessions, holding your children together for perhaps half of the math period and sending them out to do Work Places the other half. There are no new Work Places associated with this unit, but Work Places 3, which you introduced near the end of Unit 1 can certainly be used as needed. The lessons and activities in this unit are intended to be taught in sequence and we offer the planner below as a guide. Ultimately, however, you will determine your own pacing.

Although the needs of your students will guide many of your planning decisions, it's important to bear in mind that they will have many more opportunities throughout the year to pose and solve problems and communicate their thinking clearly. They will also revisit the basic operations in many different ways, not only in the context of story problems, but also in Work Place games and activities, structured group instruction, and in the Number Corner. Skills and concepts not perfectly grasped this time around will continue to develop through the months.

Unit 2 Planning Guide

SESSION 1	**SESSION 2**	**SESSION 3**	**SESSION 4**	**SESSION 5**
One Hundred Hungry Ants: Can You Line Them Up? p. 129	Ants: What Do You Know? What Do You Wonder? p. 135 **Work Places 3**	Ant Research: Looking for Information in Print and Pictures, p. 138 **Home Connection 5**	Creating an Ant Spreadsheet, Part 1, p. 142 **Work Places 3**	Creating an Ant Spreadsheet, Part 2, p. 146 **Work Places 3**

SESSION 6	**SESSION 7**	**SESSION 8**	**SESSION 9**	**SESSION 10**
Hungry Ant Story Problems: What Do You Notice? What Do You See? p. 149 **Work Places 3**	Hungry Ant Story Problems: Looking at Picture Problems, p. 152	Creating Hungry Ant Story Problems, Part 1, p. 157 **Home Connection 6**	Creating Hungry Ant Story Problems, Part 2, p. 162	**Work Sample** Solving Hungry Ant Story Problems Together, p. 169

SESSION 11	**SESSION 12**	**SESSION 13**
Work Sample Shopping for Hungry Ant Story Problems, Part 1, p. 174	**Work Sample** Shopping for Hungry Ant Story Problems, Part 2, p. 178	Looking Back at Our Solutions, p. 180 **Work Places 3** Review & Revisit **Home Connection 7**

Notes

Session 1

PROBLEMS & INVESTIGATIONS

One Hundred Hungry Ants Can You Line Them Up?

Overview

The teacher reads the book, *One Hundred Hungry Ants*, by Elinor J. Pinczes, to the class. The children then figure out what would happen if the 100 ants in the story were divided into 2 equal lines, 4 equal lines, 5 equal lines, or 10 equal lines.

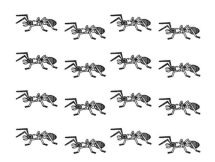

You'll need

★ the book, *One Hundred Hungry Ants*, by Elinor J. Pinczes

★ Unifix cubes divided into sets of 100 (You'll need 10 stacks of 10 cubes for every 2 students.)

★ Can You Line Them Up? problems 1–4 (Blacklines 2.1–2.4, run 10 copies of each)

Skills

★ counting by 10's and 1's

★ exploring the operation of division

★ working in pairs to solve problems

★ communicating orally and in writing

Start the lesson by explaining that the class is going to be studying ants in the next few days. Children will collect information that will help them write interesting story problems about ants for their classmates. Show the cover of the book *One Hundred Hungry Ants*, and ask students to make observations and predictions about what might happen in the story.

> **Teacher** We're going to start our study by reading a funny book about ants. What do you notice about the cover?

> **Children** It has ants on it.
> Those ants are cute!
> I see the word "Ants" at the bottom.
> The guy at the top has a napkin on.
> Two of them have forks—and that one guy has a spoon.
> They look hungry!
> Hey—that's what it says on the book! One Hundred Hungry Ants! I bet they're going to a picnic—ants are always trying to steal food at our picnics!

Once children have had a chance to share their observations, read the book aloud to them, *omitting the answers to the word problems as you go*. The first of these problems occurs six pages in, as the littlest ant says they're moving

Session 1 One Hundred Hungry Ants... (cont.)

much too slow to get the best food and suggests that the hundred of them split into 2 lines instead of 1. When you get to this point, just read,

> *"Stop," said the littlest ant.*
> *"We're moving way too slow.*
> *Some food will be long gone*
> *unless we hurry up. So...*
> *with 2 lines* (omit *"of 50"*)
> *we'd get there soon, I know."*

Then stop to discuss this idea with your students. Why would the littlest ant suggest getting into 2 lines?

Peter A line of 100 is really, really long. If they got into 2 lines they'd probably get there quicker.

Kevin If I were them, I'd just all split up and run like we do on the playground. Then they'd get there really fast.

Eloise My dad says that ants always go in lines.

Dorothy Sometimes, it just looks like they're crawling around everywhere.

As you read, be sure to omit the answers in the text as the ants split into 4 lines, 5 lines, and finally 10 lines. Do take time to discuss the wisdom of following the littlest ant's plan, and encourage speculation about how many ants would wind up in line each time.

Finally, when you've finished reading , ask the children to try the division problems posed in the story. Explain that they'll work in partners with sets of 100 Unifix cubes. Display the four stacks of problem sheets (the first of these sheets is shown below) and ask each pair of children to select one. They can

Session 1 One Hundred Hungry Ants… (cont.)

start with any of the four sheets, and if they're able to complete one before the end of the work time, they can tackle a second.

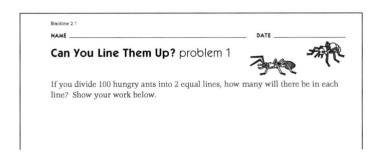

Once you've explained the sheets, remind students that they'll need to use pictures, numbers, and/or words to show their work—an answer alone won't be enough to help others understand *how* they solved the problem. You'll probably want to spend a little time brainstorming ways to get started on these problems before children go out to work.

Teacher *Suppose you and your partner choose Problem 3—the one that asks how many ants there will be in each line if they make 5 lines. How would you start? What could you do to begin to figure this one out?*

Jesse *You could use the Unifix cubes. We put 100 in each basket.*

Briana *Just like the 100 ants!*

Teacher *They're arranged in trains of 10 right now. Could that help you in any way?*

Kevin *No. I'd break them all up and then I'd put them in 5's.*

Teacher *Why?*

Kevin *Because you're going to have 5 lines.*

Hannah *I think I'd get 5 black ones and put them at the front. Then I'd line the others up behind them, kind of like we do in P.E. when we do relays.*

Whitney *Yes! We could make 5 lines and then see how many were in each line.*

Teacher *If you did that with the cubes, how would you show your work on your paper?*

Ethan *We could draw a picture of the cubes.*

Colby *We could draw a picture and write about what we did too.*

Rob *I could use numbers. I already know the answer to some of the problems in my head.*

Session 1 One Hundred Hungry Ants... (cont.)

Teacher   It will be an interesting challenge for you to see if you can explain your thinking to your partner and find some way to show it on paper.

After some discussion about how to approach the problems, send your students out with their partners. They're to choose one sheet between them, solve the problem, and show both the answer and how they got it on their paper. Many will use the Unifix cubes to help get answers, although a few may use other methods or materials. You might want to take note of *how* children use the cubes in their work. Some will break the trains of 10 into single cubes and share them out into lines using the classic "one for me, one for you" method. Others may be able to use the trains of 10 to work more efficiently.

Circulate as children work, observing and giving help where needed. You may need to offer advice and encouragement as students begin to record their work.

Hannah   We got the answer to the 4 lines problem!

Teacher   Wow! You and Nathan have really been working hard.

Nathan   We got 25 in each line.

*Teacher   I see that you've written **25** on your paper. Can you show how you got your answer?*

Hannah   We don't know what to write.

Teacher   What did you do to get the answer?

Nathan   We used the cubes.

Teacher   What did you do with the cubes?

Hannah   We broke them all into 1's. Then we put a red one at the beginning of each line. Then we kept putting 1 cube into each line until we ran out of cubes. Then we counted to see how many were in each line. It was 25.

Session 1 One Hundred Hungry Ants… (cont.)

Teacher *If you could draw a picture of the cubes and write what you just told me on your paper, I would be able to remember how you did this problem even if you weren't here to explain it.*

You will need to decide how much to ask of your students in terms of written explanations. For some, a picture with a short caption may be adequate. For others, a longer piece of writing may be in order. We often encourage children to add a bit more to their papers so others will understand their work clearly.

Blackline 2.2

NAME Hannah Nathan   DATE 10/20

Can You Line Them Up? problem 2

If you divide 100 hungry ants into 4 equal lines, how many will there be in each line? Show your work below.

25

we uzd the coobs

we kapt pooting thim in lins til we uzd them up.

Teacher *Okay! Your picture and the words you've written really help me understand how you solved the problem. Is there any way you could use numbers to make things even more clear?*

Hannah *What do you mean?*

Nathan *We could put a number on each cube.*

Hannah *Hey, wait—I've got an idea!*

Session 1 One Hundred Hungry Ants... (cont.)

Blackline 2.2

NAME ___Hannah   Nathan_____ DATE __10/20__

Can You Line Them Up? problem 2

If you divide 100 hungry ants into 4 equal lines, how many will there be in each line? Show your work below.

25

☐☐☐☐☐☐☐☐☐☐☐☐☐☐☐☐☐☐☐☐☐☐☐☐☐ 25
☐☐☐☐☐☐☐☐☐☐☐☐☐☐☐☐☐☐☐☐☐☐☐☐☐ 50
☐☐☐☐☐☐☐☐☐☐☐☐☐☐☐☐☐☐☐☐☐☐☐☐☐ 75
☐☐☐☐☐☐☐☐☐☐☐☐☐☐☐☐☐☐☐☐☐☐☐☐☐ 100

we uzd the coobs

we kapt pooting thim in lins til we uzd them up.

25 + 25 + 25 + 25 = 100

At some point, either at the end of this session or the beginning of the next, you'll want to have children share their solutions to each of the 4 problems, along with their strategies. One way to do this would be to have pairs who solved the same problem meet and discuss their work. They could then post their answers on the chalkboard for others to see. Another way would be to have volunteers share their thinking about each of the four problems with the entire group.

Session 2

PROBLEMS & INVESTIGATIONS

Ants What Do You Know? What Do You Wonder?

Overview
Children record the things they already know and make note of things they wonder about ants. Their statements and questions are then used to spark further investigation.

Skills
★ observing and describing

★ communicating orally and in writing

You'll need
★ a place on the playground or near the school to observe ants (The best kind to look for is the small common garden ant. You can often find a colony under a stone. If you can't find any ants nearby, you can omit this step.)

★ Ants: What Do You Know? What Do You Wonder? (Blackline 2.5, run a class set)

★ chart paper and a large marking pen

Over the next three days, your class will be collecting information about ants in order to pose and solve interesting story problems. One of the best ways to begin such a research project is to ask children what they already know about these insects and what they wonder. Before you ask them to do any recording, however, you may want to have your students observe some ants in action. A brief observation period may help them remember some of the things they've already learned about ants and may also spark some good questions.

If you're able to locate ants on or near your school yard, take your students out to look for about 10 minutes. Encourage them to share their observations and questions with one another as they watch. Then return to the classroom and ask them to record the things they already know about ants and the things they wonder. If you can't arrange for any kind of firsthand observation, just distribute the sheets. You might not get quite as much from children, but it's probably reasonable to assume that many of your students have

Session 2 What Do You Know?... (cont.)

had some previous experience with ants. The story you read yesterday, *One Hundred Hungry Ants*, may also have set them to thinking and wondering.

To facilitate their writing questions about ants, you might want to post the following words on the board: "what," "where," "why," "when," "how," and "can." Take a minute to read the words together and have children brainstorm at least one question about ants starting with each word before they go out to work on their sheets.

Blackline 2.5

NAME _____ DATE _____

What Do You Know About Ants? Wonder About Ants?

What do you already know about ants?

What do you wonder about ants?

The record sheet has lines and spaces in order to encourage both writing and drawing. Sometimes children who say they don't know anything can be encouraged to draw, and from there to explain their pictures. You may even choose to take dictation for a few. There are also children who simply communicate better in pictures than words, especially this early in second grade.

Collect the sheets from children as they finish. Later in the day, go through them and consolidate the information, listing each new fact on a large piece of chart paper. Be sure to include bits of misinformation as well as facts. As they learn more about ants, students will be able to add more information to the chart and eliminate the statements that aren't true.

Session 2 What Do You Know?... (cont.)

Things We **Know** About Ants

- Ants are fast.
- Ants get into people's houses.
- Ants live in holes.
- Ants can sting you!
- Ants are insects.
- They have 6 legs and 3 body parts.
- Ants have antennae to feel with.
- Army ants are big and can eat anything, even animals!
- Ants can be red or black.
- Ants are little, but they can carry things that are bigger than them.

Consolidate and record children's questions about ants on a separate sheet. These questions, along with others that emerge in the next day or two, will lend some structure to the research process. Children will be looking and listening for all the information they can, but will also be trying to answer their own questions.

Things We **Wonder** About Ants

- How big is the biggest ant?
- Can an ant's sting kill you?
- Are there army ants around here?
- How fast can ants run?
- How do ants get into our houses?
- Do ants really like sugar?
- Do ants have stingers like bees?
- Why do ants run all over each other?
- Are there really ants that can eat a whole animal?

 WORK PLACE NOTES

If there's time after students finish their statement and question sheets about ants, have them get their folders and go out to Work Places. There are no new Work Places associated with Hungry Ants; children will simply continue to use Work Places 3 from Unit 1 on the days when time allows.

Session 3

PROBLEMS & INVESTIGATIONS

HOME CONNECTIONS

Ant Research Looking for Information in Print & Pictures

Overview

Children review the facts and questions they listed yesterday. Next, they collect more information about ants by listening to some poems and a story about ants and looking at the pictures.

. . . .

Note You may want to teach this session over 2 days or at least 2 periods, reading and analyzing the poems during math period and doing the story and note sheet at another time, or even the following day.

. . . .

Skills

★ sorting information

★ observing and describing

★ taking notes

You'll need

★ the 2 charts you wrote yesterday, 1 listing the things children already know about ants and 1 listing their questions

★ wall charts of the 2 poems, "Ants Here, Ants There" and "Ants" (Blacklines 2.6–2.17, to make wall charts, run 1 copy of each page. Trim and glue the pages for each poem onto a large sheet of butcher paper. Another option is to run copies of these sheets and bind them into 2 small books.)

★ small copies of the 2 poems for children (Blacklines 2.18–2.19)

★ a book, video, film, or filmstrip about ants (See the introduction to this unit, pages 121–122, for a list of good resources.)

★ Ant Note Sheets (Blackline 2.20, run a class set plus a few extra)

★ Home Connection Blacklines HC 5.1–5.3

Open today's session by having your students read through the charts you wrote yesterday.

After reviewing the charts, explain that you are going to gather some more information about ants today, and possibly answer some of the questions children have asked by reading two poems about ants and also listening to a story (or in your classroom, perhaps it's viewing a video, film, or filmstrip instead). In any event, children need to listen as carefully as they can for new facts.

Read the first poem, "Ants Here, Ants There," to your students from the wall chart. Next, go back and take a careful look at the pictures on the chart. Take a minute to let students share comments and questions about the pictures.

Session 3 Ant Research (cont.)

Then read through the poem a second or perhaps third time with the children. You might even want to distribute small copies of the poem at this point so students can follow along on their own sheets. Finally, have them state any new facts they've learned about ants from this poem, possibly underlining some of the information on their own sheets.

Teacher Now that we've read this poem through a couple of times, what can you tell me about ants that you didn't know before? Are there any facts about ants that we haven't already listed on our chart? Look over your own copies of the poem. If you find something new, you can underline it with your pencil.

Alejandrina It says that they have special places for everything, like a place for food, a place for larvae. What's larvae, anyway?

Teacher Good question? Does anyone know?

McCall I think it means ant babies.

Teacher That's right. Ant larvae are the equivalent of caterpillars in butterflies—it's that stage in insect development when the ants are like squirmy little grubs before they go into their pupal cases and hatch out as adult ants.

Rob I didn't know that ants did that. I thought only butterflies did!

Teacher So we've learned that ants make special places for things in their tunnels and that they go through different stages in their development—first the egg, then the larva, then the pupa, and then the adult.

Session 3 Ant Research (cont.)

Repeat this reading and fact-finding process with the second poem.

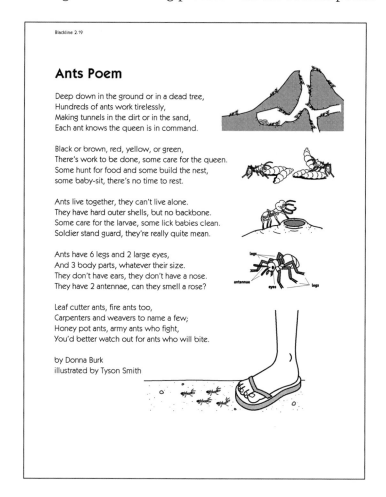

Blackline 2.19

Ants Poem

Deep down in the ground or in a dead tree,
Hundreds of ants work tirelessly,
Making tunnels in the dirt or in the sand,
Each ant knows the queen is in command.

Black or brown, red, yellow, or green,
There's work to be done, some care for the queen.
Some hunt for food and some build the nest,
some baby-sit, there's no time to rest.

Ants live together, they can't live alone.
They have hard outer shells, but no backbone.
Some care for the larvae, some lick babies clean.
Soldier stand guard, they're really quite mean.

Ants have 6 legs and 2 large eyes,
And 3 body parts, whatever their size.
They don't have ears, they don't have a nose.
They have 2 antennae, can they smell a rose?

Leaf cutter ants, fire ants too,
Carpenters and weavers to name a few;
Honey pot ants, army ants who fight,
You'd better watch out for ants who will bite.

by Donna Burk
illustrated by Tyson Smith

Peter *I didn't know that ants could live in dead trees. I thought they just lived in the ground.*

Ciel *I didn't know they came in so many colors. I thought they just came in red and black.*

Eloise *They have so many jobs to do—taking care of the queens, finding food, building the nest—even babysitting!*

Teacher *You are really digging a lot of facts out of this one little poem!*

If, after reading and analyzing the two poems, there is still energy and interest, share the ant book, video, film, or filmstrip you've found for your class. If it seems like too much, let the children go out to Work Places and resume the work at another time, perhaps even the following day. After you've shared the book or other resource and possibly read through the poems one last time, have children take some time to write and draw about some of the new things they've learned, using the Ant Note Sheet shown below.

Session 3 Ant Research (cont.)

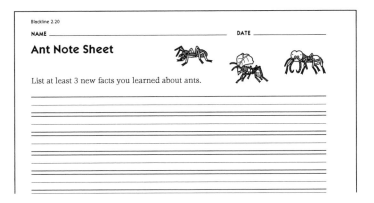

If you can find the time, it's fun to have children bring their sheets to the discussion circle when they're finished and have them each read a new fact from their paper. You can also go through their notes and add new facts to the class chart of things they know about ants.

 HOME CONNECTION 5

Activity An Hour or Bust! (Blacklines HC 5.1–5.2, pp. 19–20)
Worksheet 60 Minutes in an Hour (Blackline HC 5.3, p. 21)

In this homework assignment, children teach their families to play An Hour or Bust, and practice reading the minute hand on a worksheet full of clocks.

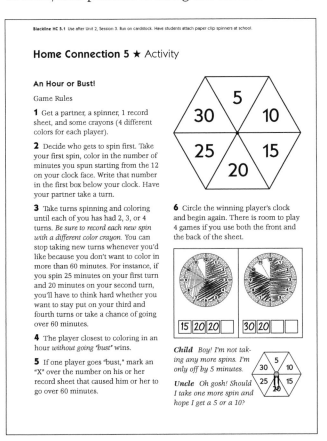

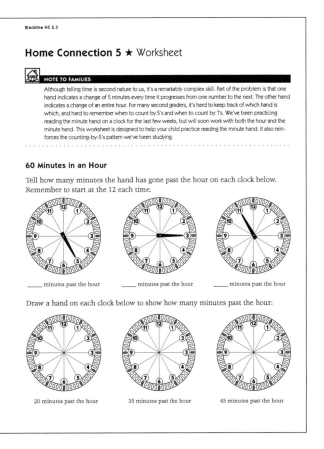

Session 4

PROBLEMS & INVESTIGATIONS

Creating an Ant Spreadsheet, Part 1

Overview

Now that your students have gathered some general information about ants, they're going to study 4 particular types: the army ant, the harvester, the leaf cutter, and the formica ant. The information will come primarily through songs about each, although individual students might be motivated to collect more facts about one or more of these ants, especially if there are resources (books, filmstrips, tapes, or the Internet) available in the classroom. As children learn each song, they'll enter notes about the ants on a spreadsheet-type organizer. A little later in the unit, they'll use these notes to help write their own ant story problems.

You'll need

★ wall charts of the 2 songs, "Army Ants" and "Harvester Ants" (Blacklines 2.21–2.27, to make the wall charts run 1 copy of each page. Trim and glue the pages of each illustrated song onto a large sheet of butcher paper. Another option is to run copies of these sheets and bind them into 2 small books.)

★ small copies of the 2 songs for children (Blacklines 2.28–2.29)

★ Ant Spreadsheet (Overhead 2.1)

★ Ant Spreadsheet (Blackline 2.30, run a class set plus a few extra)

★ any resources about ants you've gathered (books, filmstrips, tapes, Internet materials)

Skills

★ observing and describing

★ reading carefully to find information

★ organizing information on a spreadsheet

Open the session by calling children's attention to the new wall charts—one about army ants and one about harvester ants. Explain that the songs will teach them some new facts about these particular ants. Sing both songs to them and then have them sing the songs several times through with you. Take a minute for comments and questions about each song and then show your transparency of the Ant Spreadsheet at the overhead.

Session 4 Creating an Ant Spreadsheet, Part 1 (cont.)

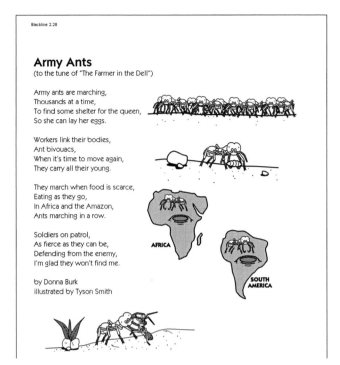

Blackline 2.28

Army Ants
(to the tune of "The Farmer in the Dell")

Army ants are marching,
Thousands at a time,
To find some shelter for the queen,
So she can lay her eggs.

Workers link their bodies,
Ant bivouacs,
When it's time to move again,
They carry all their young.

They march when food is scarce,
Eating as they go,
In Africa and the Amazon,
Ants marching in a row.

Soldiers on patrol,
As fierce as they can be,
Defending from the enemy,
I'm glad they won't find me.

by Donna Burk
illustrated by Tyson Smith

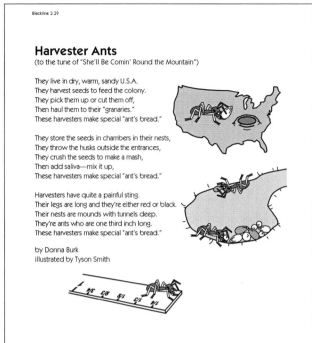

Blackline 2.29

Harvester Ants
(to the tune of "She'll Be Comin' Round the Mountain")

They live in dry, warm, sandy U.S.A.
They harvest seeds to feed the colony.
They pick them up or cut them off,
Then haul them to their "granaries."
These harvesters make special "ant's bread."

They store the seeds in chambers in their nests,
They throw the husks outside the entrances,
They crush the seeds to make a mash,
Then add saliva—mix it up,
These harvesters make special "ant's bread."

Harvesters have quite a painful sting.
Their legs are long and they're either red or black.
Their nests are mounds with tunnels deep.
They're ants who are one third inch long.
These harvesters make special "ant's bread."

by Donna Burk
illustrated by Tyson Smith

Explain that spreadsheets are charts that people use to organize and display information. Computers are often used to create them, but you're going to be making them by hand today. Take a moment to read the headings across the top of the sheet and then discuss them with your students. Do the songs provide enough information to answer each of the questions on the sheet for army ants and harvesters? What about taking a good look at the pictures on the song charts as well? Do they help?

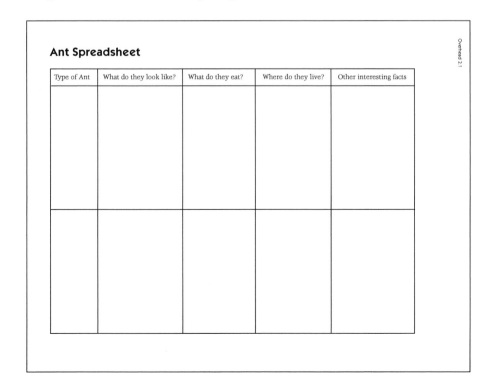

Ant Spreadsheet

Overhead 2.1

Type of Ant	What do they look like?	What do they eat?	Where do they live?	Other interesting facts

Session 4 Creating an Ant Spreadsheet, Part 1 (cont.)

Choose one of the ants to start with and work your way through each question with the students, recording on the transparency as you go.

Teacher *Let's work together to fill in the first row of this spreadsheet. Which ant shall we start with?*

Children *Army ants!*

Teacher *Okay. So we'll enter the words "Army Ants" here where it says, "Type of Ant." Now, the first question across the top of the sheet is, "What do they look like?" Does the song give us any information about the appearance of army ants?*

Joseph *Not really.*

Kevin *They're really big—I know 'cause that's what I've heard.*

Teacher *Okay, but let's stick to the information on the song chart for now.*

Kaitlin *But it really doesn't say anything about how they look.*

Teacher *Can you gather any information from the pictures?*

Children *Yeah! The pictures tell.*
Look at those soldier guys! They're huge!
They have really big heads.
They're biting up the enemy ants!
Their jaws are really weird.

Teacher *Can you describe their mandibles a bit more? What do they look like?*

Children *They're long—they look like huge elephant tusks.*
They're black and curved.
Their legs are long too—maybe because they do so much marching.

Teacher *Good observations! Let's enter your ideas on the spreadsheet.*

Ant Spreadsheet

Type of Ant	What do they look like?	What do they eat?	Where do they live?	Other interesting facts
Army Ants	They're large. They have big heads. Their jaws are long, curved, and strong. They have long legs.			

Overhead 2.1

Session 4 Creating an Ant Spreadsheet, Part 1 (cont.)

Continue in this fashion until you've made an entry for each question. It
might be a bit of a stretch, but between the pictures and the song lyrics,
you'll find something for each category, except the diet of army ants. If you
have reference materials that include army ants, you might want to have
your students look this up. On the other hand, you can just tell your children
that army ants eat all kinds of things, including other insects, spiders, and
even small mammals such as mice. Then distribute copies of the spreadsheet
to children and have them copy the information you've entered on the transparency. Encourage them to use the backs of their papers if they can't fit everything on the front. As they finish, have students go on to enter information about the harvester ant on their own, unless you feel that they need
your help and modeling to do this. (If they are able to work independently,
you should to give out individual copies of the songs at this point.) Based on
the song lyrics and illustrations alone, their finished papers might look something like this:

NAME _____Elmer_____   DATE ___10/24___   Blackline 2.30

Ant Spreadsheet

Type of Ant	What do they look like?	What do they eat?	Where do they live?	Other interesting facts
Army Ants	They're large. They have big heads. Their jaws are long, curved, and strong. They have long legs.		South America Africa	Soldiers can bite other ants' heads off. They carry their babies with them. Soldiers march on the outside.
Harvester Ants	They have long legs. They're either red or black. They're about ⅓" long.	seeds ant bread	USA in dry, warm places in mounds with deep tunnels	They gather seeds and store them in chambers called granaries. They mash up the seeds and mix them with spit to make ants' bread.

There might also have been information about one or both of these ants in
the book or other resource you shared yesterday. If students want to include
these facts or even find a few more using classroom resources, that's great.

Session 5

PROBLEMS & INVESTIGATIONS

Creating an Ant Spreadsheet, Part 2

Overview

Students learn 2 new ant songs today—one about formica ants, set to the tune of "On Top of Old Smoky," and the other about leaf cutter ants, set to the tune of "Are You Sleeping?". After they've gone over the songs several times, they create a second spreadsheet with the information they're able to gather from the song lyrics and illustrations.

Skills

★ observing and describing

★ reading carefully to find information

★ organizing information on a spread-sheet

You'll need

★ wall charts of the 2 songs, "Formica Ants" and "Leaf Cutter Ants" (Black-lines 2.31–2.39, to make the wall charts, run 1 copy of each page. Trim and glue the pages of each illus-trated song onto a large sheet of butcher paper. Another option is to run copies of these sheets and bind them into 2 small books.)

★ small copies of the 2 songs for chil-dren (Blacklines 2.40–2.41, run a class set of each song)

★ Ant Spreadsheet (Overhead 2.1)

★ Ant Spreadsheet (Blackline 2.30, run a class set plus a few extra)

★ any resources about ants you've gathered (books, filmstrips, tapes, Internet materials)

Open the session by calling children's attention to the new wall charts—one about formica ants and one about leaf cutter ants. Explain that the songs will teach them some new facts about these particular ants, both of which are very like farmers but in different ways. Sing the songs to them and then have them sing the songs several times through with you. Take a minute for com-ments and questions about each song and then distribute new copies of the Ant Spreadsheet.

If you have children who need help finding information and taking notes, keep them with you to work through at least one of the ants, while the others take small copies of the songs off to work independently. Again, the idea is to cull as much information from the songs as possible and to enter it correctly on the spreadsheet.

Session 5 Creating an Ant Spreadsheet, Part 2 (cont.)

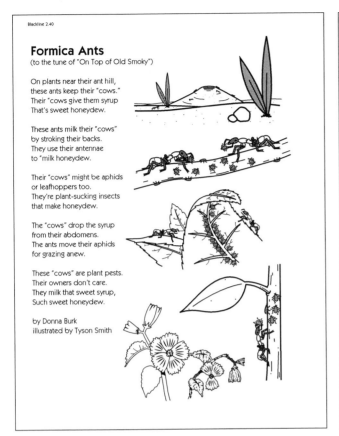

Blackline 2.40

Formica Ants
(to the tune of "On Top of Old Smoky")

On plants near their ant hill,
these ants keep their "cows."
Their "cows give them syrup
That's sweet honeydew.

These ants milk their "cows"
by stroking their backs.
They use their antennae
to "milk honeydew.

Their "cows" might be aphids
or leafhoppers too.
They're plant-sucking insects
that make honeydew.

The "cows" drop the syrup
from their abdomens.
The ants move their aphids
for grazing anew.

These "cows" are plant pests.
Their owners don't care.
They milk that sweet syrup,
Such sweet honeydew.

by Donna Burk
illustrated by Tyson Smith

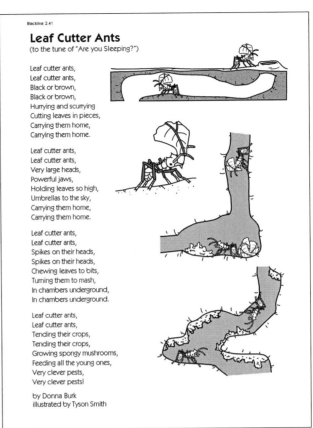

Blackline 2.41

Leaf Cutter Ants
(to the tune of "Are you Sleeping?")

Leaf cutter ants,
Leaf cutter ants,
Black or brown,
Black or brown,
Hurrying and scurrying
Cutting leaves in pieces,
Carrying them home,
Carrying them home.

Leaf cutter ants,
Leaf cutter ants,
Very large heads,
Powerful jaws,
Holding leaves so high,
Umbrellas to the sky,
Carrying them home,
Carrying them home.

Leaf cutter ants,
Leaf cutter ants,
Spikes on their heads,
Spikes on their heads,
Chewing leaves to bits,
Turning them to mash,
In chambers underground,
In chambers underground.

Leaf cutter ants,
Leaf cutter ants,
Tending their crops,
Tending their crops,
Growing spongy mushrooms,
Feeding all the young ones,
Very clever pests,
Very clever pests!

by Donna Burk
illustrated by Tyson Smith

There might also be information about one or both of these ants in the books or other resources you've shared in your classroom. If students want to include these facts or even find a few more, that's great.

Here's what their finished spreadsheets might look like if they just use the information from the song lyrics and illustrations.

Session 5 Creating an Ant Spreadsheet, Part 2 (cont.)

NAME _____John_____   DATE ___10/25___

Ant Spreadsheet

Type of Ant	What do they look like?	What do they eat?	Where do they live?	Other interesting facts
Formica Ants	They're black.	honeydew from aphids or leafhoppers		They keep aphids for cows. They milk the aphids by stroking them with their antennae.
Leaf Cutter Ants	They're black or brown. The have little spikes on their heads and thoraxes. They must be pretty strong.	spongy mushrooms		They carry leaves home. The leaves look like little umbrellas. They chew up the leaves and then grow mushrooms on them to eat.

Blackline 2.30

There is no mention made in either song of these ants' habitats. You might leave this for some of your eager beavers to track down, but if you prefer to tell your students, leaf cutter ants live in Central and South America, and formica ants can be found all over the world. If children finish early, they can collect extra information for their sheets from books and other classroom resources, help classmates with their spreadsheets, or get their folders and go off to Work Places. Have them save all their work—both spreadsheets and all the songs and poems in their folders for the next couple of sessions. They'll need some of this information to help them write their story problems.

Session 6

PROBLEMS & INVESTIGATIONS

Hungry Ant Story Problems What Do You Notice?
What Do You See?

Overview

Now that children have collected some information about ants, they're ready to begin solving and posing story problems. In this session, the teacher introduces the visual story-telling format that will be used throughout the rest of the unit by showing 2 transparencies of harvester ants in their underground nests. Children make observations about what they see.

You'll need

★ Hungry Ants: What Do You Notice? What Do You See? sheets 1–2 (Overheads 2.2–2.3)

★ overhead pen

Skills

★ observing and describing

★ gathering information from pictures

★ applying mathematics in new contexts

Open the lesson by explaining that the class is going to spend the next few days posing and solving some story problems about ants. As an introduction to the visual models you'll be using, display the first Hungry Ant transparency at the overhead. Ask your students to share anything they observe about the picture with the people sitting near them. After they've had a minute or two to talk things over, ask for volunteers to share their thinking with the whole group.

Many of the initial comments may be scientific or language-based rather than mathematical. Hopefully, students will relate what they see to some of

Session 6 What Do You Notice?... (cont.)

the things they've learned about ants over the past few days. You may hear stories about the worker ants bringing in food and storing it in an underground chamber. Children may notice worker ants going out to find more food and speculate about the ants in the lower chamber. Someone may correctly identify these ants as harvesters. As more and more observations are shared, however, some of them will involve number—it's hard to make observations about something without quantifying it in some way.

Children may observe that there are 3 harvesters in the lower chamber and 3 storing seeds. Two more are coming into the burrow and 2 are leaving. They may notice that there are 8 seeds in the pile and 4 more being added. Eventually, children may begin to combine or compare quantities—the seed total will be 12 and there are half as many being added as are already in the pile. There are 6 ants in the hole, 2 more coming in, and 2 leaving, for a total of 10. The same number of ants are leaving as are entering. There are equal numbers of ants in the 2 chambers.

It's hard to predict exactly what observations your students will make, and it may be that you'll have to do a little leading to get anything that has to do with number. If no one says anything about quantities, try asking such question as, "Are there more ants inside or outside the burrow? How many more? How do you know?" or, "How many seeds do you see in the picture?" Ideally, the children will be brimming over with quantitative as well as narrative remarks about each of the pictures, but you can certainly nudge a little if they're not.

Once you've gotten as much out of the first transparency as you're probably going to, show the second. This one also features harvester ants, but adds some new elements, including the appearance of the queen in the lower chamber, and may prompt some different observations and comments.

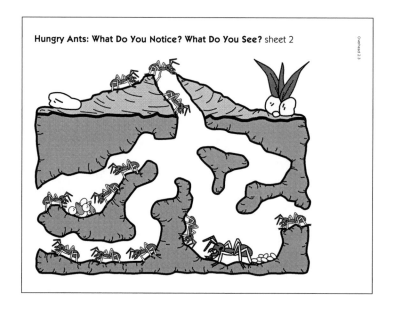

Hungry Ants: What Do You Notice? What Do You See? sheet 2

Session 6 What Do You Notice?... (cont.)

WORK PLACE NOTES

If there's time after viewing and discussing the two transparencies, send children out to Work Places. This is probably the last chance they'll have to use the games and activities in Work Places 3 until the end of the Hungry Ants unit, at which time you'll review and revisit these Work Places in preparation for the next unit.

Session 7

PROBLEMS & INVESTIGATIONS

Hungry Ant Story Problems   Looking at Picture Problems

Overview

Children analyze and solve a small collection of Hungry Ant picture problems. Children look over the picture, the math-talk bubble, and the story flap carefully before solving each problem, and as they finish, share their solutions and strategies with one another. They will use these problems as models in creating their own next session.

Skills

★ interpreting visual information

★ exploring the processes of addition, subtraction, multiplication, and division by interpreting and solving story problems

★ sharing strategies for solving problems

You'll need

★ Hungry Ant Picture Problems

★ math-talk bubbles for each picture problem (Blacklines 2.42–2.43) Run a single copy of each sheet and cut the bubbles apart. Then fasten them lightly to a wall or a board near your discussion area with loops of masking tape.

★ Unifix cubes

★ 8½" × 11" white copier paper and pencils

Note Each picture problem has three components: a picture of ants in action, a descriptive and factual story with a math problem embedded (the story flap), and a math-talk bubble that poses the problem more explicitly (see example below). There are 7 problems in this collection. If you don't get through all 7 in one math period, you can continue a second day before moving on to Session 8.

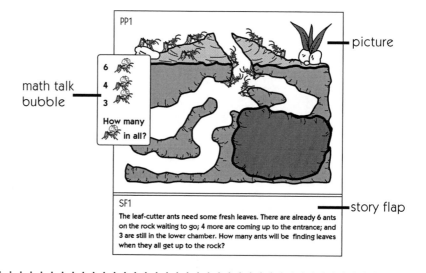

math talk bubble

6
4
3

How many ant in all?

picture

SF1

The leaf-cutter ants need some fresh leaves. There are already 6 ants on the rock waiting to go; 4 more are coming up to the entrance; and 3 are still in the lower chamber. How many ants will be finding leaves when they all get up to the rock?

story flap

Session 7 Looking at Picture Problems (cont.)

Gather your students to the discussion circle and explain that you are going to pose some story problems about ants today, and you will use pictures, numbers, and words to help. Show them the first picture and read the story on the attached flap.

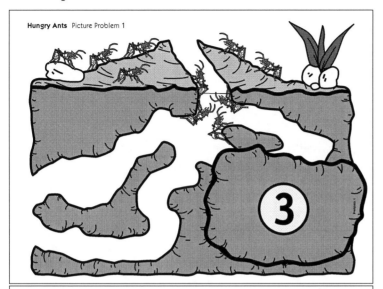

Hungry Ants Picture Problem 1

The leaf-cutter ants need some fresh leaves. There are already 6 ants on the rock waiting to go; 4 more are coming up to the entrance; and 3 are still in the lower chamber. How many ants will be finding leaves when they all get up to the rock?

Then explain that because the story is long, detailed, and maybe a little hard to remember, you have one more thing to help students understand what problem to solve, and that's a math-talk bubble. Call children's attention to the bubbles you've posted nearby and ask them if they can find the one that matches the story and the picture.

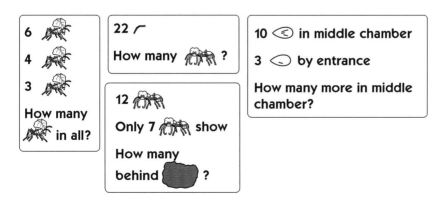

Teacher *Can you find the math-talk bubble that goes with this problem?*

Session 7 Looking at Picture Problems (cont.)

Children *I see it!*
It has the same numbers as the problem—6, 4, and 3!
I already know the answer. That bubble makes it easy!

Teacher *It sounds like a lot of you know just which bubble it is.*
Joey, could you pull that bubble off the wall and gently fasten it to
the picture?

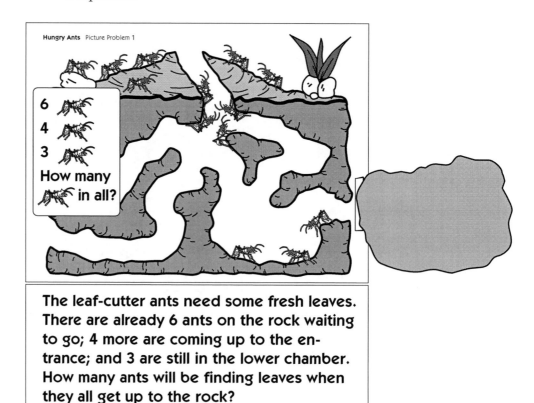

Hungry Ants Picture Problem 1

6
4
3
How many in all?

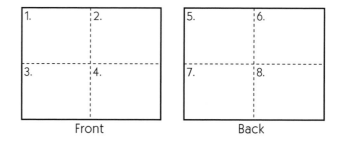

The leaf-cutter ants need some fresh leaves.
There are already 6 ants on the rock waiting
to go; 4 more are coming up to the entrance; and 3 are still in the lower chamber.
How many ants will be finding leaves when
they all get up to the rock?

After students have found the math-talk bubble that matches the first problem, explain that you are going to ask them to work the problem on paper using numbers, words, and drawings to show how they got the answer. Distribute paper and ask children to fold it in fourths and label the resulting boxes
as shown below:

1.	2.
3.	4.

Front

5.	6.
7.	8.

Back

Then ask them to work the first picture problem in Box 1 on their papers.
Some may already know the answer. Others will need to get the Unifix cubes

Session 7 Looking at Picture Problems (cont.)

or draw pictures to solve the problem. Many will draw a picture of each ant, or at least a tally mark to symbolize each ant and then count them up, starting from 1. Some will count on from 6. A few may know that 6 plus 4 is 10, and 3 more is 13. The challenge for most will be to show their work on the paper in some fashion. If you encourage children to look around as they work; to draw pictures if they can; to write number sentences to match their thinking, it won't be long before nearly everyone is writing or drawing something. Probably the most important thing you can do to encourage the kind of written communication that enables you to see how a child has solved a problem is to have students share their strategies with one another after each problem.

Teacher *As you finish the first problem, please take a minute to share your work with someone sitting nearby. Did you get the same answer? Did you use the same method to get it?*

Children *I got 13! So did I! I knew the answer right when we were looking at the picture.*

Teacher *Did anyone get a different answer? You all agree that it's 13? How did you figure it out?*

Eric *I drew a picture to get the answer.*

Teacher *I noticed that on your paper, Eric. Could you come up to the board and show the children what you did?*

IIIIII IIII III
              13

Eric *It was simple. First I drew 6 marks for the 6 ants. Then I drew 4 more. Then I drew 3. Then I counted them all to get 13.*

Teacher *Great! If Eric wanted to write a number sentence to go along with his tally marks, what could he write?*

Children *You mean like pluses and minuses and stuff? I wrote 6 + 4 + 3 because that's what you're adding—those 3 numbers.*

Teacher *Eric, would it be okay if we added those numbers to your work on the board?*

Eric *Sure.*

6   4   3
IIIIII IIII   III
  6 + 4 + 3 = 13

Session 7 Looking at Picture Problems (cont.)

Teacher *Did anyone have a different way to solve this problem?*

Rob *I figured it in my head. I know that 6 and 4 are 10, and 3 more is 13.*

Teacher *What did you write to show your thinking?*

Rob *I just put 13. I wasn't sure what to write.*

Teacher *Let's see if we can write just what you said, using numbers here on the board. First you said that 6 and 4 made 10. Let's write that.*

$$6 + 4 = 10$$
$$10 + 3 = 13$$

Teacher *Then you mentioned that 10 and 3 more made 13. Let's write that part.*

Continue working your way through the remaining six picture problems in this fashion. Each time you move on to the next problem in the set, have children share a few observations about the picture (some will be able to spot the matching math-talk bubble right away), read the story flap, find the matching bubble on the board, and fasten it to the picture. Once the problem has been clearly identified, have children work it on their papers. After most children have had enough time to work the problem, call on individuals to share their solutions. There will be times when everyone has the same answer, but in some ways, it's even more interesting when there are several different solutions. In such cases, there's a real reason to listen to others explain their thinking. If you take a little time to have students share their strategies with one another and with the group you may begin to see improvements in their ability to get something other than the answer down on paper, even within this lesson. After you've presented all seven picture problems (which may take two math periods, depending on your class), pin them up and ask children to be thinking about the type of story problem they want to pose when they start creating their own Hungry Ant problems next session.

Session 8

PROBLEMS & INVESTIGATIONS

Creating Hungry Ant Story Problems, Part 1

HOME CONNECTIONS

Overview

Over a period of 2 days, students create their own story problems, based around one of the 4 types of ants they have studied. They work from pictures to words as they create scenes, figure out what problems to pose, and then write stories and shorthand math-talk bubbles to support their picture problems. We ask them to start the process by making their pictures rather than writing their problems because so many children this age need some sort of scaffold for their writing. As they create their pictures, students begin to develop story lines that include facts about the ants they've chosen and problems to solve. After their pictures and stories are finished, children create the math-talk bubbles as a final step. Most will need this entire session to get a good start on their pictures.

Skills

★ identifying needed information to pose and solve a problem

★ posing story problems

You'll need

★ the picture problems from Session 7 posted where everyone can easily see them

★ the Ant Spreadsheets children created in Sessions 4 and 5

★ Ant Cutouts (Blacklines 2.44–2.45; run 15 copies of each sheet. (see note)

★ Home Connections Blacklines HC 6.1–6.4)

★ materials for children to create their own picture problems (see note)

The color-in method

• copies of the Ant Tunnel Background with doors taped on (Blacklines 2.46–2.47)

• scissors, crayons, glue or gluesticks

The collage method

• sheets of 9" × 12" light blue construction paper for backgrounds

• 6" × 12" pieces of light brown paper to create ant nests

• 3" × 6" pieces of gray or dark brown paper for rocks and logs

• 3" × 4" pieces of black paper for ant chamber doors

• scraps of green and brown paper for seeds, grass, leaves, plants, etc.

• scissors, crayons, glue or gluesticks and scotch tape

Note Cut copies of Blacklines 2.44 and 2.45 in half by ant type so each student can use accurate drawings of the particular ant she wants to feature in her story problem. We like to give our students the option of creating picture

Session 8 Creating Story Problems, Part 1 (cont.)

problems by taking a copy of an ant tunnel background, coloring it, and gluing pictures of ants to it (the color-in method) or by starting from scratch with colored paper for a background and smaller pieces of construction paper from which to cut nest chambers, rocks, leaves, and so on (the collage method). The materials for both methods are listed under "You'll need.")

. . . .

Explain to the children that they are going to start making story problems for each other. The idea will be for them to create problems about ants that are both factual and challenging to solve. The first decision each student will need to make is which of the four types of ants—army, leaf cutter, harvester, or formica—he wants to feature in his work. Revisit the four songs with your class and have children look over their spreadsheets to make a decision. Have each child circle the ant of her choice on one of her two spreadsheets and take a half-sheet of those particular ant cutouts to her desk or table.

NAME ___Dorothy___   DATE ___10/26___

Blackline 2.30

Ant Spreadsheet

Type of Ant	What do they look like?	What do they eat?	Where do they live?	Other interesting facts
Army Ants	They're large. They have big heads. Their jaws are long, curved, and strong. They have long legs.	grasshoppers spiders larvae	South America Africa	Soldiers can bite other ants' heads off. They carry their babies with them. Soldiers march on the outside.
(Harvester Ants)	They have long legs. They're either red or black. They're about 1/3" long.	seeds ant bread	USA in dry, warm places in mounds with deep tunnels	They gather seeds and store them in chambers called granaries. They mash up the seeds and mix them with spit to make ants' bread.

Harvester Ants

Session 8 Creating Story Problems, Part 1 (cont.)

> ***Dorothy*** *Okay! I've made my decision. I'm going to put harvester ants in my story problem. I'm going to have them gathering seeds and putting them in their granaries!*

Although the factual information students include in their story problems might not be any more complex than using the name of the ant, the correct ant cutout, and some reference to its correct food or habitat, a choice of ant type will give children a starting point. The picture problems you shared yesterday are also posted on the board as resources. These problems are meant to be examples to give children ideas about the types of story problems they'd like to pose.

If they need to, students can even copy your picture problems, although they'll have to change the numbers and find other ways to make their problems a little more challenging than yours. (Second graders often make problems more challenging by using bigger numbers, but it's wise to limit them to 25 ant cutouts each—the number on a half-sheet—and encourage them to use odd numbers and operations like subtraction and division rather than just using big numbers in an addition problem. Finding the difference between 9 and 13 is considerably more challenging than adding 10 and 8.)

Before children go out to work, take time to model the process of creating a picture problem. Using either the color-in method or the collage method, prepare your background as the children watch, making sure to take into account the type of ant you've chosen to feature. If you're using the color-in method, plan to start with your background sheet partly colored so your demonstration doesn't take too much time. Once the background is prepared, go ahead and start gluing on ants. Keep things open-ended and fluid as you work, talking to yourself and the children all the while.

Session 8 Creating Story Problems, Part 1 (cont.)

Teacher *Let's see. I'm going to use army ants in my story problem. They're going to be in a temporary nest because the queen has to lay her eggs. There are going to be a few soldier ants guarding the entrance to keep the queen extra safe. I have my background sheet ready—I've colored in the sky, put in some extra grass, and colored in the dirt around the tunnels. I'm ready to put the ants in now. I think I'll start with 6 soldier ants, inside, guarding the entrance tunnel and 3 outside on the rocks. Now I'll put 6 ants in the lower chamber and cover them over with a flap so you can't see them.*

Teacher *This is getting kind of interesting now. What kinds of problems could I pose with the ants arranged this way?*

Jesse *You could ask how many ants in all.*

Hiroki *You could ask if there are more guarding the entrance or standing on the rocks.*

Kaitlin *You could pretend that all the ants are going to hide in the lower chamber because an anteater comes along. Even army ants would be afraid of an anteater!*

Teacher *Those are all good ideas. I'll have to think about it some more as I keep working. Right now, I'm going to send you out to get started on your pictures. Again, if you're not quite sure what to do, have a look at your spreadsheets and the picture problems on the board. They might give you some ideas. Remember that you only have 25 ant cutouts. Your job is to make challenging problems even though the numbers can't be enormous this time around.*

Session 8 Creating Story Problems, Part 1 (cont.)

Call the children one by one to gather their materials. Circulate as they work, asking them what kinds of problems they have in mind. Some will have things all planned out from the beginning. Others will begin to generate a plan as they go. A few will be perfectly happy cutting, coloring, and gluing without a thought in the world about posing a story problem. For now, that's okay. You'll have a chance to catch them again tomorrow. Ultimately, you'll have to work with some children individually to help them pull problems out of their pictures.

At the end of your math time, have students collect their cut pieces and pile them on top of their background papers and spreadsheets. Be sure they label the background papers with their names so you can distribute them easily tomorrow.

 HOME CONNECTION 6

Activity The Ant Path Game—3 in a Row! (Blacklines HC 6.1–6.3, pp. 23–25)
Worksheet Measuring Ant Paths (Blackline HC 6.4, p. 26)

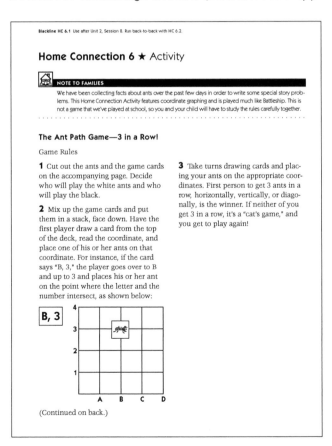

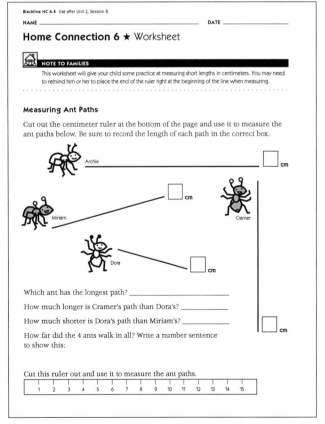

Session 9

PROBLEMS & INVESTIGATIONS

Creating Hungry Ant Story Problems, Part 2

Overview

The teacher opens the lesson by revisiting the picture problem he created during Session 8. The class generates several problems that might be posed by looking at the picture. The teacher selects one, writes a story to support it, and adds any necessary clues to his picture. Then the children complete the pictures they started the other day, write their stories, and add math-talk bubbles, question marks, and other needed clues to their picture problems. To prepare for Sessions 10, 11, and 12, the teacher types each student's story in large print and attaches it to the bottom of his or her picture problem.

Skills

★ generating a variety of problems based on a single picture

★ identifying needed information to pose and solve a problem

★ writing story problems

★ explaining in words why a solution is correct

You'll need

★ the picture problem you created yesterday

★ a half sheet of lined paper and a narrow tipped black felt marker for writing so that everyone can see

★ a piece of white construction paper cut into a talking bubble shape as shown here:

The children will need

★ the picture problems they started working on during Session 8, along with all the supplies they'll need to complete their work

★ their Ant Spreadsheets

★ half sheets of lined paper to write their own stories

★ white construction paper cut into talking bubble shapes

★ glue or gluesticks

Gather the children into your discussion circle and explain that today they're going to finish their story problems. Some of them are further along than others, but by the end of the math time today, they will need to have finished their picture problems and written the stories and math-talk bubbles to go along with them. Show your picture problem from Session 8 and talk with students about some of the problems you could possibly pose, and how. Then choose one of their ideas, and write a story to accompany the picture. Finally, add a talk bubble to your picture to clarify the mathematics. The goal is to wind up with a picture in which the problem is posed in numbers and sym-

Session 9 Creating Story Problems, Part 2 (cont.)

bols, accompanied by a factual and interesting piece of writing that presents
the problem in narrative form.

Teacher *Here's my picture from yesterday. I've done some more think-*
ing about it. What are some of the problems I could pose with this pic-
ture? What could I ask other people to figure out about it?

Hannah *They could figure out how many ants there are in the whole*
picture.

Eloise *But what if they didn't know that there were 6 ants behind the*
door to the lower chamber?

Teacher *That's a good question. I'd have to let them know somehow.*
What else could I have people figure out?

Briana *You could have them figure out how many ants behind the*
door.

Andrew *But how could they do that? Would they just have to guess?*

Teacher *Not if I gave them some kind of clue. I've been thinking about*
that idea of having people figure out how many behind the door. There
are a couple of problems like that up on the board from the other day. I
might look at them to get some ideas.

Eric *Oh, like that one where the bubble says 12, but all you can see is*
7 ants guarding the nest? And there are some hiding behind the door?

Teacher *That's what I'm thinking of. I'm going to write a story to go*
with this picture that will tell about these army ants but also give a
problem to solve.

Session 9 Creating Story Problems, Part 2 (cont.)

Here I go. The army ants made a temporary nest because it was time for the queen to lay her eggs. They wanted to post plenty of soldiers near the entrance to the nest to keep the queen safe. There were supposed to be 15 of them on duty, but there were only 6 at the tunnel entrance and 3 on the rocks. How many were still coming up from the lower chamber?

Gavin *There are 6!*

Teacher *How did you know that?*

Gavin *I remembered from yesterday when you put 6 behind there.*

Children *Me too! Yeah, I remember that!*

Teacher *What if you hadn't see me glue the 6 behind the door? Would you still have been able to figure it out?*

Sarah *Sure. I can see 6 in the tunnel and 3 on the rocks. That's 9. If there were supposed to be 15, there'd have to be 6 behind the door because I know 9 + 6 = 15.*

Kaitlin *I can go 6, 7, 8, 9. That's how many in the tunnel and on the rocks. Then keep going—10, 11, 12, 13, 14, 15—so I know there are 6 behind the door.*

Teacher *Now I have my picture and my story. I need one more thing, and that's a math-talk bubble to paste onto the picture that tells people what I want them to solve, even without reading the story.*

Colby *Is that like the cartoon bubble things in the picture problems up on the board?*

Teacher *Exactly. The talk bubble tells what the math problem is without all the details of the story. It shows people just what they need to solve. Let's see. I'm trying to get people to figure out how many ants are behind the door, so I could put a question mark on the door. And my*

Session 9 Creating Story Problems, Part 2 (cont.)

bubble can say "15 ants" because that's how many soldier ants are supposed to be on duty. But I'll also have to write that there are 6 in the tunnel and 3 on the rocks, like this:

Needless to say, the discussion you'll have in your classroom will depend on the picture problem you put together. The main points to communicate to the children are:

1. Finish your picture. Be sure that it gives accurate information about the type of ant you've chosen. You wouldn't want to show harvester ants living in a jungle scene or formica ants getting honeydew from spiders, for instance.

2. When you finish your picture, make a final decision about the problem you're going to pose and write a story that poses the problem. Your story must also say true things about the type of ant you've chosen. You may find your Ant Spreadsheet helpful here. Use a half sheet of writing paper for your problem and glue it to the back of your picture problem when you're finished.

3. After the picture and the story are complete, put a math-talk bubble and perhaps a question mark into your picture to make the problem very clear. Your classmates should be able to understand what you want them to do without reading your story. The story adds more detail and interest, but your picture problem should be able to stand alone. If you can't figure out what to put in your bubble, or you're not sure where to put a question mark, come and see me.

. . . .

Note *Don't be discouraged if a fair number of children need help with their math-talk bubbles. The reason we think these shorthand clues are important is because they help nonreaders know what to do and they also reinforce the idea*

Session 9 Creating Story Problems, Part 2 (cont.)

that the children are writing story problems rather than stories. The most common mistake students make in writing story problems is to forget to pose the question or the problem. Having to create a math-talk bubble to accompany the story really forces the issue, but you'll probably have to help many of your students figure out exactly what to write in these bubbles. If nothing else, this serves as a last check on your part that a child knows what problem she is trying to pose. If she doesn't and it's not clearly spelled out in her story, this will be an opportunity to help her define what it is she wants others to figure out.

· ·

4. When you're completely finished, show your problem to at least one other child. Have him look over the picture and the math-talk bubble to see if he can figure out what your problem is, and then read the story to see if he's right. Then see if he can solve your problem. If he can't, have him try to help you fix it so it can be solved. If neither of you can figure out what to do to get your problem to work, bring it to me.

To prepare for Sessions 10–12
Before you can move into the next three sessions, you'll need to type a large copy of each child's story problem to serve as a story flap, and about ten smaller copies to be used by children as they solve one another's problems. Here's one relatively easy way to accomplish this task:

1. Make sure you can read each student's story problem before you sit down to type. This whole production is a bit like publishing the stories children write, and a little legwork before the typing session can save headaches!

2. If possible, on a computer, type the text of each story problem in bold lettering, font size 14. Correct children's spelling, punctuation, and grammar as you see fit—the goal is to make the story portion of each problem as legible as possible. As you end a story problem, type the child's name, and press return 2 or 3 times to leave several spaces between one story problem and the next:

> **The enemy was coming, so the soldier ants had to hide by the entrance to their nest. Pretty soon, all you could see were 12 antennae sticking out from behind the rocks. How many ants were hiding?**
> **Rob**
>
> **The harvester ants were working hard. 3 were down in the lower chamber taking care of the eggs. 5 were on the rocks looking for food. 9 were in the middle chamber cleaning up. How many ants in all?**
> **Cassie**

Session 9 Creating Story Problems, Part 2 (cont.)

3. When you're finished typing each problem, you'll probably have a page or two of text. Run spell-check, proofread, and print out a copy. Save this copy to run through the copy machine. You'll make ten copies of these problems and cut them apart to be used in Sessions 11 and 12.

4. Now highlight the entire text, if you're working on computer. Change the page setup to sideways or "landscape," and enlarge the text to font size 36 bold. Suddenly, your document will be 7 to 10 pages longer, and you'll want to check through before you print again to make sure that you haven't cut someone's problem off in the middle of the page. Respace as necessary and print it out.

5. Cut these stories apart and scotch tape them to the bottoms of the corresponding picture problems, as shown below.

The little harvester ants are very busy moving eggs to the lower chamber to keep them warm. They started with 15 eggs and still have 9 left to move. How many have they aleard moved?
Alyssa

6. As mentioned above, run ten copies of the sheets of small text. Cut the problems apart and put them into half envelopes labeled with each child's name. That is, all ten copies of Alyssa's text go into her envelope. (Just take a half class set of the long, legal-size envelopes, lick the flaps and seal them, and then cut them in half widthwise. Label each envelope-pocket with a child's name and reuse these pockets for story problems throughout the year.) In Sessions 11 and 12, you'll post each picture problem on the wall with its envelope of small strips directly beside it. When children come along and want to solve a problem, they'll pull a small strip out of the envelope, glue it to their paper, and work the problem in the space below.

Session 9 Creating Story Problems, Part 2 (cont.)

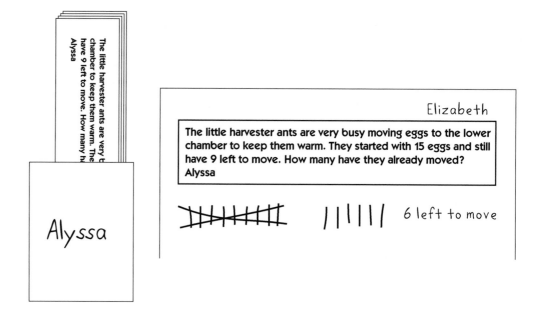

The little harvester ants are very busy moving eggs to the lower chamber to keep them warm. They started with 15 eggs and still have 9 left to move. How many have they already moved?
Alyssa

6 left to move

7. Once the picture problems and small story problem strips are prepared, you're ready for Sessions 10, 11, and 12. You'll just need the picture problems with story flaps for Session 10. Sessions 11 and 12 will require both the picture problems with typed story flaps and the small story problem strips in envelopes.

Session 10

PROBLEMS & INVESTIGATIONS

Solving Hungry Ant Story Problems Together

WORK
SAMPLE

Overview

Before this session, the teacher goes through children's completed picture/story problems and selects 2 or 3 for the class to work on together. As each of these problems is presented to the group, children work to show their strategies and solutions on paper. Answers, strategies, and methods of symbolizing these things are shared. Some children use pictures to show their thinking while others use numbers and/or words. Children who are at a loss as to how to show anything other than the answer are encouraged to borrow ideas from classmates. Even though their work is somewhat collaborative, children's work sheets may be saved as work samples.

Skills

★ solving story problems

★ exploring the idea of symbolizing the problem statement and the solution process

★ explaining why a solution is correct

You'll need

★ 2 or 3 student-posed story problems you have preselected for whole-group work today

★ blackline copies of the text of these story problems (See example on the next page.)

★ pencils

★ clipboards if you plan to have children work on the floor

★ Unifix cubes and/or tile for children who want or need manipulatives

★ the rest of the student-posed picture problems, prepared as described in Session 9 (pages 166–168)

. . . .

Note In preparation for this lesson, you will need to go through your students' finished picture/story problems, select two or three that seem moderately challenging, type the text of each, and run blackline copies. (See example on the next page.)

. . . .

When you meet with your students, congratulate them on a job well done. They've written their first story problems of the year, and they're all terrific. You might even want to hold up each picture problem for everyone to admire. Next, explain that you've selected two or three for everyone to work on together today. Tomorrow, all the problems will be available. The two or three you're going to do as a whole group today will help everyone get "warmed up."

Session 10 Solving Story Problems (cont.)

_____

Name and Date

Hungry Ant Story Problems

1. One day, there were 13 red garden ants going to look for food. 8 of them were already the the door. How many were still in the lower chamber taking care of the queen? by Danielle

2. A little harvester ant went out to look for food and found a big piece of cake! She came running back to tell the others. Soon, 16 ants were on the trail. How many antennae did they have in all? by John

Have children get ready to work—they'll each need a blackline copy of the problems you've selected for them to work today. They'll also need a hard surface on which to write (their desks or clipboards), a pencil, and Unifix cubes or tiles if they think they might like to have some materials to help them solve the problems. Explain that you'll be reading each problem together, taking time to work, and then sharing solutions and strategies with one another.

The challenge for students will be to show how they figured the problems out on paper, because the person who wrote each problem will be very curious to know exactly how they did it. Let them know that writing the answer alone won't be adequate. If they figured it out in their head, they'll need to show something about how they were thinking, using either words, numbers, or pictures, or a combination of these elements. If they used manipulatives, they'll need to draw a picture of what they did and perhaps add a number sentence or some words to explain their actions. Showing one's thinking on paper isn't always easy, and some students may be at a bit of a loss, especially the first time around. Encourage them to share methods with each other and hang in there—it will be a little easier each time they try it.

When everyone is set to go, hold up the first picture problem you've selected. You can read it, or you can have the child who wrote the problem read it. The

Session 10 Solving Story Problems (cont.)

words will be on everyone's page, so you might have the whole class read it together a second time around. Give any clarification needed and let children go to work. Encourage them to use their heads, pictures, their fingers, Unifix cubes, or tiles, to help them figure it out. Remind them to show their thinking as completely as possible, and be prepared to have a number of them just put down an answer the first time around.

After many of the children have an answer and appear to have something down on paper, take a few minutes to share solutions and strategies. As at other times, we like to have several students share their answers. If they're all the same, we always ask if anyone got a different answer. Hearing the answers, whether alike or different, seems to set up more of a desire on the children's part to listen to one another's strategies. After soliciting answers from several children, ask volunteers to share their strategies. You might even want to have them come up to the overhead, chalkboard, or easel to show their thinking. The pictures and number sentences some children have invented may help others see how to show their thinking. A picture may be particularly instructive for a child who's locked into numbers; number sentences (e.g., 9 + 5 = 14) might become useful shorthand tools for children who don't yet know how to use them.

Children are often fascinated to see how many different approaches there are to a single problem, and how many different ways there are to communicate one's thinking. We encourage students to add ideas to their own papers as others are presenting their thinking. In this way, they begin to learn how to communicate their mathematical thinking both orally and in writing.

Once you have gone through one of the student-posed problems, repeat the whole procedure with the other one or two problems you've chosen for the day's work. End the session by reassuring the children that everyone's story problem will be available tomorrow and that they'll get to choose which problems they want to work. (Someone will be sure to ask, both today and tomorrow, whether or not they can solve their own story problems. We always tell children that they can, as long as they're willing to show their thinking on paper.)

Looking at Children's Work

◀ **ASSESSMENT TIPS**

At the conclusion of the lesson, collect students' sheets, take some time to look them over, and then save them in work sample files for future reference. Because their work was somewhat collaborative, you might not place a great deal of weight on individuals' papers. On the other hand, looking through the sheets may trigger thoughts or memories about the comments or contributions made by specific children. Here are some things to keep in mind as you look at each paper:

Session 10 Solving Story Problems (cont.)

• Has the child made any attempt to show her thinking? Is there something on the page to indicate how she got her answers? (Given a problem like: "One day, there were 13 leaf cutter ants going to look for new leaves. Eight of them were already by the door. How many were still in the lower chamber taking care of the queen?", did the student simply write "5" or "five," or did she give other clues to her thinking? In addition to the answer to this problem, we have seen things like 8 | | | | |, which seems to indicate some kind of counting-on procedure. Use of tally marks alone is also quite common: ₦₦₦₦₦| | | | |. In this configuration, the child has apparently made 13 tally marks and crossed out 8 of them (the 8 ants by the door) to discover that there must still be 5 in the lower chamber.

• Has he been able to use number sentences of any kind to symbolize the transactions in the story problems? Is he using standard notation or invented symbols? For the problem above, we have seen some students write **13 − 8 = 5**. We have also seen **8 + 5 = 13**. Both are couched in standard notation; these children are familiar with addition and/or subtraction symbols and can use them correctly. Children sometimes use combinations of invented and standard notation, such as **8 + 1 1 1 1 = 13**, or **8 9 10 11 12 13**, both of which indicate a counting-on strategy.

• If she hasn't used number sentences, has she been able to use pictures or diagrams to show her thinking? Tally marks, each mark standing for one thing, may be one of the most common sketch methods known to second graders. Some, however, use more literal pictures, as shown below.

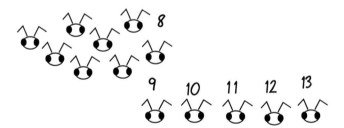

• If he's using number sentences to show the transactions in the problems, which operations does he choose? At this time of year, it's most common to see addition. Some children will also use subtraction; very few will use multiplication or division sentences yet. Given the problem about antennae ("16 ants, how many antennae?"), you might see everything from drawings of ants in which every antennae has been counted individually to quick sketches of ant heads where the antennae are counted by 2's. You might also see 16 pairs of tally marks or the following number sentence: 2 + 2 + 2 + 2 + 2 + 2 + 2 + 2 + 2 + 2 + 2 + 2 + 2 + 2 + 2 + 2 = 32. It would be unusual to see 16 × 2 = 32, but it's possible.

Session 10 Solving Story Problems (cont.)

• Do her incorrect answers demonstrate any kind of logic? Do look at incorrect answers and erasures carefully—sometimes they yield interesting information, especially if accompanied by pictures, words, or number sentences that offer clues to the child's thinking. A child who answers the problem above with 16 instead of 32 might have started drawing ants and stopped when she got to 16 antennae instead of 16 ants. Her response demonstrates logic and some definite skills (counting by 2's, using pictures to show thinking, taking time to show the answer clearly); it's just that she hasn't fully understood the problem.

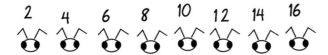

8 ants hav 16 antenas

Session 11

PROBLEMS & INVESTIGATIONS

WORK SAMPLE

Shopping for Hungry Ant Story Problems, Part 1

Overview

The teacher posts students' completed picture problems on the wall, along with the small story problem strips. Then she models how to "shop" for a story problem by selecting one from the collection, gluing the small story strip to a half-sheet of paper, working it through with students' help, and re-cording her strategies and solutions on the paper. Finally, the children leave the discussion circle a few at a time to shop for problems themselves. They select and work one problem at a time, completing as many as they can during this session (usually 2 or 3). Shopping continues next session.

You'll need

★ the student-posed picture problems, prepared as described in Session 9 (pages 166–168) and displayed at children's eye-level on the walls of your classroom

★ a half envelope with 10 reduced copies of the problem text pinned up beside each story problem

★ 100–200 half sheets of white copier paper (5½″ × 8½″)

★ glue or gluesticks

★ Unifix cubes

★ tile

Skills

★ solving story problems

★ exploring the idea of symbolizing the problem statement and the solu-tion process

★ explaining with pictures, numbers, and/or written words why a solution is correct

The little harvester ants are very busy moving eggs to the lower chamber to keep them warm. They started with 15 eggs and still have 9 left to move. How many have they alread moved?
Alyssa

Explain to your students that today and tomorrow, they're going to have a chance to choose the story problems they want to solve, and that you'll model the shopping process very carefully for them so they'll know exactly what to do when they go out to work. Most of them will be quite excited about this chance to choose and work at their own pace, and will pay close attention.

Start by cruising along the wall, admiring all the wonderful picture problems. It's so hard to choose, but you know you'll have a chance to do more than one. Stop in front of one that would be moderately challenging to many of

Session 11 Shopping for Story Problems, Part 1 (cont.)

your students. Read it aloud, and then take one of the small strips out of the envelope beside the problem, double-checking that the text matches the problem you just read.

Bring the small strip back to your discussion circle, take a half piece of copier paper and glue the small strip to the top of your paper.

> **15 harvester ants are supposed to gather seeds today, but some of them are still taking care of the eggs in the lower chamber. 7 are waiting on the rocks, ready to go. How many are still in the lower chamber? by Ali**

Read the problem once more to the children and begin to talk to them and yourself about how to solve this problem.

Teacher *This is an interesting problem. I think I'll start by writing down the numbers I know about. Let's see—7 and 15.*

Sherwin *Now just add them—it's 22!*

Teacher *Is that what I need to do?*

Children *Yes!*
No! Wait a minute! You can't add them. You're trying to figure out how many are under the door to the lower chamber. There aren't 22!

Teacher *What should I do?*

Peter *There are 7 on the rocks, right? But 15 are supposed to look for food. Just count on from 7 until you get to 15.*

Eloise *Right! Then you'll know how many are missing. 7—8, 9, 10, 11, 12, 13, 14, 15! How many is that?*

Teacher *Maybe this would be a good time to write some things on my paper. Let's see.*

> **15 harvester ants are supposed to gather seeds today, but some of them are still taking care of the eggs in the lower chamber. 7 are waiting on the rocks, ready to go. How many are still in the lower chamber? by Ali**
>
> 7   15
> 7 8 9 10 11 12 13 14 15
> | | | | | | | |

Teacher *So, how many ants are still in the lower chamber?*

Session 11 Shopping for Story Problems, Part 1 (cont.)

Children *I don't know!*
Look under the flap on Ali's picture!
Count the tally marks you made!

Teacher *Good idea. Help me out, okay? 1, 2, 3, 4, 5, 6, 7, 8. What does that tell me?*

Sarah *There are 8 ants still below.*

McCall *7 plus 8 makes 15! You should write a number sentence to show.*

Teacher *Okay! Also, if there are supposed to be 15 ants going out to hunt for food and I can only see 7 of them, I can subtract 7 from 15 to show that there are still 8 in the lower chamber.*

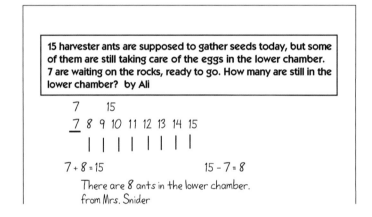

As you record your solution and strategies, emphasize the idea that this is almost like writing a letter to Ali. You really want her to understand how you figured things out. She already knows the answer to her own problem; what she doesn't know is how other people are going to solve it. Emphasize, also, the importance of signing your name, so she'll know who did the problem. Remind the children that they're welcome to use the Unifix cubes or tile to help them solve the problems.

Once you've modeled the whole procedure, send the children out a few at a time to choose the problems they are going to work. Remind them that they're to find one they want to solve (even their own is okay), take the story problem strip from the envelope next to the picture problem, glue it to the top of a half sheet of paper, record their solution and strategies as clearly and fully as they can, sign their name, put the paper in a designated place to dry, and start again. *Let them know that if any of the envelopes run out of small story strips, they're to find other problems to solve. Part of the reason we only put ten strips in each envelope is to insure more even coverage. If everyone in class chooses a particular problem, it's more likely that some of the other problems won't get done.*

Session 11 Shopping for Story Problems, Part 1 (cont.)

In the time that remains after you introduce the activity, some students will only get to two or three problems, while others will get to more. If some have trouble reading or understanding the problems, suggest that they ask the child who wrote the problem to help them. If that doesn't work, have them consult other children before they come to you. Finish up the session by collecting any half-finished papers and reassuring children that they'll have more time tomorrow to work on these problems.

To Prepare for Session 12

To prepare for the second day of shopping, gather all the papers the students did this session and sort them by the names of the children who wrote the problems (not the names of the children who solved them). Once you've sorted them, go through to find out if there are any problems that haven't yet been tried. If such is the case, rehang these problems in more accessible locations and label them with yellow sticky notes to signal that they need some responses.

Be sure to save all the completed papers from this session and the next. You'll need them for Session 13, and you may also want to place them in children's work sample files when the unit is finished.

Session 12

PROBLEMS & INVESTIGATIONS

WORK SAMPLE

Shopping for Hungry Ant Story Problems, Part 2

Overview

The teacher calls attention to the problems on the wall that have been marked with yellow sticky notes. These are the problems that haven't yet been solved and need special attention today. She reviews the shopping procedure and children go back out to work.

Skills

★ solving story problems

★ exploring the idea of symbolizing the problem statement and the solution process

★ explaining with pictures, numbers, and/or written words why a solution is correct

You'll need

★ the student-posed picture problems displayed at children's eye-level on the walls of your classroom

★ a half envelope with reduced copies of the problem text pinned up beside each story problem

★ 100–200 half sheets of white copier paper (5½" × 8½")

★ glue or gluesticks

★ Unifix cubes

★ tile

In your introduction to the children today, tell them that there are a few problems that haven't been solved by anyone, possibly because they were hidden away or too hard to reach. Explain that you've rehung them and labeled them with sticky notes, and that students need to get to them today.

If you feel it's necessary, review the shopping process, or at least have children tell you the steps. Next, distribute any half-finished problems from the day before for students to complete. Finally, send the rest of your youngsters out one by one to shop for new problems. If the energy for this activity is high and children are working well, you may want to continue until the end of the math period. If interest begins to wane mid-period, have students clean up and move on to another activity. Chances are that they'll want to continue shopping for the entire hour, though.

To prepare for Session 13

To prepare for the final session, gather all the papers the students have completed over the past two days. Sort them by the names of the children who wrote the problems (not the names of the children who solved them). Tomorrow, you'll turn the papers back to the problem authors. Susannah's problem, for instance, may have received six responses. Susannah will have an opportunity to look over these responses and think about which ones she understands and which ones are more difficult to comprehend, and why. She and the other children will begin to think about how to communicate their strategies and solutions even more effectively the next time around.

Session 13

PROBLEMS & INVESTIGATIONS

HOME CONNECTIONS

Looking Back at the Solutions

Overview

The children look over all the responses to the problems they wrote. Some of the papers they get back may not have names on them. Others may only state the answer or be too messy to read. This session provides a powerful opportunity for students to consider the things that make for effective written communication in mathematics.

You'll need

★ all the story problem responses children have written over the past 2 days, sorted by original author (That is, each child will receive all the responses to his or her problem.)

★ Home Connection Blacklines HC 7.1–7.4

Skills

★ thinking about the elements that constitute effective written communication in mathematics

Even though this is a short lesson, it carries a lot of weight and is important to children. Many will really want to see how classmates have responded to their problems. Before you hand out the papers, you might want to talk to your students about being supportive of children who tried their problems. If someone got the wrong answer, the job is to read through the explanation and try to understand the other child's thinking. If someone's handwriting is a little hard to read, see if you can get help from the child who wrote the response to figure out what it says. Emphasize the fact that everyone worked hard and did the very best they could. This will be a great opportunity for children to begin to see why some written responses are more effective than others, and can be very productive if handled in a positive spirit.

Distribute the responses to their owners and give youngsters a few minutes to read their "mail." Children who didn't receive many responses might be encouraged to share theirs with someone else. When most of your students have had a chance to read through their papers at least once, you might ask some of the following questions:

• How did you feel about the responses to your problem?
• Were there things that made some of them hard to understand?
• What made some of them easy to understand?
• Were any more interesting to read than others? Why?
• Do you think your problem was too hard, too easy, or just right for most of your classmates?
• Next time we write story problems for each other, will you make yours easier or more challenging. Why?

Session 13 Looking Back at the Solutions (cont.)

Finally, after everyone has read his or her "mail," collect all the papers. When you have time, sort them into piles by the children who solved the problems this time. Ashley's pile will contain all the problems she solved, for instance. Staple each pile together and place it in the child's work sample file, along with his or her own picture problem. By the end of the year, you'll have several batches of problems and solutions for each child, and it's particularly interesting to look at the changes that will occur over the months. If you're interested in analyzing children's strategies and solutions right now, you might look back at the Assessment Tips section in Session 10 (pages 171–173).

WORK PLACE NOTES

If you have time at the end of this lesson, review Work Places 3. It may have been a week or more since your students have worked at these activities and they will probably be excited to go back to them. When you think enough of your children remember what to do, send them out with their Work Place folders. Remind them to complete any of the activities they weren't able to get to after you started the Hungry Ants unit. If they've completed all six Work Places, they're free to return to their favorites, marking their planners as they go to show their progress.

Session 13 Looking Back at the Solutions (cont.)

HOME CONNECTION 7

Activity How Long is a Foot? (Blacklines HC 7.1–7.2, pp. 27–28)
Worksheet Solving Ant Story Problems (Blackline HC 7.3–7.4, pp. 29–30)

This homework assignment gives students an opportunity to develop some measuring sense, and also to solve some ant story problems with their families. If you like you can substitute the problems your students have written for the problems provided in the Home Connections worksheets.

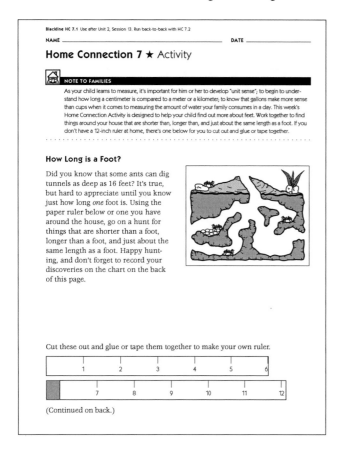

Blackline HC 7.1 Use after Unit 2, Session 13. Run back-to-back with HC 7.2

NAME _____ DATE _____

Home Connection 7 ★ Activity

NOTE TO FAMILIES

As your child learns to measure, it's important for him or her to develop "unit sense"; to begin to understand how long a centimeter is compared to a meter or a kilometer; to know that gallons make more sense than cups when it comes to measuring the amount of water your family consumes in a day. This week's Home Connection Activity is designed to help your child find out more about feet. Work together to find things around your house that are shorter than, longer than, and just about the same length as a foot. If you don't have a 12-inch ruler at home, there's one below for you to cut out and glue or tape together.

How Long is a Foot?

Did you know that some ants can dig tunnels as deep as 16 feet? It's true, but hard to appreciate until you know just how long *one* foot is. Using the paper ruler below or one you have around the house, go on a hunt for things that are shorter than a foot, longer than a foot, and just about the same length as a foot. Happy hunting, and don't forget to record your discoveries on the chart on the back of this page.

Cut these out and glue or tape them together to make your own ruler.

```
|    1    2    3    4    5    6 |
|    7    8    9   10   11   12 |
```

(Continued on back.)

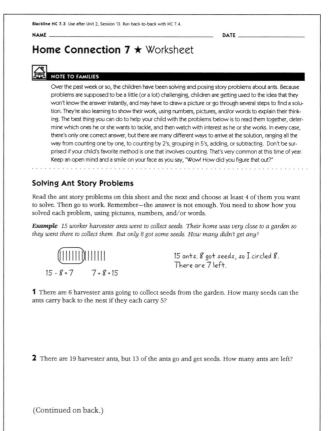

Blackline HC 7.3 Use after Unit 2, Session 13. Run back-to-back with HC 7.4.

NAME _____ DATE _____

Home Connection 7 ★ Worksheet

NOTE TO FAMILIES

Over the past week or so, the children have been solving and posing story problems about ants. Because problems are supposed to be a little (or a lot) challenging, children are getting used to the idea that they won't know the answer instantly, and may have to draw a picture or go through several steps to find a solution. They're also learning to show their work, using numbers, pictures, and/or words to explain their thinking. The best thing you can do to help your child with the problems below is to read them together, determine which ones he or she wants to tackle, and then watch with interest as he or she works. In every case, there's only one correct answer, but there are many different ways to arrive at the solution, ranging all the way from counting one by one, to counting by 2's, grouping in 5's, adding, or subtracting. Don't be surprised if your child's favorite method is one that involves counting. That's very common at this time of year. Keep an open mind and a smile on your face as you say, "Wow! How did you figure that out?"

Solving Ant Story Problems

Read the ant story problems on this sheet and the next and choose at least 4 of them you want to solve. Then go to work. Remember—the answer is not enough. You need to show how you solved each problem, using pictures, numbers, and/or words.

Example *15 worker harvester ants went to collect seeds. Their home was very close to a garden so they went there to collect them. But only 8 got some seeds. How many didn't get any?*

15 ants. 8 got seeds, so I circled 8.
There are 7 left.

$15 - 8 = 7$ $7 + 8 = 15$

1 There are 6 harvester ants going to collect seeds from the garden. How many seeds can the ants carry back to the nest if they each carry 5?

2 There are 19 harvester ants, but 13 of the ants go and get seeds. How many ants are left?

(Continued on back.)

unit 3 ▲ addition, subtraction & probability

addition subtraction & probability

. . . .

What's Going to Happen in This Unit?

Addition, Subtraction & Probability is a unit about adding and subtracting. This unit helps students understand how the basic operations work and reviews standard notation. It also helps children discover which of the basic addition and subtraction facts they already know and how they can build on these to learn some of the combinations that are less familiar to them. Strategies for solving facts are developed, from counting on and counting backwards to using known facts to solve the unknown. Children come to understand that if they can add 10's quickly (i.e., 10 + 6 = 16), they can also add 9's and even 8's with relative ease ("9 + 6 = 15 because I can move 1 from the 6 to the 9 to make it 10 + 5, which is 15."). They also find that some sets of facts, like the doubles (3 + 3, 4 + 4, 5 + 5, etc.) serve as springboards to learning others, like the subtract halves (6 – 3, 8 – 4, 10 – 5, and so on) or the neighbor numbers (3 + 4, 4 + 5, 5 + 6, and so on).

This unit helps students develop strategies by presenting certain collections of facts in relation to one another rather than as random bits of information to be memorized. After a brief review of standard notation in both horizontal and vertical form, students are asked to construct a class chart of addition facts, from 0 + 0 to 10 + 10, as shown on the following page, and several days later, a class subtraction chart. Through putting these charts together and examining them closely, the children themselves begin to see many relationships between various combinations; pattern reemerges as a major theme.

> **Ali** *All the ones along the top row add 0's. There are lots of 0's in that row.*

> **Gavin** *And the top numbers in that first row go 0, 1, 2, 3, 4, 5, 6, 7, 8, 9, 10—right in order.*

> **Alyssa** *The answers go in order too.*

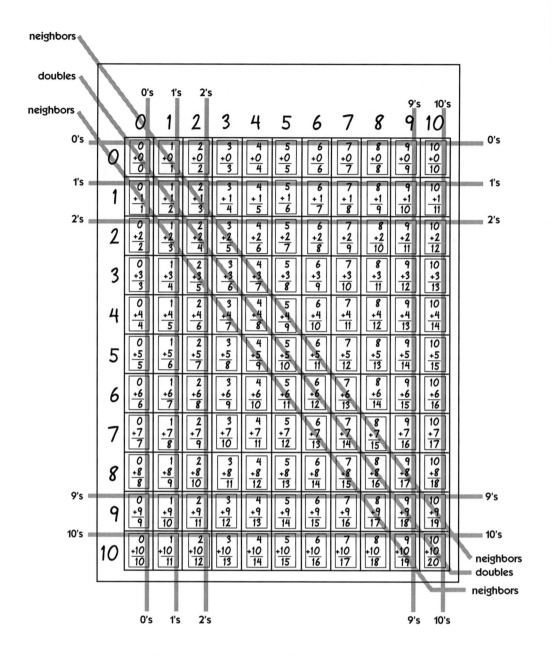

Rob *That's because when you add 0 to any number, you just get the same number. Like 3 + 0 = 3.*

Kaitlin *The cards down the left side all add 0's too. Those are so easy.*

John *Down the right side, it's adding 10's every time. Those are easy too.*

Evelyn *You mean like 10 + 0, 10 + 1, 10 + 2, 10 + 3…?*

John *Yes! And the answers are just 10, 11, 12, 13, and on and on.*

Danielle *Everything on this chart keeps going in order!*

Joey Rose *Look! I found the double ones going in this diagonal row. You can see 0 + 0, then 1 + 1, 2 + 2, 3 + 3, 4 + 4—all the doubles.*

Once the class addition and subtraction charts have been developed and discussed, a set of games and activities that promote counting on, counting backwards, and working with fact families is introduced. These games quickly resurface as Work Places 4, so children are able to practice the strategies independently while learning new ones during whole group lessons.

The second set of games and activities, introduced after a brief side trip into the world of geometry to create a fall/winter character quilt, features very direct study of facts that add and subtract 0's, 1's, and 2's. Other fact groups that receive close attention are doubles and neighbors, 10's and 9's, subtract halves (8 – 4, 10 – 5, 12 – 6, etc.) and run away 1's (13 – 3, 14 – 4, 15 – 5, and so on). Again, these whole group games and activities quickly reappear in the Work Places. Work Places 5 allows children another period of independent practice that extends over two weeks or more. In total, students will receive almost five weeks of intensive work with addition and subtraction facts to 20. The facts and strategies they learn during this time will be revisited almost daily over the coming months in the Number Corner.

Although the individual interviews done early in the fall offered some opportunity to examine children's knowledge of basic facts and strategies, there are several other assessments in Unit 3. There are two timed tests, one on addition facts and the other on subtraction, given very early in the unit and again at the end. Rather than simply solving as many of the facts as they can in the allotted time, students are encouraged to search for the ones that are easiest, do them first, and then return to the harder ones. In this way, teachers are able to get some handle on which facts the children actually know as opposed to how fast they can count forwards or backwards. (Standard timed tests are usually accompanied by a flurry of flying fingers, as children race to complete every fact on the sheet, even those with which they are almost entirely unfamiliar.) Students and teachers alike compare the results of the "before" and "after" tests, and in most cases are able to see some real progress over the five weeks.

The other assessment tool in Unit 3 is an observation checklist to be used by the teacher as students visit the games and activities featured in Work Places 4 and 5 (see following page). Ideally, teachers will have a chance to observe all their students using facts and strategies "in context" at least once over several weeks. With smaller groups, there may even be a chance to observe some students more than once.

Blackline 3.7

NAME _____ DATE _____

Work Places 4 & 5 Arithmetic Observation Sheet

Addition and Subtraction	Comments
Uses fingers	
Uses other manipulatives	
Counts on	
Counts backwards	
Works from Doubles to add (6 + 7 = 13 because 6 + 6 = 12)	
Works from Doubles to subtract (12 – 6 = 6 or 12 – 5 = 7 because 6 + 6 = 12)	
Works from 10's to add (9 + 5 = 14 because 10 + 5 = 15)	
Works from 10's to subtract (15 – 9 = 6 because 15 – 10 = 5)	
Works from other known facts to add or subtract	
Knows +0's, –0's	
Knows +1's, –1's	
Knows + – Doubles	
Knows + – Neighbor Number Facts	
Knows + – 10's	
Knows + – 9's	
Knows other addition or subtraction facts	

What's the Big Idea? Basic Facts

While there is some debate about teaching standard "recipes" for multi-step procedures like carrying or borrowing, long division, or averaging, very few educators question the idea that children need to know basic addition, subtraction, multiplication, and division facts. The issues we deal with in classrooms day to day revolve around when and how. Each fall in second grade we see children who know most addition and subtraction facts and have developed their own strategies to solve the ones they haven't yet mastered. We also see students who count both quantities on their fingers and then recount the total to solve 2 + 3 or 4 + 2. Between the two extremes, there are youngsters who know some facts and cope with the rest reasonably well by counting on or counting backwards (although there's often some confusion about which number to start on when they're doing "countbacks"). In general, our students are often somewhat less proficient than we'd like, and the task of teaching them addition and subtraction facts to 20 by the end of the year seems a bit daunting.

In his book, *Learning From Children* (Addison Wesley, 1985), Ed Labinowicz cites research about fact acquisition among primary children. One study

(Thornton, 1978) showed that second graders who were taught strategies for solving addition and subtraction facts did better as a group on timed tests than children who had simply been required to memorize their facts. On the strength of this and other studies by Thiele (1938), Swenson (1949), and Rathmell (1978), Thornton recommended that derived thinking strategies be taught systematically prior to drill and practice. "Children capable of derived strategies are better able to interrelate the combinations and remember or retrieve them. Children who forget combinations learned as isolated facts in drill have never constructed the relations and therefore have no basis for reconstruction." (Labinowicz, 1985)

While there are a great many strategies, some of which seem to be more accessible to second graders than others, we have decided to focus on a few big and basic ideas. The first is *counting on*. This is the bottom-line way to solve an addition problem. While not as efficient as some other strategies, it's faster than counting all the way from one in order to total two numbers. It also requires a tremendous level of comfort with counting, and is not easy or obvious to some of our students, but can be learned by most.

The second is *counting backwards* to subtract. This technique seems to be favored by children as they move away from straight finger computation (e.g., putting up 9 fingers, taking down 4, and counting the remainder to solve 9 – 4). Counting backwards has some built-in limitations because you have to keep track of how many backward "jumps" you're making as you actually perform the task. In essence, you're doing a double count—forwards and backwards at the same time.

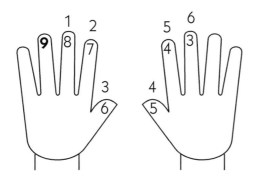

"9 – 6...let's see. I have to go back 6 numbers."

There's also the confusion of which number to start on. If you're trying to figure 9 – 6, do you count the 9 (9, 8, 7, 6, 5, 4), or do you jump back to 8 to start (9—8, 7, 6, 5, 4, 3)? Because of these limitations, we teach our students that counting backwards works well if they're only subtracting 1, 2, or 3 from a number. We encourage them to find other strategies if the subtrahends are larger.

Looking at the entire collection of addition or subtraction facts on a chart helps children find and use other strategies.

Most students agree that adding 0, 1, or 2 to a number or subtracting 0, 1, or 2 from a number is easy. Adding or subtracting 0 makes no change at all. Adding or subtracting 1 is like saying the next number up or the number that comes before. Adding or subtracting 2 is a little more challenging, but if nothing else, can be counted on or backwards from the other number very quickly.

$\begin{array}{r} 2 \\ +0 \\ \hline 2 \end{array}$	$\begin{array}{r} 1 \\ +4 \\ \hline 5 \end{array}$	$\begin{array}{r} 6 \\ +2 \\ \hline 8 \end{array}$		$\begin{array}{r} 2 \\ -0 \\ \hline 2 \end{array}$	$\begin{array}{r} 4 \\ -1 \\ \hline 3 \end{array}$	$\begin{array}{r} 6 \\ -2 \\ \hline 4 \end{array}$
+0's	+1's	+2's		−0's	−1's	−2's

Many children regard adding 10 to a single digit number or subtracting 10 from a "teen" as very easy too. To add, they will tell you that you just "pop" the other number into the 0's spot. One little boy told us that it was easy for him to remember because the 10 simply picked the other number up and carried it off in his backpack. When they subtract 10's, they comment that only the 1's are left. Both operations require some understanding of place value, but seem to come fairly easily.

$\begin{array}{r} 10 \\ +5 \\ \hline 15 \end{array}$	$\begin{array}{r} 15 \\ -10 \\ \hline 5 \end{array}$		$\begin{array}{r} 15 \\ -5 \\ \hline 10 \end{array}$
+10's	−10's		run away 1's

Related to this are what our children have christened the "run away 1's." These are subtraction facts in which the number in the 1's place is subtracted from a teen number. These facts are seen by some second graders as very simple because "only the 10 is left."

Doubles are another group of facts considered easy by many youngsters. It is common to hear children as young as 5 or 6 chanting the doubles addition facts up to 5 + 5 or 6 + 6. Beyond that, things get a little more challenging, but children seem to be able to commit these facts to memory quite easily. Subtracting doubles is a "snap" —when you take something away from itself, nothing is left.

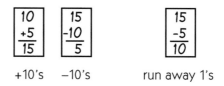

$\begin{array}{r} 4 \\ +4 \\ \hline 8 \end{array}$	$\begin{array}{r} 4 \\ -4 \\ \hline 0 \end{array}$
+ doubles	− doubles

Once children are familiar with the doubles, another group of addition facts, the "neighbor numbers," becomes accessible. We teach children to recognize a neighbor as two numbers that "live next door." Then we ask them to double the lower number and add 1 more ("5 + 4 = 9 because 4 + 4 = 8 and 1 more is 9."). It is important to know that this strategy and others are based on the methods some children develop independently. Given no coaching at all, there are children in every class who volunteer that 5 + 4 is easy either because 4 + 4 = 8 and 1 more is 9, or 5 + 5 = 10 and 1 less is 9.

+ doubles   + neighbors   – neighbors   – halves

Two other groups of facts that spring from the addition doubles are the "subtract neighbors" (5 – 4) and the "subtract halves" (8 – 4). Subtracting two numbers that live next door to each other, like 5 and 4, is nearly as easy as subtracting doubles. The answer is always 1 because neighbors are exactly 1 apart.

While not quite as obvious, "subtract halves" are also fairly simple. As children start to understand that subtraction is the reverse of addition, they'll often tell us that 8 – 4 is easy because 4 + 4 = 8. This is not apparent to all children, however, and in some ways seems to be a matter of development. Before the idea of reversibility starts to take hold, the ability to see the relationship between the two sets of facts, and the ease with which they can be solved just isn't there.

A final group of facts that takes its cue from a very easy set is the "add 9's."

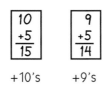

+10's   +9's

While children with lots of number sense may have realized that you can move 1 from the 5 to the 9 to make 9 + 5 into 10 + 4, which is 14, others can be helped to see this by using a model in which they can literally move a counting chip from one side to the other.

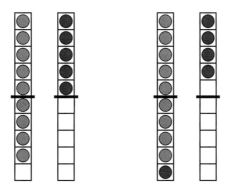

"9 + 5? That's easy! Just move a black one over to make it 10 + 4. It's 14!"

It should be noted that once children have either started to memorize or understand the strategies for all these groups of facts—the 0's, 1's, 2's, doubles, neighbors, 10's, and 9's, there aren't that many facts left on the charts (see shaded area in Addition Chart below). In essence, memorizing the very easy facts and using them to develop strategies to solve some of the more challenging combinations cuts the whole task down to size and makes it seem more manageable for both students and teachers.

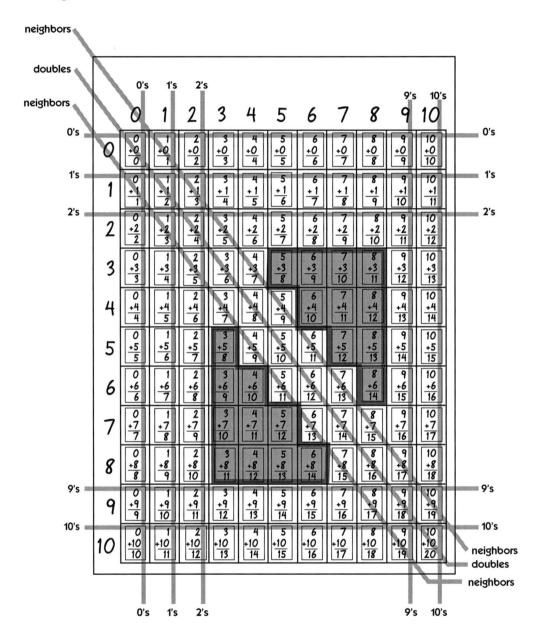

Once children know +0's, +1's, +2's, +10's, +9's, doubles, and neighbor numbers, there aren't many facts left to learn.

As a last comment about the mathematics in this unit, we have tried to layer our instruction enough to accommodate students at both ends of the spectrum. Children for whom very little about addition and subtraction is easy or obvious will get lots of repetition and practice at a very basic level. They will probably not master many of the facts or strategies within this five-week period, but will have a good foundation from which to build in the months to come.

There are also some challenges for children who already know most of the basic facts and strategies. Quite a few of the games, including Roll & Add, Shake, Reach & Record, Roll & Subtract, and Crossing the Pond make use of dice, spinners, and tile. At a very basic level, each one of these activities provides lots of practice adding and subtracting. At a more sophisticated level, these games are also experiments in probability. More able students are challenged to consider which combinations are most likely to come up on the dice and spinners and why. They are encouraged to experiment with the numbers of tile they place in their bags for Shake, Reach & Record, and asked to make predictions about how the shapes of their graphs will change as a result. They are given the opportunity to change the placement of their markers in Crossing the Pond mid-game, based on the data they've collected to that point. While you will extend these opportunities to every child in your classroom, students who are ready to move beyond simple addition and subtraction will seize on them eagerly and begin to unravel some of the mysteries of probability, while others practice at a more basic level.

· ·

How Do I Sequence My Instruction For This Unit?

There are 24 sessions in the Addition, Subtraction & Probability unit. Some of the sessions open with a problem or investigation, while others begin with a new game that will soon appear in the Work Places. (Games are played by the whole group, but children usually go off to work on problems or investigations by themselves, with partners, or in small groups.) As they finish, they get their work folders and begin Work Places. There may be occasions when an investigation will take the entire hour or more and there won't be time for Work Places. There will be other days when you'll want to use the entire session to introduce a new set of Work Places and have the children choose where to begin.

The lessons and activities in this unit are intended to be taught in sequence and we offer the planner below as a guide. Ultimately, however, you will determine your own pacing. It may take you longer than five weeks to get through the material, especially the first year you use the program. If you find yourself falling way behind schedule, you may choose to omit Sessions 9, 10, and 11. Although these three sessions provide a welcome break and some important geometry instruction, they aren't integral to the unit, and may be skipped.

We strongly encourage you to supplement the sessions in this unit with the Number Corner calendar routines each day, even though they're not shown in the planning guide below. The November routines feature quite a bit of work with basic operations and place value counting as children build tile arrays for the day's date and look at the number of days they've been in school as shown on a hundreds grid. Observations are recorded in the form of number sentences, and children practice using standard notation for addition, subtraction, multiplication, and division many times throughout the month. We think you'll find it worth the extra 15 or 20 minutes a day to pick up these Number Corner routines, many of which serve to reinforce the arithmetic skills taught in Unit 3.

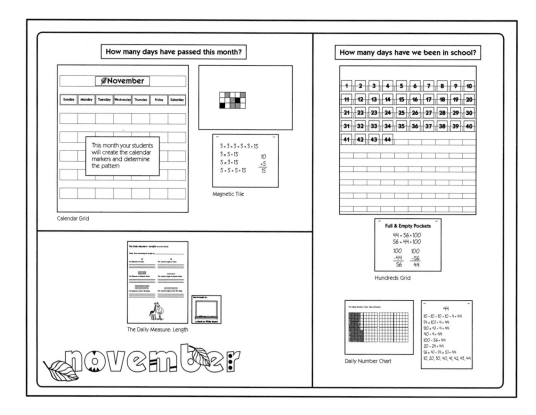

Unit 3 Planning Guide

SESSION 1	SESSION 2	SESSION 3	SESSION 4	SESSION 5
12 Ways to Make 11 (Reviewing standard notation for addition and subtraction) p. 195	Get the Facts: Addition (Developing a chart of addition facts) p. 198	**Assessment** Which Addition Combinations Are Easiest For You? p. 203 Roll & Add: A Probability Game (Counting on to add) p. 208	Shake, Reach & Record (Exploring addition fact families and probability) p. 211	Get the Facts: Subtraction (Developing a chart of subtraction facts) p. 214

SESSION 6	SESSION 7	SESSION 8	SESSION 9	SESSION 10
Assessment Which Subtraction Combinations Are Easiest For You? p. 219 Roll & Subtract: A Probability Game, p. 221	Make the Sum (Exploring addition fact families) p. 224	Getting Started with Work Places 4, p. 243 Introduction to Cats & Mice (Exploring subtraction as a process of finding the difference) p. 243	Fall/Winter Character Quilt—Making the Quilt Blocks (Spatial problem solving) p. 247	Fall/Winter Character Quilt—Designing the Quilt Layout (Exploring symmetry) p. 252
	Introduce Work Places 4		**Work Places 4** ———————————————→	
Home Connection 8				

SESSION 11	SESSION 12	SESSION 13	SESSION 14	SESSION 15
Fall/Winter Character Quilt—Choosing the Quilt Layout, p. 255	Cover Up, Part 1 (Exploring sums of doubles and neighbors) p. 258	Cover Up, Part 2 (Exploring sums of doubles and neighbors) p. 261	Battling Bugs (Exploring subtraction as a process of finding the difference) p. 266	Kids in the House (Searching for addition combinations to 16) p. 268
Work Places 4 ———→				
Home Connection 9				

SESSION 16	SESSION 17	SESSION 18	SESSION 19	SESSION 20
Crossing the Pond: A Probability Game (Practicing subtraction facts to 12) p. 272	Scout Them Out 1: Adding & Subtracting 0's & 1's, p. 277	Getting Started with Work Places 5, p. 297	Scout Them Out 2: Adding & Subtracting 2's & 10's, p. 299	Scout Them Out 3: Adding & Subtracting Doubles & Neighbors p. 302
Work Places 4	**Introduce Work Places 5**		**Work Places 5** ———————————————→	
Home Connection 10				

Unit 3 Planning Guide (cont.)

SESSION 21	SESSION 22	SESSION 23	SESSION 24	
Scout Them Out 4: Adding Doubles & Neighbors; Subtracting Halves, p. 308	Scout Them Out 5: Adding 10's & 9's; Subtracting 10's & Run Away 1's, p. 312	**Assessment** Which Addition Combinations Are Easiest For You Now? p. 318	**Assessment** Which Subtraction Combinations Are Easiest For You Now? p. 318	
Work Places 5 ⟶				
Home Connection 11				

Session 1

PROBLEMS & INVESTIGATIONS

12 Ways to Make 11

Overview

The teacher reads *12 Ways to Get to 11*, a delightful picture book that shows all kinds of combinations for 11. Students look, listen, and write one or more number sentences for some of the pages, recording what they see with numbers and operation symbols. Emphasis is placed on standard notation for addition and subtraction.

You'll need

★ *12 Ways to Get to 11*, by Eve Merriam

★ chart paper and marking pen, or chalk and chalkboard

★ paper and pencils; also clipboards if you plan to have students sit in a discussion circle to do this lesson

Skills

★ developing understandings of addition and subtraction

★ using standard notation to symbolize basic operations

★ symbolizing visual information

★ adding and subtracting whole numbers

Now that you've completed the first story problem theme with your students, the time seems ripe to move into a unit that takes a rather explicit look at addition and subtraction—the processes, the notation, and the facts themselves. 12 Ways to Make 11 is a transition lesson designed to review standard notation for addition and subtraction.

To begin today's lesson, reflect back on the story problem work you've done over the past two weeks. Note that children have used words, pictures, and numbers to solve each other's story problems. Some students might also have used number sentences—especially addition and subtraction sentences—to express their thinking. Let them know that you are headed into a unit that will help them become even more familiar with how to express addition and subtraction in numbers and symbols. The lessons and Work Places will also help them become more proficient with some of the basic addition and subtraction facts they'll need as they encounter more challenging math problems through the year.

Today you are going to read the children a simple and charming picture book by Eve Merriam, and ask them to write number sentences to match the words and pictures in the book. Some of your students might not be quite sure what a number sentence is at the beginning of the lesson, but most will

Session 1   12 Ways to Make 11 (cont.)

by the end. Before you start reading, have your students fold their papers into eighths and number each box, as shown below. This will help them organize their work as you move from page to page, and help you interpret what they've written later.

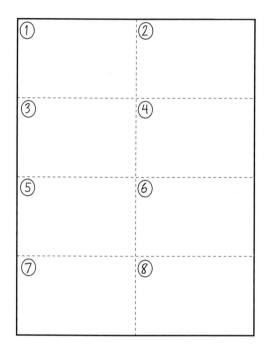

The opening pages of this book show the counting sequence from 1 to 12 with 11 left out, and pose the question, "Where's 11?" The next two pages show a little girl in the forest picking up pine cones. The text reads, "Pick up 9 pine cones from the forest floor and 2 acorns." If need be, count with your students to confirm that the pine cones plus the acorns total 11, and then challenge them to come up with a number sentence that matches the picture and the words. Have them record their ideas in the first box on their papers. Some children may be a little lost; others will write 9 + 2. A few (maybe more) will probably write "9 + 2 = 11." In any event, have several children share their ideas, and be sure to record "9 + 2 = 11" on your board or chart paper. Those who aren't quite sure what to do should be encouraged to copy your model. Be sure to show the number sentence in vertical, as well as horizontal form. It's possible, too, that someone might have written, "4 + 5 + 2 = 11" to match the numbers that can be seen on each page. If so, this should be discussed as another way to record what's seen.

The next page shows an elephant looking at 6 peanut shells and 5 pieces of popcorn. Again, the challenge is to come up with a written number sentence that reflects what's seen on the page. While 9 + 2 would work in some ways, it wouldn't reflect the words and pictures on the page, and the point is to use the picture as a departure point. Solicit several suggestions and then ask if it's possible to write a subtraction sentence about the picture. You might get

Session 1 12 Ways to Make 11 (cont.)

11 – 5 = 6 or 11 – 6 = 5. You might even get 6 – 5 = 1 (to reflect the difference between the number of peanuts and pieces of popcorn). Any of these responses would be acceptable. If no one can come up with anything for subtraction, model at least one possible response, asking students to copy your work on their papers.

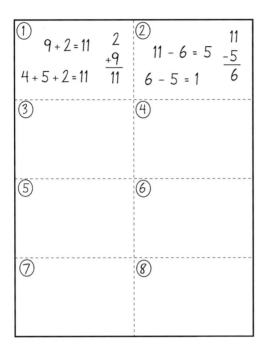

The book continues to show all sorts of combinations for 11, some much more complex than the first two pages. As the complexity grows, so does the opportunity for diverse number sentences. You won't want to have students write number sentences for more than eight of the pictures, but they will certainly enjoy looking at the entire book.

Session 2

PROBLEMS & INVESTIGATIONS

Get the Facts Addition

Overview

Given that acquisition of addition facts and use of standard notation are basic skills in the broadest sense, we want to set the task clearly before our students. In order to do this, we have them work together to create a class chart of addition facts to 20. Through generating all the possible 2-addend combinations and organizing them on a chart, children will begin to see patterns and relationships and also to realize that the job of learning the basic facts is finite and manageable. We also want to help them continue to develop number sense—a sense that numbers are not random, useful patterns do exist, and that it's possible to work from the things one knows to the things with which one is not so familiar.

You'll need

★ a 36" × 50" butcher paper chart as shown below

★ 130 2" × 3" white construction paper slips

★ pencils, marking pens, and glue

★ 2 trains of 10 Unifix cubes in 2 different solid colors for each group of 2 or 3 children in your class

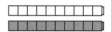

★ 10 small cards for the numbers 0–4 and 6–10

| 0 | 1 | 2 | 3 | 4 |
| 6 | 7 | 8 | 9 | 10 |

Skills

★ using standard notation to symbolize basic operations

★ finding all the 2-addend combinations for the numbers 0 through 20

★ discovering number patterns

★ looking at how addition facts relate to one another

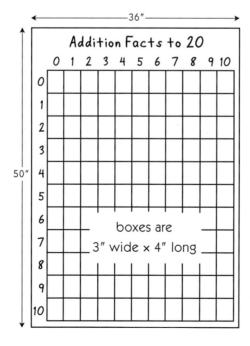

Session 2 Get the Facts: Addition (cont.)

To open this lesson, let the students know that you are headed into a unit that will help them become even more familiar with how to express addition and subtraction in numbers and symbols, as well as put a collection of useful facts and strategies at their fingertips. As they encounter more challenging problems through the year, it will be increasingly useful to "just know" that 6 + 6 is 12 or that 10 + 7 is 17. Understanding, too, that subtraction is the reverse of addition or that adding 9's is almost as easy as adding 10's will make things easier and more fun as the challenges grow.

Show the large, blank chart you've drawn and invite children to make observations. Then explain that you are going to use it to collect and organize all the addition facts they will be studying this year. Once the chart is put together, they may be surprised to discover how many of the facts they already know and how many of the ones they don't know seem pretty easy. Next, take 2 trains of Unifix cubes in 2 different colors and use them to help generate all the combinations for the 5's column on the chart as children watch and help. Record each combination on a slip of construction paper.

> *Teacher   I'm going to make all the addition facts for the 5's column on this chart. First, I'll get myself 5 Unifix cubes in 1 color.*

> *The first number I'm going to add to this collection is 0. What's 5 + 0?*

> *Children   Easy—5 + 0 is 5!*

> *Teacher   That's it? Okay, I'm going to write that on one of small pieces of paper, using large, neat printing. I'm also going to use vertical notation. That means going up and down instead of sideways, like this:*

$$\begin{array}{r} 5 \\ +0 \\ \hline 5 \end{array}$$

> *Teacher   Now I'll add 1 to my collection of 5. I want to be sure to show it with my Unifix cubes and to use the other color, like this:*

> *What number sentence can I write to show what I've just done with my cubes?*

> *Children   5 + 1 = 6.*

> *Teacher   Okay, that's what I'll write on my next slip of paper.*

$$\begin{array}{r} 5 \\ +1 \\ \hline 6 \end{array}$$

Session 2 Get the Facts: Addition (cont.)

Teacher *You can probably guess what's going to come next...*

Children *Yes—you're going to add 2 more.*
You're just going to keep your 5 and keep adding more and more to it, like 5 + 0, 5 + 1, 5 + 2, 5 + 3.
You're making an adding pattern with 5's!

Teacher *You're right, but I'm going to stop when I get to 5 + 10, because I only have 10 cubes in the second color, and this chart has no room for adding more than 10 to a number.*

Continue in this fashion until you've written slips of paper for 5 + 0 = 5 all the way to 5 + 10 = 15. Then, with the children's help, place the slips you've written on the chart (which should be lying flat so the slips stay in place).

Teacher *I want to use my slips to start filling in this addition chart. To place the slip that says 5 + 0 = 5, I'll look for a 5 along the top of the chart and a 0 along the side and place the slip in the box where the two meet, like this:*

And to place 5 + 1 = 6 and 5 + 2 = 7, I'll look for the top and side numbers, going from the top first.

Kaitlin *Your cards are going straight down.*

Teacher *That's right—straight down the 5's column. Would you like to place the slip that says "5 + 3 = 8"?*

Kaitlin *Sure—it will go in the box right underneath the last one.*

Teacher *That's right. Let's work together to get the rest of my slips placed.*

Session 2 Get the Facts: Addition (cont.)

	0	1	2	3	4	5	6	7	8	9	10
0						$\frac{5+0}{5}$					
1						$\frac{5+1}{6}$					
2						$\frac{5+2}{7}$					
3						$\frac{5+3}{8}$					
4						$\frac{5+4}{9}$					
5						$\frac{5+5}{10}$					
6						$\frac{5+6}{11}$					
7						$\frac{5+7}{12}$					
8						$\frac{5+8}{13}$					
9						$\frac{5+9}{14}$					
10						$\frac{5+10}{15}$					

After all your number facts have been placed, let each small group of students choose one of the numeral cards 0 through 4 or 6 through 10 you've prepared. This is the number for which they are going to write all the facts that belong on the chart. Then have each group gather 2 trains of Unifix cubes, pencils, and a supply of construction paper slips. They will use the first train of Unifix cubes to show their starting number (the number on their card). They will use the second train to show what happens as they add 0 to their number, then 1, then 2, then 3, then 4, and so on, up to 10. As they work, they will record their addition facts on the small slips of paper and then place their slips where they belong on the class chart. You may want to have them write their combinations in pencil first and then trace over them in marking pen once you've checked them.

Session 2 Get the Facts: Addition (cont.)

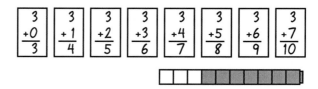

Hannah There! We have them all.

John No, we don't. We have to keep going until we add 10 to our number, not 'til we get an answer of 10.

Hannah Oh, yeah! We still have to do 3 + 8, 3 + 9, and 3 + 10. Okay.

If your students aren't as systematic as Hannah and John, don't despair. Most, in fact, will work in fairly random fashion and may need to be encouraged to find a way to check and see if they have really added all the numbers, 0 through 10, to their starting number. In the end, the chart itself will serve as a checking tool. If a combination has been left out, there will be a hole in the chart, which some children will be able to fill by looking at the numbers first along the top and then along the side.

	0	1	2	3	4	5	6	7	8	9	10
0	0 +0 0	1 +0 1	2 +0 2	3 +0 3	4 +0 4	5 +0 5	6 +0 6	7 +0 7	8 +0 8	9 +0 9	
1	0 +1 1	1 +1 2	2 +1 3	3 +1 4	4 +1 5	5 +1 6	6 +1 7	7 +1 8	8 +1 9	9 +1 10	10 +1 11
2		1 +2 3	2 +2 4	3 +2 5	4 +2 6	5 +2 7	6 +2 8	7 +2 9	8 +2 10	9 +2 11	10 +2 12

Teacher Looks like we have a couple holes in our chart. Can you tell what's missing?

Children There's one missing in the top row and one in the third row. What are they?
There's a 10 along the top and a 0 on the side in that first row.
It must be 10 + 0!
Yes—that's it. Who had 10? They need to write another slip.

It will probably take an hour to get the addition chart put together. You'll find yourself moving at a rather quick pace, as you encourage children to find all the possibilities. Before anything gets glued down, be sure to gather your group around the chart so the children can help check to be sure all the slips are there and correctly placed.

Session 3

ASSESSMENT

Which Addition Combinations Are Easiest For You?

Assessment

Children take a 4-minute timed addition test. Instead of working through fact by fact, however, they find and do the problems that seem easiest to them first, only going back to do the others if they still have time. There are 42 combinations on the sheet, and while a few of your students might be able to complete them all in the time allotted, many will only get to the ones that involve adding 0, 1, 2, or 10, and perhaps the doubles. Analyzing the results will give you some sense of the facts and strategies each child already knows and which are still challenging. This assessment will be repeated at the end of the unit and will provide one way to see some of the growth that has taken place over the course of 5 or 6 weeks.

You'll need

★ the addition chart you made with your class during Session 2

★ Addition Assessment Sheet (Blackline 3.1, run a class set)

★ pencils and erasers

Skills

★ practicing addition combinations to 20

★ discovering number patterns

★ looking at how addition facts relate to one another

★ thinking about which addition facts seem easier than others and why

Start the lesson by having children take a good look at the addition chart they helped create during Session 2. Ask them to talk with one another about the things they notice. After they've had a few minutes to talk among themselves, invite them to share comments and ideas with the group. Do they notice any patterns or other interesting things about the chart? Can they spot combinations that they already know by heart or that seem especially easy to solve? Why are some of the combinations so easy? What do they do when they come to combinations they don't already know?

Once children have had a chance to share their thoughts, remind them that this chart shows all the basic addition facts. Reassure them that they already know some of these. Others will be easy to learn, while a few may present more of a challenge. Let them know that you plan to spend lots of time over the next few weeks getting more familiar with this collection of facts, and that you'll continue to work on them all year long.

Explain that right now, you want to find out which facts are easy for each child and which seem more challenging. In order to get this information,

Session 3 Which Addition Combinations… (cont.)

you're going to ask each of them to do a sheet of addition. This sheet has many of the facts they see on the addition chart—combinations that add 0, 1, 2, 9, and 10; and doubles and neighbors. They'll have 4 minutes to work on it, and rather than going from the top to the bottom of the sheet, fact by fact, *they'll need to scan through and do the easiest ones they can find first. If they have more time after that, they can go back and tackle some of the combinations that seem harder.*

Blackline 3.1

NAME _____   DATE _____

Addition Assessment Sheet Which Facts Are Easiest For You?

Go through the facts below and do the easiest ones first. Then, if you have more time, go back and do the others.

$\begin{array}{r}0\\+\ 3\\\hline\end{array}$	$\begin{array}{r}0\\+\ 8\\\hline\end{array}$	$\begin{array}{r}4\\+\ 0\\\hline\end{array}$	$\begin{array}{r}9\\+\ 0\\\hline\end{array}$	$\begin{array}{r}1\\+\ 4\\\hline\end{array}$	$\begin{array}{r}1\\+\ 7\\\hline\end{array}$	$\begin{array}{r}1\\+\ 9\\\hline\end{array}$
$\begin{array}{r}5\\+\ 1\\\hline\end{array}$	$\begin{array}{r}2\\+\ 4\\\hline\end{array}$	$\begin{array}{r}2\\+\ 5\\\hline\end{array}$	$\begin{array}{r}2\\+\ 8\\\hline\end{array}$	$\begin{array}{r}3\\+\ 2\\\hline\end{array}$	$\begin{array}{r}6\\+\ 2\\\hline\end{array}$	$\begin{array}{r}7\\+\ 2\\\hline\end{array}$
$\begin{array}{r}4\\+\ 10\\\hline\end{array}$	$\begin{array}{r}4\\+\ 9\\\hline\end{array}$	$\begin{array}{r}10\\+\ 3\\\hline\end{array}$	$\begin{array}{r}9\\+\ 3\\\hline\end{array}$	$\begin{array}{r}10\\+\ 5\\\hline\end{array}$	$\begin{array}{r}9\\+\ 5\\\hline\end{array}$	$\begin{array}{r}6\\+\ 10\\\hline\end{array}$
$\begin{array}{r}9\\+\ 7\\\hline\end{array}$	$\begin{array}{r}10\\+\ 7\\\hline\end{array}$	$\begin{array}{r}2\\+\ 2\\\hline\end{array}$	$\begin{array}{r}3\\+\ 3\\\hline\end{array}$	$\begin{array}{r}4\\+\ 3\\\hline\end{array}$	$\begin{array}{r}4\\+\ 4\\\hline\end{array}$	$\begin{array}{r}5\\+\ 4\\\hline\end{array}$
$\begin{array}{r}5\\+\ 5\\\hline\end{array}$	$\begin{array}{r}5\\+\ 6\\\hline\end{array}$	$\begin{array}{r}6\\+\ 6\\\hline\end{array}$	$\begin{array}{r}6\\+\ 7\\\hline\end{array}$	$\begin{array}{r}7\\+\ 7\\\hline\end{array}$	$\begin{array}{r}7\\+\ 8\\\hline\end{array}$	$\begin{array}{r}8\\+\ 8\\\hline\end{array}$
$\begin{array}{r}8\\+\ 9\\\hline\end{array}$	$\begin{array}{r}9\\+\ 9\\\hline\end{array}$	$\begin{array}{r}9\\+\ 10\\\hline\end{array}$	$\begin{array}{r}10\\+\ 10\\\hline\end{array}$	$\begin{array}{r}5\\+\ 3\\\hline\end{array}$	$\begin{array}{r}5\\+\ 7\\\hline\end{array}$	$\begin{array}{r}8\\+\ 6\\\hline\end{array}$

Distribute the papers, pencils, and erasers and make provisions for children to do their own work. *Don't forget to put the class addition chart away for now.* Have them put names and dates on their papers and begin at your signal. Let them work for 4 minutes and then collect the papers. You may want to take a few minutes to discuss the experience. Was everyone able to find some facts that seemed easy? Did other combinations seem hard? Were there some they had to leave unfinished this time? Reassure students that the work you'll be doing over the next few weeks will help. They'll have a chance to take this test again at the end of unit and will probably notice some changes in their own performance by then.

Session 3 Which Addition Combinations... (cont.)

Looking at Children's Work

Here are some things to think about as you look over each student's paper after this lesson.

1. Have the facts been done from top to bottom, right to left, or in a more random fashion, as shown below?

Blackline 3.1

NAME _____ DATE _____

Addition Assessment Sheet Which Facts Are Easiest For You?

Go through the facts below and do the easiest ones first. Then, if you have more time, go back and do the others.

0 + 3 **3**	0 + 8 **8**	4 + 0 **4**	9 + 0 **9**	1 + 4 **5**	1 + 7 **8**	1 + 9 **10**
5 + 1 **6**	2 + 4 **6**	2 + 5 —	2 + 8 —	3 + 2 **5**	6 + 2 —	7 + 2 —
4 + 10 **14**	4 + 9 —	10 + 3 **13**	9 + 3 —	10 + 5 **15**	9 + 5 —	6 + 10 **16**
9 + 7 —	10 + 7 **17**	2 + 2 **4**	3 + 3 **6**	4 + 3 **7**	4 + 4 —	5 + 4 —
5 + 5 **10**	5 + 6 —	6 + 6 —	6 + 7 —	7 + 7 —	7 + 8 —	8 + 8 —
8 + 9 —	9 + 9 —	9 + 10 —	10 + 10 **20**	5 + 3 —	5 + 7 —	8 + 6 —

If the paper looks a bit like Swiss cheese (full of holes), there's a good chance the child understands the idea of finding the easy facts first and is able to do so. If, on the other hand, the facts in the first 2 or 3 rows have been done quite methodically and there's been no apparent attempt to skip down to easier work below (like 2 + 2 in the fourth row or 5 + 5 in the fifth row), it's possible that the child doesn't understand what to do or, in fact, finds no facts particularly easier than others. Maybe they are all difficult and simply have to be done using fingers or counting from 1 each time.

2. Which facts have been completed? As you look at the paper, you've probably noticed that the facts have been grouped: +0's and +1's in the top row; +2's in the second row; 10's and 9's in the third row; doubles and neighbors in the fourth, fifth, and sixth rows; and a few miscellaneous facts at the very

Session 3 Which Addition Combinations… (cont.)

bottom. Did the child do all the +0's, +1's, a few of the lower doubles, and some of the 10's? All the +0's, +1's, +2's, and most of the doubles?

3. Is there any indication that the child may have used the answer from one fact to help with another? We deliberately set up the sheet to make this possible: 9 + 5, for instance, sits right beside 10 + 5. Children who know the answer to 10 + 5 and see the relationship between the two will often do both. Children who have little or no sense relationship between facts may do the 10's and not touch the 9's.

4. How many out of the 42 have been completed correctly? You'll want to store these papers in children's work sample files and pull them out again at the end of the unit when you have a second sample for both addition and subtraction. Both you and the students may be interested to compare the "before" and "after" sheets at that point.

Some Thoughts on Timed Testing

While, in general, we don't advocate the practice of timed testing in primary classrooms, we've chosen to make an exception in this unit. Why? Mainly because we want to get a sense of whether or not there are facts that stand out to our students as being easier than others. Can they cruise through a sheet of random addition facts and find the combinations that seem really simple to them? Which facts are those, and why? Putting a 4-minute time limit on the project is one way to encourage children to get the "easy ones" done first and then go back to work on the harder ones—not a bad practice when it comes to taking tests. Without the time limit, there are children in our classes who might spend 20 minutes or more completing the sheet, insisting that all the facts are easy for them. That's not the point.

The other reason we've chosen to put a time constraint on this exercise is that we want children to understand that at some point, it's very handy to know some addition and subtraction facts by heart. Speed, in fact, does pay when it comes to basic addition and subtraction. If you happen to know that 5 + 5 = 10, it's easier to figure 5 + 6, 4 + 5, 10 – 5, 10 – 4, 10 – 6, and even 50 + 50 or 500 + 500. We're hoping that this brief timed exercise will give children a sense of what they already know and what they can learn. Having the chance to take both the addition and the subtraction tests now and once again in 5 or 6 weeks will give students and teachers a chance to see growth and change.

There are, of course, limitations to this exercise. You may have a few students for whom none of the addition or subtraction facts are easy right now. These may be the same children who won't make a lot of growth within the time frame of this unit. For them, the facts and strategies will need to be taught and reviewed over and over throughout the year. Perhaps there will be children in your group who do know some basic facts, but feel so anxious in a

Session 3 Which Addition Combinations… (cont.)

testing situation that they won't be able to show what they know. There may be others who can't read, process, or write quickly enough to get much down on the paper in 4 minutes. Still others may have a hard time bringing enough focus to the task to produce much.

You'll have to make provision for these children as you see fit. Perhaps some will need a little longer than 4 minutes, or a chance to go back and revisit the sheet a day later for an additional 4 minutes. It's important for them to understand, though, that the point isn't to complete the sheet in 4 minutes. The point is to find the combinations that seem easy and get them done.

With some students, the information you collected when you did individual interviews will be much more useful than what you'll see here. It's important to bear in mind that these assessments *are only one small measure of growth and change.* You've already conducted interviews with each of your students. We've provided an observation checklist for you to use as you watch children at the Work Places during this unit as well. The Work Places 4 and 5 activities will provide you with many opportunities to watch children exercise their knowledge of facts and strategies in context. Children will also have repeated opportunities to develop facility with basic facts throughout the year—especially through the Number Corner activities and the Home Connection assignments, but also in the course of many of the other units.

Session 3 Roll & Add

Roll & Add

Overview

Children play a whole-group dice game to practice the skill of counting on. The probability of rolling some combinations more than others is also considered. This game will appear in the next set of Work Places.

Skills

★ counting on as a strategy for adding numbers

★ recording data on a graph

★ using experimental data to predict probability

You'll need

★ two ¾" wooden cubes for every 2 children; number one cube from 5 to 10 and number and dot the other cube from 0–5 (use a permanent black fine felt-tip pen to do your numbering)

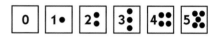

★ Roll & Add record sheets (Blackline 3.2, run a half-class set)

★ 3" sticky notes

Once you've finished the addition assessment with your group, gather children into a discussion circle and explain that one of the easier ways to add two numbers, if they don't already know the answer, is to count on. In order to practice this skill, you are going to teach them a new game, which they will play today and again in the next set of Work Places. Tell them that in a few minutes they will work in pairs to do a little investigation with dice (or "number cubes" if you prefer). Show them that they will be working with a numbered die and a die that has both numbers and dots, as shown below.

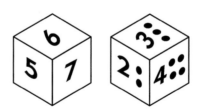

"6—7, 8, 9; the answer's 9!"

Explain that with their partner they will roll, add (by counting on from the plain number to the number with dots, if they don't already know the answer), and record. They will keep doing this until 3 columns on their graphs are filled to the top.

Session 3 Roll & Add (cont.)

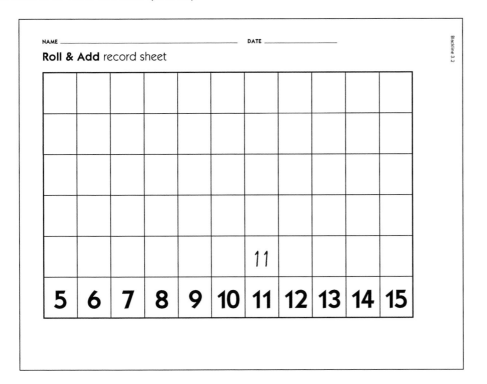

NAME _____ DATE _____

Blackline 3.2

Roll & Add record sheet

						11				
5	**6**	**7**	**8**	**9**	**10**	**11**	**12**	**13**	**14**	**15**

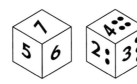

"I got 7 and 4. That's 7—8, 9, 10, 11. So I'll write an 11 on my graph.

Demonstrate with a pair of dice and a record sheet, but before you start, ask if they think any of the numbers will have a better chance of being first to fill a column. Repeat this question several times as you work, asking children to explain their thinking each time. Chances are, if you roll a particular number several times in the space of a few minutes, many students will be convinced that it will be the winner. Others may be convinced that every number has an equal chance, and whatever number takes the lead is pure chance or due to how you're tossing the dice. A few may say that it would be hard to get a 5 or a 15 because there's only one way to roll either number (5 + 0 and 5 + 10).

Demonstrate the process of rolling and recording until at least 1 of the columns on your paper is filled. Then send students out in partners to work until 3 columns are filled. Before they go, show them how to write first, second, and third in shorthand (1st, 2nd, and 3rd) so they can note the numbers that win on their papers.

Session 3 Roll & Add (cont.)

NAME ___Eloise_____   DATE ___November 5___

Roll & Add record sheet

Blackline 3.2

				1st	3rd	2nd				
				10	11	12				
				10	11	12				
			9	10	11	12	13			
		7	8	9	10	11	12	13		
5	6	7	8	9	10	11	12	13	14	
5	**6**	**7**	**8**	**9**	**10**	**11**	**12**	**13**	**14**	**15**

As they finish, have pairs of children post their results on a class chart you've drawn on the chalkboard. All they have to do is to write their winning number on a 3″ sticky note and post it above the appropriate number on the board. (If they're really interested in looking at the results, you might have them post their second and third place winners, each on its own color sticky note, on the chart.)

When everyone's finished and has posted their results, have a look at the chart together. What do they notice about the data? What can they observe? Did some numbers come up as first place winners more often than others? Why? Would it happen the same way if you repeated the whole experiment?

Session 4

PROBLEMS & INVESTIGATIONS

Shake, Reach & Record

Overview

Students conduct another probability experiment, this time featuring tile pulled out of a bag. The question being investigated is: If you put 10 green tile in a bag and 10 yellow tile, shake them up, and then pull out 7, how many greens are you likely to get? How many yellows? If you repeat this many times, replacing the tile each time and shaking the bag again, are certain combinations of 7 more likely to come up than others? While conducting this experiment, students are seeing and recording all the 2-addend combinations for 7 over and over, as well as creating graphs to show their data. This activity will appear in the next set of Work Places.

You'll need

★ Shake, Reach & Record 7's record sheet (Overhead 3.1)

★ 10 yellow overhead tile and 10 green overhead tile in a paper lunch sack

★ 3" sticky notes

Each child will need

★ Shake, Reach & Record 7's record sheet (Blackline 3.3, 1 copy)

★ 10 yellow tile and 10 green tile in a paper lunch sack (Use the tile from your base ten kits.)

Skills

★ seeing and recording all the 2-addend combinations for 7 using standard notation

★ recording data on a graph

★ using experimental data to predict probability

Much like Roll & Add, this activity is another opportunity to practice addition facts while conducting informal probability investigations. This time, the experiments involve tile sampling. With the record sheet shown on the following page, for example, one would pull 7 tile out of the sack, record how many greens and yellows came out, put the tile back in the sack, shake it, and repeat the process.

Session 4 Shake, Reach & Record (cont.)

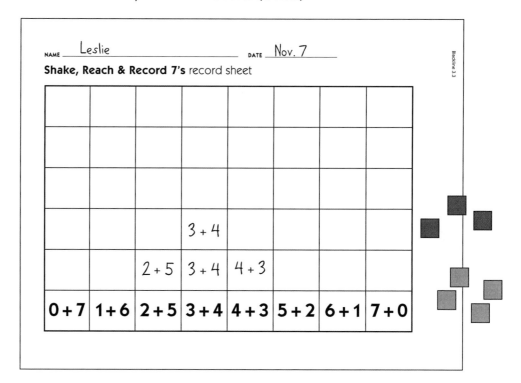

NAME _Leslie_   DATE _Nov. 7_

Blackline 3.3

Shake, Reach & Record 7's record sheet

			3 + 4				
		2 + 5	3 + 4	4 + 3			
0 + 7	**1 + 6**	**2 + 5**	**3 + 4**	**4 + 3**	**5 + 2**	**6 + 1**	**7 + 0**

Leslie I pulled out 3 greens and 4 yellows this time, so I'll
have to write down 3 + 4 on my record sheet. I've gotten
3 + 4 two times now. I wonder what I'll get next time.

To start the lesson, show your overhead transparency of the record sheet. As
always, ask children to talk with one another about what they notice. Then
take a minute to have a few volunteers share with the group. Your students
may notice that each combination along the bottom of the sheet adds up to 7.
They're almost sure to notice some patterns in the numbers and will be curious to know what you're planning to do with the sheet.

Explain that this is another game to help them practice addition facts. Show
them your sack and, while they watch, count 10 green and 10 yellow overhead tile into the sack. Shake the sack well, reach in, and pull out 7 tile. Set
them on the overhead platform for all to see, and explain that you want to
record the results of your sample by writing down how many greens you got
first, and then how many yellows. Once the numbers have been recorded,
place the 7 tile back in the bag, shake it again, and draw out 7 more. Record
your results, put the tile back, and repeat several more times. Be sure to emphasize the fact that you're returning the tile to the bag each time, shaking it
well before each draw, and counting the greens *before* the yellows as you record.

Once you've gone through the steps 4 or 5 times, ask the children what they
think might happen as you continue to work. Do they think that you're more
likely to pull any particular combinations out of the bag? Do they see any
combinations they think might be harder to get? Why? The fact that you have

Session 4 Shake, Reach & Record (cont.)

equal numbers of green and yellow may make this experiment simpler to think about than Roll & Record, but if your students are anything like ours, they'll find it easier to observe the results of probability than to explain them. Nevertheless, we think that questions involving probability are worth pursuing; this isn't the last time they will come up this year.

When you think most of your students understand what to do, send them out to work on their own 7's sheets, with the understanding that they're to shake, reach, and record 7's until two of their columns have reached the top. Again, have them keep track of first and second place winners on their sheets. As children finish, have them record their first place winners on sticky notes and graph them on the board, as shown below. Discuss the class graph at the end of the math period. What do students notice about the graph? Why did so many children pull combinations of 3 and 4 or 4 and 3 out of the bag? Why weren't there more combinations of 0 and 7 or 1 and 6 pulled out? If you repeated this experiment tomorrow, would the results be similar or different? Why?

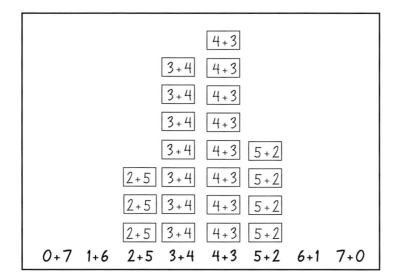

Session 5

PROBLEMS & INVESTIGATIONS

Get the Facts Subtraction

Overview
Students work together to create a chart of subtraction facts

Skills
★ using standard notation to symbolize basic operations

★ listing subtraction facts for the numbers 0 through 18

★ discovering number patterns

★ looking at how subtraction facts relate to one another

You'll need
★ a large chart made of two 60″ lengths of 36″-wide butcher paper (Cut 1 length in half lengthwise, glue or tape it to bottom of the 60″ × 36″ piece, as shown below.)

★ 220 white construction paper slips, 2″ × 3″

★ pencils, marking pens, and glue

★ 20 Unifix cubes in a single color for each pair of children in your class

★ 14 small cards numbered 5–18

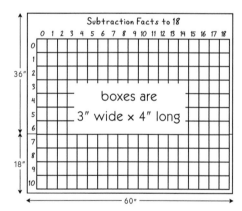

This lesson parallels the session in which students created a class addition chart. As they did before, pairs of students will work together to generate and record facts for a given number. Their work will then be organized onto a chart. The interesting thing is that the shape of this chart will turn out differently than the addition chart. As shown on the chart on the next page, the shaded boxes will be filled in and the white boxes will remain blank.

Session 5 Get the Facts (cont.)

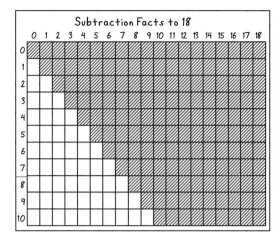

To begin the lesson, show the large blank subtraction chart you've drawn up and invite children to make observations. How are the shape and dimensions of this one the same as the addition chart? How are they different? Then explain that you are going to use it to collect and organize many of the subtraction facts they'll be studying this year. Once the chart is put together, the students may be surprised to discover how many of the facts they already know and how many of the ones they don't know seem pretty easy. With the children's help, generate subtraction facts for the numbers 0, 1, 2, 3, and 4. Start each time by taking 0 away from the "target number," then 1, then 2, and so on, until you've reached the point of taking the number away from itself. Record each combination on a construction paper slip.

Teacher *I want to make a set of subtraction cards for 0. I'm going to start by taking 0 away. What is 0 – 0?*

Children *0!*

Teacher *That's it? Okay, I'm going to write that on one of these slips of construction paper, using large, neat printing. I'm also going to use vertical notation, just like we did on the addition chart.*

Teacher *Now let's think about 1. What's 1 – 0?*

Children *0!*
No, 1. If you have 1 and take 0 away, you'll have 1 left.
Any number take away 0 is just itself. Taking 0 away is easy!

Teacher *Okay. So 1 – 0 = 1. How about 1 – 1?*

Children *1 – 1 = 0!*

Teacher *Have I gone as far as I can subtracting numbers from 1?*

Session 5 Get the Facts (cont.)

Sarah *You could keep going and get negative numbers. My mom told me about those.*

Teacher *That's true. What would happen if you subtracted 2 from 1?*

Sarah *You'd get negative 1.*

Teacher *How does that work?*

Sarah *Well, if you take 1 away from 1, you get 0. If you take 2 away, you have to go below 0. It's like when it gets so cold the temperature is below 0.*

Teacher *We can come back to the subject of negative numbers later—they are fascinating. But if we don't include them yet, do we have all the possibilities here?*

Sarah *Yes.*

$$\begin{array}{r} 1 \\ -0 \\ \hline 1 \end{array} \qquad \begin{array}{r} 1 \\ -1 \\ \hline 0 \end{array}$$

Teacher *Now, how about 2? If I look at the differences between 2 and 0, 2 and 1, and 2 and 2, what three facts do I end up with?*

Children *2 – 0 = 2.*
2 – 1 = 1.
2 – 2 = 0.
That's all! You can't go any further.
This is kind of easy, it's like a pattern each time.
Yes—you take away more each time and get smaller and smaller answers.

$$\begin{array}{r} 2 \\ -0 \\ \hline 2 \end{array} \qquad \begin{array}{r} 2 \\ -1 \\ \hline 1 \end{array} \qquad \begin{array}{r} 2 \\ -2 \\ \hline 0 \end{array}$$

Continue in this fashion until you've generated the subtraction facts for the numbers 0 through 4. With children's help place the slips you've written on the chart (which should be lying flat so the slips stay in place).

Teacher *I want to use my slips to start filling in this subtraction chart. To place the paper that says 0 – 0 = 0, I'll look for a 0 along the top of the chart and a 0 along the side and place it in the box where the two meet, like this:*

Session 5 Get the Facts (cont.)

	0	1	2	3	4	5	6	7	8	9	10	11	12	13	14	15	16	17	18
0	0 −0 0																		
1																			

And to place 1 − 0 = 1 and 1 − 1 = 0, I'll look for the top and side numbers, always looking along the top first.

	0	1	2	3	4	5	6	7	8	9	10	11	12	13	14	15	16	17	18
0	0 −0 0	1 −0 1																	
1		1 −1 1																	

Ethan *That's weird how it moved over.*

Teacher *Why did it do that?*

Ethan *Because you were matching up the numbers on the top and the side.*

Teacher *That's right. If we did want to fill that empty space, what would we have to put in?*

Caroline *1 − 0 = 1—no, you have to say the top first. It would be 0 − 1! It would be a negative number, like Sarah was talking about!*

Teacher *We can fill the empty spaces later, if you want to include negative numbers on your chart, but let's not, for now. Where do the rest of these slips belong?*

	0	1	2	3	4	5	6	7	8	9	10	11	12	13	14	15	16	17	18
0	0 −0 0	1 −0 1	2 −0 2	3 −0 3	4 −0 4														
1		1 −1 0	2 −1 1	3 −1 2	4 −1 3														
2			2 −2 0	3 −2 1	4 −2 2														
3				3 −3 0	4 −3 1														
4					4 −4 0														

After all your combinations have been placed, let each pair of students choose one of the numeral cards 5 through 18 you've prepared. This is the number for which they are going to find subtraction facts. Then have each pair get 20 Unifix cubes in a single color, a pencil, and a supply of white construction paper slips. They will use the Unifix cubes to form the subtraction facts for their number, record their combinations on slips, and put the cards where they belong on the class chart.

Session 5 Get the Facts (cont.)

. . . .

Note   Be sure to let children know that with the numbers over 10, they need to stop at the point of taking away 10. The chart won't accommodate combinations like 12 – 11 or 17 – 14. The fact that the chart itself stops at 10 going down the side may serve as a reminder, but if they wind up making extra slips, it won't be the end of the world. Those slips just won't have any place on the chart.

. . . .

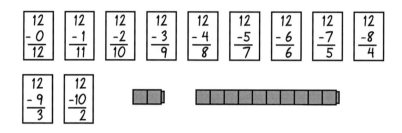

Kevin   *Do we have them all?*

Cassie   *Yes. We don't have to go any farther than 10. There's no place on the chart for 12 – 11 and 12 – 12.*

Kevin   *We got a lot of papers for 12, didn't we?*

Few of your students will be as systematic as Kevin and Cassie. Most will probably work in fairly random fashion and may need to be encouraged to find a way to check and see if they have really generated all the subtraction facts with differences greater than or equal to 0 for their number (e.g., 5 – 0, 5 – 1, 5 – 2, 5 – 3, 5 – 4, and 5 – 5 for 5). In the end, the chart itself will serve as a checking tool. If a combination has been left out, there will be a hole in the chart, which some children will be able to fill by looking at the numbers on the top and the side.

It will probably take the entire math period to get the subtraction chart put together. Move at a rather quick pace as you encourage children to find all the possibilities and place their slips on the chart correctly. Unless you are able to supervise the placement very closely, you might want to wait until all the slips are placed before allowing children to glue them down.

If you have time at the end of the period, ask children to share observations about the chart with one another. There are all sorts of interesting patterns to be found. In two of our classes, the students became very intrigued with the growing numbers of empty spaces that preceded the second through eleventh rows on the chart. As they talked about what would have to go into those spaces, a nice discussion about negative numbers emerged, led by a child who'd been introduced to the idea at home. It's quite possible that the subject won't come up in your classroom, but if it does, we encourage you to follow your students' lead. We are often surprised at what happens when we "leave the lid off."

Session 6

ASSESSMENT

Which Subtraction Combinations Are Easiest For You?

HOME
CONNECTIONS

Overview

Children take a 4-minute timed subtraction test. Instead of working through fact by fact, however, they first find and do the problems that seem easiest to them, only going back to do the others if they still have time. There are 42 combinations on the sheet, and while a few of your students might be able to complete them all in the time allotted, many will only get to the ones that involve subtracting 0, 1, 2, or 10, and perhaps the doubles. Analyzing the results will give you some sense of the facts and strategies each child already knows and which are still challenging. This assessment will be repeated at the end of the unit and will provide one way to see some of the growth that's taken place over the course of 5 or 6 weeks.

You'll need

★ the subtraction chart you made with your class during Session 5

★ Subtraction Assessment Sheet (Blackline 3.4, run a class set)

★ pencils and erasers

★ Home Connections Blacklines HC 8.1–8.4

Skills

★ practicing subtraction facts

★ discovering number patterns

★ looking at how subtraction facts relate to one another and to addition facts.

Start the lesson by having children take a good look at the subtraction chart they helped create during the last session. Ask them to talk with one another about the things they notice. After they've had a few minutes to talk among themselves, invite them to share comments and ideas with the group. Do they notice any patterns or other interesting things about the chart? Can they spot subtraction facts that they already know by heart or that seem especially easy to solve? Why are some of these facts so easy? What do they do when they come to subtraction facts they don't already know?

Once children have had a chance to share their thoughts, explain that this chart shows many of the basic subtraction facts. Most students already know some of them. Others will be easy to learn, while a few may present more of a challenge. Let them know that you plan to spend lots of time over the next few weeks getting more familiar with this collection of subtraction facts, and that you'll continue to work on them all year long.

Explain that right now, you want to find out which facts are easy for each child and which seem more challenging. In order to get this information,

Session 6 Which Subtraction Combinations… (cont.)

you're going to ask each of them to do a sheet of subtraction exercises, just as they did addition the other day. This sheet has many of the facts they see on the subtraction chart—pairs of numbers whose differences are 0, 1, 2, or 10; doubles and neighbors. They'll have four minutes to work on it, and rather than going from the top to the bottom of the sheet, fact by fact, *they'll need to scan through and do the easiest ones they can find first. If they have more time after that, they can go back and tackle some of the more difficult ones.*

Blackline 3.4

NAME _____   DATE _____

Subtraction Assessment Sheet Which Combinations Are Easiest For You?

Go through the facts below and do the easiest ones first. Then, if you have more time, go back and do the others.

3 − 0	8 − 0 **8**	14 − 0	9 − 0	4 − 1	7 − 1	10 − 1
12 − 1	5 − 2	8 − 2	11 − 2	7 − 2	6 − 6	6 − 5
10 − 10	10 − 9	15 − 15	15 − 14	4 − 2	4 − 3	12 − 12
12 − 6	12 − 7	10 − 5	10 − 6	8 − 4	8 − 5	6 − 3
15 − 10	15 − 9	12 − 10	12 − 9	18 − 10	18 − 9	12 − 2
14 − 4	16 − 6	13 − 3	20 − 10	16 − 8	16 − 9	16 − 10

Distribute the papers, pencils, and erasers and make provisions for children to do their own work. *Don't forget to put the class subtraction chart away for now.* Have them put names and dates on their papers and begin at your signal. Let them work for four minutes and then collect the papers. You may want to take a few minutes to discuss the experience. Was everyone able to find some facts that seemed easy? Did other combinations seem hard? Were there some they had to leave unfinished this time? Reassure students again that the work you'll be doing over the next few weeks will help them know more facts by heart and also learn some ways to more quickly figure combinations they don't already know. Tell them that they will have a chance to take this test again at the end of the unit, and will probably notice some changes in their own performance by then.

ASSESSMENT TIPS ▶ **Looking at Children's Work**

Please see the remarks under this section in Session 3 (pages 205–207).

Session 6 (cont.)

PROBLEMS & INVESTIGATIONS

Roll & Subtract

Overview

Children play a whole-group dice game to practice the skill of subtracting by counting backwards. Like counting on, this strategy is much favored by second graders. It's not particularly efficient when the subtrahends are larger than 3 because it becomes quite cumbersome. Nevertheless, we want to acknowledge the strategy and give "count backs" their due. The dice are set up so children are taking 1, 2, or 3 away each roll. We'll share other strategies for taking away larger numbers later in the unit. As with Roll & Add, the probability of getting some combinations more than others is also considered. This game will appear in the next set of Work Places.

You'll need

★ two ¾" wooden cubes for every 2 children; number one cube from 5 to 10 and number and dot the other cube from 0–3

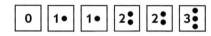

★ Roll & Subtract record sheets (Blackline 3.5, run a half-class set)

★ 3" sticky notes (optional)

Skills

★ counting backwards as a strategy for subtracting 1, 2, or 3 from a larger quantity

★ recording data on a graph

★ using experimental data to predict probability

Once students have finished the subtraction assessment, gather them into a discussion circle and explain that one of the ways children often try to subtract two numbers if they don't already know the answer, and there isn't an easier strategy, is to count backwards. This is a useful method when subtracting small quantities. The technique is so common that's it's worth acknowledging and encouraging, as long as it only involves counting back 1, 2, or 3 numbers. Combinations like 8 – 1, 8 – 2, and 8 – 3 might be handled with count backs; 8 – 6 is probably too far a distance to count back. In order to practice count backs, you are going to teach them a new game, which they will play today and again in the next set of Work Places. Tell them that in a few minutes they will work in pairs with a numbered die and a die that has both numbers and dots.

Explain that with their partner they will roll, subtract (by counting backwards from the numeral on the undotted die the number of times indicated by the dots on the other die), and record.

Session 6 Roll & Subtract (cont.)

"I rolled a 9 and a 2. That means I have to count back 2 times—
9—8, 7. The answer is 7, so that's what we'll show on our paper."

They will keep doing this until 3 columns on their graphs have filled to the top. Demonstrate with a pair of dice and a record sheet. Be very explicit, to the point of writing it on the chalkboard, that when you use the count back technique, you name the first number and jump backwards from that number, as on a gameboard, rather than counting the number itself.

10 **3** :·

Teacher If I roll a 10 and a 3, that means I want to subtract 3 from 10. Because 3 is such a small number to subtract, I'm going to use count backs. I say the number and count back 3 times: *10*—9, 8, 7. It's like playing a game and having to move 3 squares back.

| 0 | 1 | 2 | 3 | 4 | 5 | 6 | 7 | 8 | 9 | 10 |

When you think most of the children know what to do, send them out to work in partners. Remind them that they're to play until 3 columns have come to the top, and show them again how to write "1st," "2nd," and "3rd," so they can keep track of the winning numbers. If this entire task is fairly easy for many of your students, you might want to post class results in terms of numbers that place first. This could be done with sticky notes on the chalkboard the same way you did for Roll & Add. If you do decide to look at class results, it's interesting to ponder the question of why 5's, 6's, and 7's often seem to come in before any of the other numbers.

Session 6 Roll & Subtract (cont.)

 HOME CONNECTION 8

Activity These Beans Have Got to Go! (Blacklines HC 8.1–8.2, pp. 31–32)

Worksheet What is it About Those Middle Numbers? (Blacklines HC 8.3–8.4, pp. 33–34)

It's homework time again. This week's activity and worksheet provide some practice with addition facts in the context of a new probability game.

Blackline HC 8.1 Use after Unit 3, Session 6.

Home Connection 8 ★ Activity

 NOTE TO FAMILIES

One of the very best ways to learn addition and subtraction facts is to play games. This game is particularly interesting in that winning is not just a matter of luck. Each player places his or her beans on the numbers shown below and takes turns spinning the 2 spinners and adding the 2 numbers that come up. Anytime you have a bean on the sum you spin, you get to take it off the board. The trick is figuring out how best to place your beans before you start. As adults, we know that there are certain sums that are going to come up more often than others. It is far easier to spin a 7 than a 2, for instance, simply because there are more combinations for 7 on the spinners. You can get a 7 by spinning 1 + 6 or 2 + 5 or 3 + 4. The only way to get a 2 is by spinning 1 + 1. Your child will probably want to place a bean on every number "just to be safe," but will learn through experience that the middle numbers usually come up more often.

These Beans Have Got to Go!

You'll need 24 beans, buttons, coins, or other small markers in 2 different colors to play this game (e.g., 12 black beans and 12 white beans, or 12 white buttons and 12 brown buttons).

Game Rules

1 Each player needs to place his or her beans on the board. You can place more than 1 bean on a particular number. Here's a sample set-up:

| 2 | 3 | 4 | 5 | 6 | 7 | 8 | 9 | 10 | 11 | 12 |

2 Decide who will start and have that player spin the 2 spinners and add the 2 numbers. If it's your turn and you have a bean sitting on the sum of the 2 numbers you spun, you can remove it. If, for instance, you spin 4 + 3, and you have a bean sitting on 7, you can take it off. You can only take 1 bean off at a time.

3 Take turns spinning and removing beans if you can. The first player to get all his or her beans off the board wins. Play the game several times and see if you can figure out the best way to place your beans.

Blackline HC 8.3 Run back-to-back with HC 8.4

NAME _____ DATE _____

Home Connection 8 ★ Worksheet

 NOTE TO FAMILIES

This worksheet is designed to help your child begin to understand why the middle numbers tend to come up more often in the game you just played. If your child doesn't fully comprehend what's going on, don't worry. It takes a long time to understand probability, and we'll play many more games like this throughout the year.

What Is It About Those Middle Numbers?

Are you wondering why the middle numbers keep winning on the the game you just played? Fill in the sums on the addition table shown below and follow the instructions for coloring them in, and you may begin to see why it's a better idea to put your beans on the 6 and the 7 instead of the 2 and the 12.

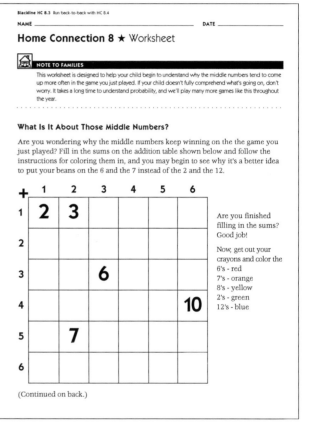

+	1	2	3	4	5	6
1	2	3				
2						
3			6			
4					10	
5		7				
6						

Are you finished filling in the sums? Good job!

Now, get out your crayons and color the

6's - red
7's - orange
8's - yellow
2's - green
12's - blue

(Continued on back.)

Session 7

PROBLEMS & INVESTIGATIONS

Make the Sum

Overview
Children learn to play a card game that can be easily tailored to provide practice with specific addition combinations for 5 through 15. After playing this new game in small groups, children are introduced to the new Work Places.

You'll need
★ 8 decks of Make the Sum cards

Skills
★ practicing addition combinations for 7 (or other quantities) in a problem-solving context

To start the lesson today, you might review the territory you've covered over the past few sessions. So far, you've looked at standard notation for addition and subtraction, created class addition and subtraction charts, thought about why some addition and subtraction facts are easier than others, practiced counting on and counting backwards as possible strategies, and looked at all the 2-addend combinations for the number 7. Today, you're going to play another game that will provide practice with many of the combinations for a target number.

Gather your students into a discussion circle where everyone can see, and choose three volunteers to play Make the Sum with you. Display a deck of number cards and explain that because you're playing for 7's today, you will need to set aside all the cards that are more than 7. With the help of your three volunteer players, discard all the 8's, 9's, and 10's. When all the cards greater than 7 have been set aside, shuffle the deck.

Then set the stack of cards face down. Take turns around your little group of four players drawing a card from the top of the deck. The object of the game is to collect combinations of cards that add to 7; so if you draw a 2, just leave it face up beside the deck to be used as community property. If the next player in the group then draws a 5, she can combine it with the 2 to make 7. She gets to keep those two cards and then it's the next player's turn. (Play always continues around the circle—players don't get an extra turn when they collect a combination.) If a player draws a 7 from the deck, he or she gets to keep it.

Sometimes it's possible that a number of cards can be drawn without anyone being able to make the sum. If you had a collection of cards like the ones shown on the next page and you drew a 1, you could combine it with the 2 and the 4 to make 7.

Session 7 Make the Sum (cont.)

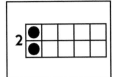 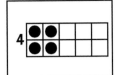 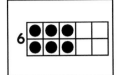 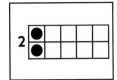

In fact, combinations that involve more than two cards are very desirable be-cause the person who has the most cards in the end wins. Play continues around the circle until no more combinations of 7 can be made. Players then count their cards to determine the winner.

Take the time to model this game all the way through to the end. Then send your students off in groups of three or four to play the game several times. You can either have them continue to play for 7's, or you can let them know that the game can be played for any number, 5 through 15. If you decide to have them play the game at this more open-ended level, be sure they under-stand that they need to start by "setting the deck"; that is, discarding any cards above the number they're playing for, just as you discarded all the 8's, 9's, and 10's to play for 7. The exception to this rule is when playing for 10's and above. In any of these cases, you'll need the entire deck. If children want to play for sums other than 7, they'll need to negotiate with their groups. If they can't agree on a target sum, advise them to play for a different sum each game.

We usually let our students play as many games as they can get through in 10 minutes and then have them regroup, with the understanding that they'll find Make the Sum in the set of Work Places which you're getting ready to introduce.

Notes

Session 7 Work Places 4

WORK PLACES

Introduce Work Places 4

Overview
The teacher introduces a new set of Work Places, many of which build on previous lessons. After the activities have been introduced, the children choose a place to begin if there's still time.

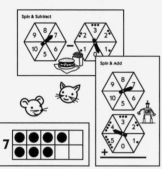

You'll need
★ Work Place baskets 4A–4F set up as shown below

★ a work folder for each child with a copy of the Work Places 4 Planner stapled to the front (Blackline 3.6)

★ Work Places 4 & 5 Arithmetic Observation sheet (Blackline 3.7, run a class set and label each with a child's name)

Work Places 4 Setup

4A Shake, Reach & Record

This Work Place basket will need

✓ Shake, Reach & Record record sheets (Blacklines 3.8–3.12, run 15 copies of each sheet and place in a folder)

✓ 6 probability containers each filled with 10 green and 10 yellow tile from the base ten pieces

4B Make the Sum

This Work Place basket will need

✓ 3 decks of Make the Sum cards

4C Spin & Add

This Work Place basket will need

✓ 6 Spin & Add spinners

✓ Spin & Add record sheets (Blackline 3.13, run 30 copies and place in a folder)

Session 7 Work Places 4 (cont.)

4D Spin & Subtract

This Work Place basket will need

✓ 6 Spin & Subtract spinners

✓ Spin & Subtract record sheets (Blackline 3.14, run 30 copies and place in a folder)

4E Cats & Mice

This Work Place basket will need

✓ 3 Cats & Mice spinners

✓ Cats & Mice record sheets (Blackline 3.15 and/or 3.16, run 30 copies and place in a folder)

✓ crayons or colored pencils

4F Bucket O'Bugs Subtraction

This Work Place basket will need

✓ math bucket of bugs

✓ Bucket O'Bugs record sheets (Blackline 3.17, run 30 copies and place in a folder)

✓ Bucket O'Bugs Subtraction cards (Separate cards by fact family, then put each family into it's own ziplock bag.)

✓ 6 pieces of green felt or graphing mats

This part of Session 7 opens with an introduction to the fourth round of Work Places. Most of these games and activities will be fairly familiar to the children. Your class will have played whole-group versions of Spin & Subtract, Spin & Add, and Shake, Reach & Record. You will want to review these activities quickly and take more time with Bucket O'Bugs Subtraction. We recommend that you save Cats & Mice until next session when you can give it more attention.

In preparation for this session, you'll want to read through the descriptions of the Work Places on the next few pages. Each description explains how to play the game or do the activity, and includes some "instructional considerations" for you to bear in mind as you introduce the Work Places. Set up your Work Place baskets as shown on the previous page. Staple the new Work Place planners to children's work folders.

As you begin this part of the session, gather your students in a discussion circle and explain that you have some new Work Places to introduce. Then show them the materials in each Work Place basket (except for Cats & Mice).

Session 7 Work Places 4 (cont.)

When you've modeled Work Places 4A through 4D and 4F, show the children their work folders with the new planners attached. Explain that all of the Work Places except for Make the Sum involve record sheets, which students will store in their folders as they work their way through the activities. As usual, they'll be expected to complete each of the activities once before they come back to any of them a second time. They are to keep track of their progress by coloring in the stars on the Work Place planners.

Before you send your students out to choose their Work Places, you might want to point out that one of the activities—Make the Sum—requires partners. Cats & Mice, which you'll introduce tomorrow, also requires partners. Talk with students about how they might find partners when they decide to go to these games. Some students may already be traveling in pairs. Others may be able to look around as they finish an activity and spot someone else who looks available. A few may still need help to find a partner effectively. If this continues to be an issue for more than a few of your students, you might consider pairing them each day before they go out to Work Places, or perhaps assigning them a Work Place partner for the duration of this round.

Observing Children During Work Places

◄ ASSESSMENT TIPS

The purpose of this set of Work Places and the next is to help children identify some of the easier addition and subtraction combinations and strategies, review standard notation, and become more proficient with basic addition and subtraction facts. One of the reasons so many of the whole group lessons revolve around the Work Places themselves in this unit is because games are so effective at helping children to gain ease and comfort with basic facts.

Besides being highly effective teaching tools, these games and activities provide wonderful opportunities for assessment. For that reason, we have included an observation sheet (Blackline 3.7) that lists some of the behaviors and skills you might look for while children are engaged in this round of

Session 7 Work Places 4 (cont.)

Work Places and the next. We suggest that you target two or three children each day by attaching their sheets to a clipboard. Direct your observations only to these few children on a given day, and then move on to another group of two or three the next day. Although you probably won't be able to observe all the things listed on the sheet for each student, we hope you'll find it possible to observe some of your children's skills as they do Work Places 4 and 5 over the next few weeks.

Blackline 3.7

NAME _____ DATE _____

Work Places 4 & 5 Arithmetic Observation Sheet

Addition and Subtraction	Comments
Uses fingers	
Uses other manipulatives	
Counts on	
Counts backwards	
Works from Doubles to add (6 + 7 = 13 because 6 + 6 = 12)	
Works from Doubles to subtract (12 – 6 = 6 or 12 – 5 = 7 because 6 + 6 = 12)	
Works from 10's to add (9 + 5 = 14 because 10 + 5 = 15)	
Works from 10's to subtract (15 – 9 = 6 because 15 – 10 = 5)	
Works from other known facts to add or subtract	
Knows +0's, –0's	
Knows +1's, –1's	
Knows + – Doubles	
Knows + – Neighbor Number Facts	
Knows + – 10's	
Knows + – 9's	
Knows other addition or subtraction facts	

Session 7 Work Places 4 (cont.)

WORK PLACE 4A

Shake, Reach & Record

This Work Place basket will need

★ Shake, Reach & Record record sheets (Blacklines 3.8–3.12, run 15 copies of each and place in a folder)

★ 6 probability containers, each filled with 10 yellow tile and 10 green tile (Use the green and yellow tile from your sets of base ten pieces as they are just a little smaller than the square inch tile and slightly easier to pick up.)

Skills

★ seeing and recording all the 2-addend combinations for 6, 7, 8, 9, and 10 using standard notation

★ recording data on a graph

★ exploring probability

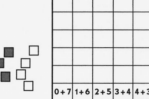

0+7	1+6	2+5	3+4	4+3	5+2	6+1	7+0

To Work

1. Choose a sheet and take a container of tile.

2. Shake the container well, reach in, and draw out the number of tile shown on your sheet. Record the number of greens and the number of yellows in the column that matches the combination you pulled out. That is, if you're working on 7's and you pull out 3 greens and 4 yellows, you would record 3 + 4 in the correct column. Remember to always record the greens first and then the yellows.

3. Put the tile back in the container, give it a good shake to mix them up, and draw out your tile number again. Continue in this manner until two of your columns reach the top. Mark the first and second place winners as they come in, if you like.

Session 7 Work Places 4 (cont.)

NAME ___Evan___ DATE ___11/13___

Blackline 3.9

Shake, Reach & Record 7's record sheet

			1st 3 + 4	2nd 4 + 3			
			3 + 4	4 + 3			
			3 + 4	4 + 3	5 + 2		
		2 + 5	3 + 4	4 + 3	5 + 2		
		2 + 5	3 + 4	4 + 3	5 + 2	6 + 1	
0 + 7	**1 + 6**	**2 + 5**	**3 + 4**	**4 + 3**	**5 + 2**	**6 + 1**	**7 + 0**

Instructional Considerations for Shake, Reach & Record

In this Work Place version of the whole group activity you've already done with your students, the children can choose the number with which they wish to work. There are sheets for 6's, 7's, 8's, 9's, and 10's. You, of course, can also assign sheet levels to particular students, but we find that given the choice children make pretty wise decisions for themselves. Youngsters who aren't very solid with facts for 6's and 7's tend to choose those sheets. Children more confident with addition facts will usually go for the 8's, 9's, and 10's.

You might want to have children begin each sheet by placing a star at the top of the column they believe will fill first. Even though some are likely to erase their stars and switch them to the winning column midway through, the mere act of making a prediction about the column that's most likely to fill to the top first leads to some nice intuitive thinking about probability.

You can emphasize or downplay the probability angle, depending on the needs and interests of your class. Children who are still grappling with standard notation and facts to 10 may need to concentrate on the basic activity. Children who are quite proficient with addition facts may enjoy collecting data from their own records and those of their classmates to ferret out trends and patterns. They can be challenged to try to figure out whether some combinations really are more likely to be pulled out of containers loaded equally with green and yellow tile. Changing the tile proportions may further student thinking too. A container of tile with 10 green and 10 yellow seems to yield lots of 2 + 4's, 3 + 3's, and 4 + 2's if you're pulling out 6 at a time. What would happen if all the tile in the container were green? What if the container had twice or three times as many green as yellow tile (14 greens and 7 yellows, for instance, or 15 greens and 5 yellows)? These are explorations that may transform an otherwise humdrum activity into a very meaningful investigation for some of your more able students.

Session 7 Work Places 4 (cont.)

WORK PLACE 4B

Make the Sum

This Work Place basket will need

★ 3 decks of Number cards

Skills

★ practicing addition combinations for
the numbers 5 through 15

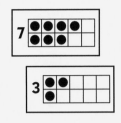

7 + 3 = 10

The purpose of Make the Sum is to provide practice with addition combinations for the numbers 5 through 15. There is a certain amount of problem solving to this drill and practice game as children are continually searching for the combinations to make a particular number rather than responding to the number facts in a rote fashion.

. . . .

Note When you introduced this game earlier in the session, students played in groups of three or four. In the Work Place version of the game, they can play in pairs.

. . . .

To Work

1. Start by talking with your partner about your target sum. You can play for 5's all the way through 15's. Once you've agreed on a sum, prepare the deck by setting aside all the cards higher than your sum. If, for instance, you decide to play for 7's, you'll need to go through the deck and discard all the 8's, 9's, and 10's. If you play for 10's or above, you'll need the full deck—no discards are necessary.

2. Once your deck is set, take turns drawing cards and placing them face up beside the deck. The object of the game is to combine cards to make your target sum. If the sum you've chosen is 7 and you draw a 7, you may keep it. If you draw a 3, you'll have to place it face up beside the deck where it will be available to you or your partner. If your partner then draws a 4, she may combine it with your 3 and take both cards. A sample sequence of play is shown below:

Session 7 Work Places 4 (cont.)

Partner A draws a 3. She has to leave it face up and can't use it.

Partner B draws a 4. She can combine it with the 3 and take both cards.

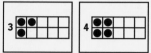

Partner A draws a 7, which she's allowed to keep.

Partner B draws a 2, which she has to leave face up.

Partner A draws a 4, which she has to leave face up also—she can't make a 7.

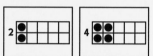

Partner B draws a 5, which she can combine with the 2, and is able to take the 2 cards. So far, she's the lucky one.

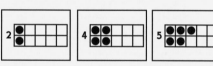

3. Play continues back and forth until no more cards can be combined to make the target sum. It's important to note that no one gets extra turns—if you win a set of cards, play still reverts to your partner. It's also important to know that combinations can be made with more than two cards. Seven, for instance might be made with a 1, a 2, and a 4, or even two 1's, a 2, and a 3.

4. When as many as possible of the cards have been used, partners count their cards to determine the winner. It is possible that a few cards may remain at the end because they can't be combined to make the target sum.

Teacher We'll have to leave the last 2 cards, but at least we can put the 1, 2, and 4 together to make 7.

Session 7 Work Places 4 (cont.)

WORK PLACE 4C

Spin & Add

This Work Place basket will need
★ 6 Spin & Add spinners

★ Spin & Add record sheets (Blackline 3.13, run 30 copies and place
in a folder)

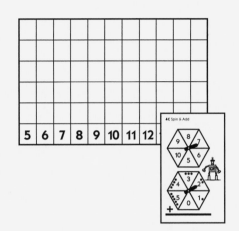

5	**6**	**7**	**8**	**9**	**10**	**11**	**12**	

Skills
★ counting on as a strategy for adding numbers

★ practicing addition combinations
for the numbers 5 through 15

★ recording data on a graph

★ exploring probability

The object of Spin & Add is to provide more practice with addition facts for
the numbers 5 through 15. Children are encouraged to use counting on as a
means of figuring the combinations they don't already know. Like Shake,
Reach & Record, Spin & Add offers an opportunity to explore probability, as
there is a greater likelihood of spinning some sums than others.

To Work

1. Get a double spinner and a record sheet. Spin both spinners and figure the
sum. If you already know the answer, just record it on the record sheet. If
you don't, say the number shown on the upper spinner and count on from
there, using the dots shown on the bottom spinner.

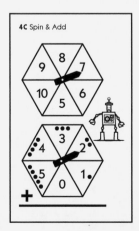

"I got 7 plus 2 on my spinner.
Let's see, that's 7—8, 9; the
answer is 9."

The record sheet is intended to be used as a graph, and answers should be recorded from the bottom to the top of each column.

Session 7 Work Places 4 (cont.)

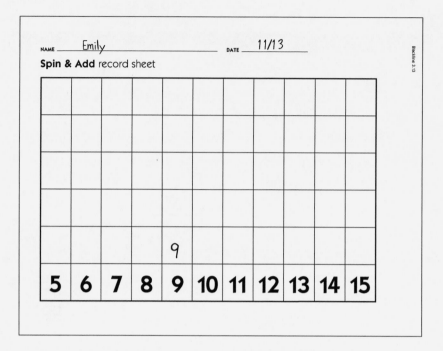

2. Continue spinning and adding in this fashion until at least three columns are filled. You can keep track of the winners by marking them "1st," "2nd," and "3rd."

Instructional Considerations

An alternative to having children record the totals on their record sheets is to have them write the full number sentences. Students who are just becoming proficient with counting on may do better recording just the totals, but youngsters who seem to know some of the facts easily, and count on quickly to find the ones they don't, can certainly handle writing the full number sentences each time.

Session 7 Work Places 4 (cont.)

As with Shake, Reach & Record, the probability aspect of this game can be played up by encouraging children to place a star at the top of the column they think will fill first. Children who are already proficient with facts might enjoy collecting class results as their friends do this activity. Are there any columns that appear to fill first on a regular basis? Why? (Second graders are likely to think it's all in the flick of the spinner, but you might nudge them a bit by asking them to figure out how many different ways there are to spin a 5, a 15, a 10, and an 11. Are there more combinations for some of the numbers than others? Why?)

WORK PLACE 4D

Spin & Subtract

This Work Place Basket will need
★ 6 Spin & Subtract spinners

★ Spin & Subtract record sheets (Blackline 3.14, run 30 copies and place in a folder)

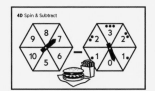

Skills
★ counting backwards as a strategy for subtracting 1, 2, or 3 from a larger quantity

★ practicing subtraction facts to 10

★ recording data on a graph

★ exploring probability

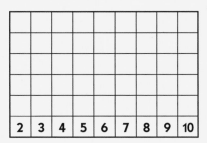

The object of this activity is to provide more practice with subtraction facts to 10, using "count backs" as a strategy to figure the differences if they're not already known.

To Work

1. Get a double spinner and a record sheet. Spin both spinners and figure the difference between the two numbers. Record the result on your sheet, working from bottom to top.

2. Continue spinning, figuring, and recording until at least three of your columns fill to the top.

Session 7 Work Places 4 (cont.)

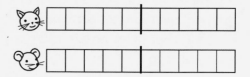
WORK PLACE 4E

Cats & Mice

This Work Place basket will need

★ 3 Cats & Mice spinners

★ crayons or colored pencils

★ Cats & Mice record sheets (Blackline 3.15 and/or 3.16—see note below and Instructional Considerations, run copies of one or both sheets and place in a folder.)

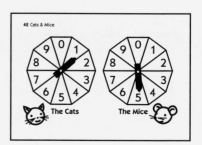

Skills

★ exploring subtraction as a process of differencing

★ recording data on a graph

★ adding strings of numbers and comparing the totals

. . . .

Note *The version of the game explained below is fairly challenging. Read through the directions here to decide whether or not you want to model this version or the "getting started" version described under Instructional Considerations.*

. . . .

To Work

1. Decide with your partner which of you is going to represent the mice and which of you will represent the cats. Take turns spinning the spinner, coloring in the number indicated on your ten strip, and recording it to the side.

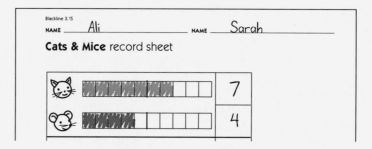

2. When you've each taken three turns, total your points and color in the two trains near the bottom of the sheet to compare the quantities. Record the results at the very bottom of the sheet with a subtraction sentence.

3. Play the game a second time, so each player will have a record sheet to put in his or her folder.

Session 7 Work Places 4 (cont.)

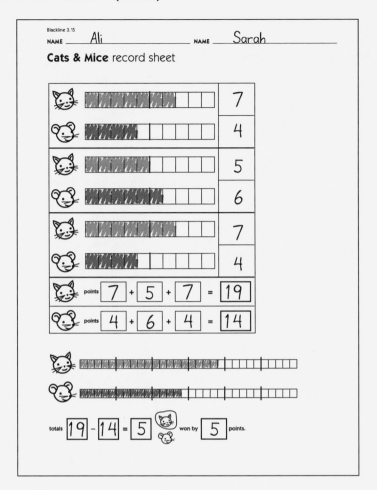

Instructional Considerations for Cats & Mice

If you feel that this record sheet is just too hard for your children to handle independently, you might use the "getting started" version (Blackline 3.16). The record sheet on Blackline 3.16 simply requires the children to spin, color, and record the difference as a single number rather than in the form of a subtraction sentence. Perhaps you'll want to offer both sheets 3.15 and 3.16 at the Work Place and give students the option of choosing the easier or the more challenging version of this game.

Session 7 Work Places 4 (cont.)

WORK PLACE 4F

Bucket O'Bugs Subtraction

This activity has two main purposes. One is to provide practice with standard subtraction notation. The other is to teach and review the process of subtraction. There are two ways to model the activity, however. One way teaches subtraction as a process of taking away, and might be considered the more basic of the two. The other teaches subtraction as a process of determining differences. You'll probably want to consider both and choose the one that best suits the needs of your class. If most of your children seem fairly confident with "take aways," you might want to give serious thought to trying the difference model. (We don't recommend modeling both formats unless you want to cause mass confusion among your students.)

. . . .

Option 1 The Take Away Model

This Work Place basket will need

★ Bucket O'Bugs record sheets (Black-line 3.17, run 30 copies and place in a folder)

★ math bucket of bugs

★ Bucket O'Bugs Subtraction cards (Separate cards by fact family, then put each family into it's own ziplock bag.)

★ 6 pieces of 8" × 12" green felt or other fabric (green construction paper will work too)

Skills

★ understanding subtraction through story problems

★ practicing subtraction facts

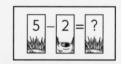

To Work

1. Choose a set of Bucket O'Bugs Subtraction cards. These cards will help you tell some simple story problems. Get a piece of green felt from the tub and a handful of bugs.

2. Read the first card in your set and tell a story to match the number sentence.

"There were 6 bugs crawling around in the grass. 4 of them disappeared down under the ground into their holes. How many were left in the grass?"

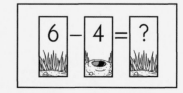

Session 7 Work Places 4 (cont.)

3. Act out the story with your bugs and green felt. (The felt will serve as grass and the bugs going underground can just zip right under it.)

4. Record the entire subtraction sentence on your record sheet.

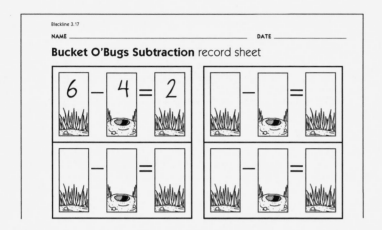

5. Work your way through the set of cards you've chosen.

Instructional Considerations for Bucket O'Bugs: Take Away Model
When you model this activity for your class, be sure to actually tell a story for each card in the set. After you've told two or three, have the children read the number sentences with you and take turns telling stories to match. (Even though the action is the same each time, there are all sorts of reasons why the bugs might crawl into their holes, including wind, rain, enemies, or mothers calling them home for dinner.) When students do this activity on their own, they can either tell stories to themselves or work with partners, taking turns setting up the bugs and telling the stories as they each record on their own sheets.

. . . .

Option 2 The Difference Model

You'll need
★ Bucket O'Bugs record sheets (Blackline 3.17, run 30 copies and place in a folder)

★ the math bucket of bugs

★ Bucket O'Bugs Subtraction cards (Separate cards by fact family, then put each family into it's own ziplock bag.)

★ 6 graphing mats (See Note on following page)

Skills
★ exploring subtraction as a process of determining differences

★ practicing subtraction facts

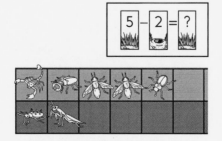

Session 7 Work Places 4 (cont.)

. . . .

Note *If you want to try the difference model for Bucket O'Bugs Subtraction, you'll need to make your own graphing mats. For each mat, just take a 6" × 20" strip of brown construction paper, glue a 3" × 20" strip of green construction paper on top, and mark it off into 2" × 3" rectangles.*

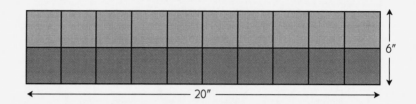

. . . .

To Work

1. Choose a set of Bug Subtraction cards. These will help you tell some simple story problems. Get a differencing mat from the tub and a handful of bugs.

2. Read the card and set up a graph to match the number sentence.

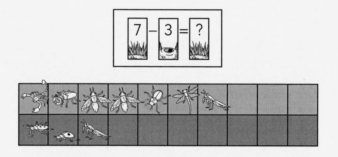

"There were 7 bugs in the grass (set 7 bugs on the green side of the graph) and 3 bugs in the dirt (set 3 bugs on the brown side of the graph). How many more bugs were in the grass than in the dirt?"

3. Record the entire subtraction sentence on your record sheet.

4. Work your way through the set of cards you've chosen.

Instructional Considerations for Bucket O'Bugs Subtraction: Difference Model
The tricky part of this activity will be for the children to understand why subtraction is used as a way to note difference. They'll surely be able to lay out the graph each time and figure the difference. However, recording the results as an outcome of subtraction when they've mostly experienced subtraction as a process of take away will probably be a bit of a stretch. It may help them to say something like "The difference between ___ and ___ is ___" as they record each number sentence.

When children do this activity on their own, they can either set up the graphs themselves or work with partners, taking turns setting up the bugs on the graphs as they each record on their own sheets.

Session 8

WORK PLACES

Getting Started with Work Places 4

Overview

Before sending students out to do Work Places today, be sure to introduce Cats & Mice. This is a complex and interesting game because it features the idea of subtracting by finding the difference between 2 sets rather than taking away part of a set.

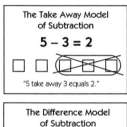

The Take Away Model of Subtraction

$5 - 3 = 2$

"5 take away 3 equals 2."

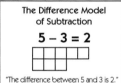

The Difference Model of Subtraction

$5 - 3 = 2$

"The difference between 5 and 3 is 2."

You'll need

★ work baskets 4A–4F set up for Work Places 4

★ a work folder for each child with a copy of the Work Places 4 Planner stapled to the front (Blackline 3.6)

★ Work Places 4 & 5 Arithmetic Observation Sheets (Blackline 3.7; if you've decided to use these sheets, you might want to have 2 or 3 labeled with children's names and ready to go. Or, you might need to spend today's Work Place time making sure things are going smoothly as this is only the second day for these activities.)

Introduction to Cats & Mice

Overview

While "take away" is a common way of thinking about subtraction, the difference model also occurs on a daily basis. It is the way we compare quantities, distances, heights, weights, and so on. The Cats & Mice game introduces your children to differencing and offers both a standard version and an easier version.

You'll need

★ Cats & Mice gameboard (Overhead 3.2) or Cats & Mice gameboard: Getting Started Version (Overhead 3.3)

★ overhead pens in 2 different colors

Skills

★ exploring subtraction as a process of finding the difference between 2 numbers

★ recording information on a graph

★ adding strings of numbers and comparing the totals

Session 8 Introduction to Cats & Mice (cont.)

Although primary children frequently think of subtraction as a process of taking something away, it is used to find differences quite often in daily life. Determining differences is how we compare quantities, distances, heights, weights, and so on. If we listen to the ball game and find that the Blazers have 42 points while the Sonics only have 26, we quickly calculate how many points the Blazers are ahead by finding the difference. If Fred is 6′3″ and David is 5′10″, we compare their two heights to discover that Fred is 5″ taller. We examine differences rather than removing quantities when we interpret graphs in the newspaper. We believe that in the primary grades it is important to introduce and practice subtraction both as a process of taking away and finding differences.

Unless instructed otherwise, children will usually figure differences by working up from the smaller number—counting up from 26 to 42, or even working in chunks of 10 (26, 36, 37, 38, 39, 40, 41, 42—the Blazers are winning by 16!). The difficulty lies not in determining the difference itself but in the formal notation used to record the transaction. If the Cats have 2 points and the Mice have 5, most children will be able to tell you that the Mice are winning by 3. Few will be able to record the difference in the form of a subtraction sentence, however. Even among very able children you're likely to see 2 + 3 = 5 or 2 − 5 = 3 (both of which might be considered valid, but nontraditional statements).

If you want to introduce the idea of finding differences without pushing the notation just yet, you'll see that there's an easier version of the Cats and Mice record sheet available. Some teachers begin with the "getting started" version, in which children compare differences without using the formal subtraction notation, and then move into using the more challenging record sheet a week or so later.

Session 8 Introduction to Cats & Mice (cont.)

If you choose to start with the more challenging sheet, explain that one way people use subtraction is as a way to find the difference between two sets of objects. If they're playing a game, for instance, and the score is 6 to 2, how much are they ahead by? Many children will answer 4, and if you ask them how they figured it out, they're likely to tell you that they counted up from 2 until they got to 6, although some might say that they knew the difference between 6 and 2 was 4, or that they just took 2 away from 6 to get 4. In any case, explain that the difference between 6 and 2 can be shown as a subtraction sentence: 6 − 2 = 4. Then tell them you're going to introduce a game that will help them practice finding and recording differences, and that everyone will get to play, together at first, and then during Work Places.

Show the transparency of the game sheet on the screen and divide your students into two teams: the cats and the mice. Have a volunteer from each group come and spin for their team. Record the two numbers by writing them and coloring them in on the ten-strips, as shown below.

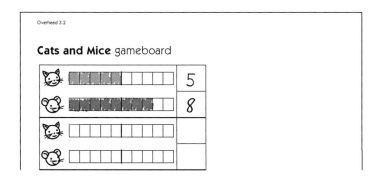

Continue until all three rounds have been played. Then, with the children's help, add all the mice points, all the cat points, and color in the totals at the bottom of the sheet. After finding the difference between the two final scores visually, record it as a subtraction sentence, using the boxes at the very bottom of the sheet (see following page).

You might want to leave the completed overhead up on the screen for the remainder of the math period. Some of our students have found it helpful to refer to as they play their first game of Cats and Mice independently at Work Places.

Session 8 Introduction to Cats & Mice (cont.)

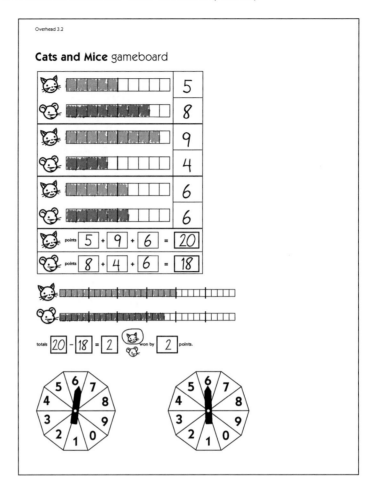

. . . .

Note *If this game and its accompanying record sheet are too hard for your group, introduce the "getting started" version of Cats & Mice (see below), which allows children to compare quantities and record differences without using standard notation. They can use the more complex record sheet later on.*

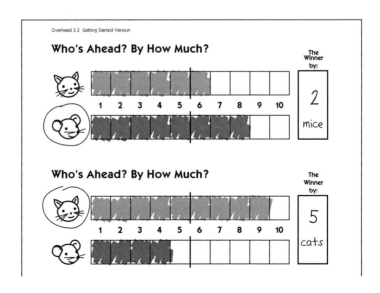

. . . .

Session 9

PROBLEMS & INVESTIGATIONS

Fall/Winter Character Quilt Making the Quilt Blocks

Overview

Even though quilt making doesn't have much to do with basic arithmetic facts, we've included a character quilt in this unit as a change of pace, and also as a way of connecting number and geometry. The numbers of quilt blocks that result from the children's work will have a great deal to do with how the quilt is eventually laid out. Each child will have a chance to grapple with these numbers as he or she attempts to create a quilt layout design that has some symmetry and balance. Today, children will look at the different quilt block characters and choose the one they'd like to make.

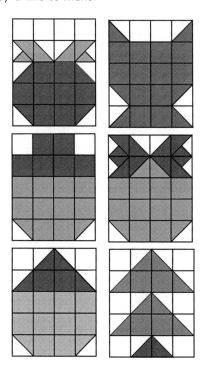

You'll need

★ *The Josephina Story Quilt,* by Eleanor Coerr (optional)

★ Fall/Winter Character Quilt Blocks, sheets 1 and 2 *or* 1 and 3 (Overheads 3.4–3.6)

★ Fall/Winter Character Quilt Blocks, sheet 1 (Blackline 3.18, run a half-class set and cut in half)

★ Fall/Winter Character Quilt Blocks, sheets 2 *or* 3 (Blacklines 3.19–3.20, see Note 1 on the next page)

★ 1" construction paper squares cut in the following colors: yellow, red, green, black, brown, tan (or manila), and orange (See Note 2 on the next page.)

★ scraps of construction paper in yellow, green, blue, brown, red, pink, and black for adding features to the cats and scarecrows or woodcutters

★ glue

★ scissors

Skills

★ observing and describing pictures made of squares and triangles

★ investigating some of the relationships between squares and right triangles

★ exploring wholes, halves, and fourths

★ solving spatial problems

Session 9 Fall/Winter Character Quilt (cont.)

. . . .

Notes

1. The fall/winter character quilt blocks have been printed two to a page; run them and then cut them apart. The number you print depends on your class size; 15 or 20 of each will be probably be more than enough. If you wind up teaching this unit in late fall or early winter, be sure to have a look at the woodcutter and fir tree quilt blocks shown on Blackline 3.20. These two in combination with the apple and the cat will make a quilt better suited to late November, December, or even January, than the pumpkin and the scarecrow.

2. It's hard to be scientific about how many construction paper squares to cut. If you have an Ellison Die Cutter that cuts 1″ squares for pattern blocks, this will be a relatively easy task. If you don't, a paper cutter does the trick, but it's enough work not to want to cut too many extra squares. Four to five sheets of 12″ × 18″ construction paper in each color cut into 1″ squares will probably be enough. If you have extra, save them for next year. You'll need red, green, and yellow for the apple; black or brown and yellow for the cat; tan, black, and yellow for the scarecrow or the woodcutter; green, orange, and yellow for the pumpkin; and green, yellow, and brown for the fir tree. Yellow is the background color for all of the blocks, and the placement of the other colors is fairly self-evident. If you really enjoy this sort of project, you might consider using white construction paper that's been sponge-painted gray or orangey-brown to create calico cats instead of plain black or brown.

3. There are many ways to organize your materials, but one way that works for us is to set up a table for each quilt block. That way, the children who choose to make the pumpkin block can go to that table and find the pumpkin block blacklines; orange, green, and yellow squares; glue and scissors—everything they'll need for that particular block clearly laid out.

4. Be sure to make a sample of each quilt block for display before you start this project. Even though the quilt block patterns indicate what color to put where, it's easier for some children to understand what to do if they can see a premade sample. The apple, the pumpkin, and the fir tree are fine as shown, but the scarecrow, woodcutter, and cat are much more appealing with added features cut from construction paper. The cat picks up lots more life with whiskers and green eyes. The scarecrow and woodcutter are really darling with shaggy yellow or brown hair; blue, green, or brown eyes; cheeks; and smile—all created from construction paper scraps and glued on. If you show such features on your premade samples, the children will add features to theirs too.

Session 9 Fall/Winter Character Quilt (cont.)

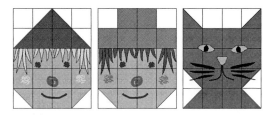

To begin this lesson, you might read *The Josephina Story Quilt* to your children. This story of a pioneer family moving westward does much to explain how and why people made quilts in "olden times," and is a nice way to introduce the idea that a quilt block can be a picture of something. In the case of the Josephina story quilt, each block that Faith made pictured a part of her journey or something she wanted to remember. Some of the blocks she made were traditional, and others look to be designs she may have created on the spot. Although our fall character blocks aren't traditional, they certainly serve as a nice way to capture and remember the fall or winter season.

Reading, discussing, and appreciating this book takes at least half an hour, and may be something you want to do during story time the day before your math lesson. It's certainly optional, but we find that adding a social and historical component to our paper patchwork lessons through the year deepens the experience for students.

Whether or not you choose to open with a story, the children will be excited to see the new quilt blocks. Take a few minutes to display the transparency of each block at the overhead.

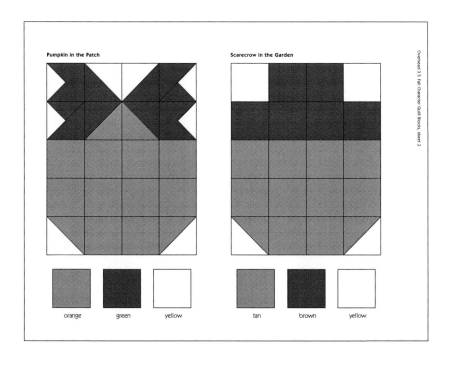

Session 9 Fall/Winter Character Quilt (cont.)

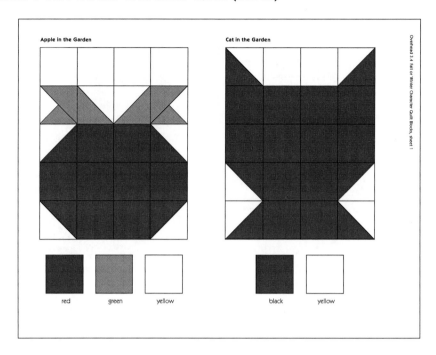

As you show the blocks, ask your students to share their observations with each other and with the group. What do they notice, what do they see? Some may notice the overall pictures—the apple, the cat, the pumpkin, and the scarecrow. If you give them a little time, they may also begin to talk about the shapes they see: the fact that some of the triangles are smaller than others, the fact that it takes more squares to make the red part of the apple than the leaves, the fact that the cat has pointy triangle ears, and that triangles have been used to create its neck and shoulders. Some children may even begin to talk about the area of each block, noticing that, in each case, they can see a 4 × 5 rectangle. You probably won't want to have them discuss every block in depth, but do take time to show all four and discuss at least two of them. You may be surprised at just how much your students have to say about them.

Once they've had a chance to get a good look at the quilt blocks, explain to your students that they'll each have a chance to make one. (Some will want to make all four blocks and will wonder why they have to choose just one. It is a hard choice, and once the project is finished, you may want to leave out your extra patterns and construction paper squares for youngsters to make some of the other blocks at their leisure.) You'll probably want to show your premade samples and briefly model some effective gluing techniques before you send children off to work.

Be sure to remind students to put their names on the backs of their blocks before they start gluing. You'll also want to explain that every shape on the blocks, except for the features on the cat and scarecrow, has been cut from a 1″ square. Most children will see how to cut the larger triangles pretty easily, but the smaller triangles on the pumpkin and apple blocks might pose a chal-

Session 9 Fall/Winter Character Quilt (cont.)

lenge to some. If you don't show them how to cut these shapes beforehand, it can be very interesting to see how your students go about doing it for themselves. Don't worry if they're not very scientific about it at this stage. They'll have many other opportunities to work with shapes through the year.

When most of your children seem to understand what to do, send them off to work on the blocks of their choice. *It doesn't matter which block each child chooses, but you will need to make sure that you wind up with even numbers; an odd number of any one of the blocks will make tomorrow's design problem almost insurmountable.* Once they've settled down to work, you can take a quick survey to see how many of each block you'll have. In the event that five children have chosen to make the scarecrow and seven have chosen to make the pumpkin, you might make one extra of each of these yourself, or have a child who finishes quickly make an extra of each. *You'll also want to end up with a total that makes a nice rectangle—with 26 blocks, for instance, you'll only be able to create a 1 × 26 or a 2 × 13 rectangle, neither of which look much like a quilt. On the other hand, 24, 28, 30, or 32 blocks all factor into dimensions for nice quilt-shaped rectangles.*

Completed blocks can be set to dry in a designated spot. When dry, trim away the excess white paper. You may also want to press them under some heavy books overnight. This will make the construction paper squares lay flatter and make the blocks themselves easier to handle when you begin to figure the quilt layout.

WORK PLACE NOTES

Send your students out to Work Places with their folders as they finish their quilt blocks.

Session 10

PROBLEMS & INVESTIGATIONS

Fall/Winter Character Quilt Designing the Quilt Layout

Overview

Children use colored squares on graph paper to figure out a layout design for the fall character quilt.

Skills

★ creating rectangular arrays for a given number

★ exploring symmetry, balance, and pattern

You'll need

★ the fall character quilt blocks created by your class during Session 9 (Again, be sure you have an even number of each block—odd numbers of blocks won't work.)

★ 1" square tile (ceramic, wood, or plastic will do; these are optional)

★ 1" Square Graph Paper (Blackline 3.21, 1 sheet per child)

★ 1" squares of construction paper in the following colors: red, orange, black, and brown (or red, green, tan, and brown if your class has made the apple, fir tree, woodcutter and cat blocks)

★ crayons, scissors, and glue

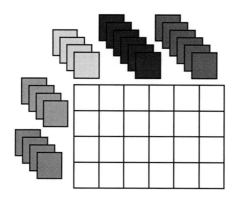

Start by complimenting your children on a job well done. The quilt blocks are wonderful and will make a terrific quilt. If you have time, you might have your students figure out the dimensions of the finished quilt. Do this by getting your group to count the number of finished blocks. Then have the children work with partners to count out that number of square inch tile for themselves. Challenge them to discover the rectangles that can be made with that many blocks. (If your class made 30 quilt blocks, for instance, children will quickly discover that they can make 1 × 30, 2 × 15, 3 × 10, and 5 × 6 rectangles with their tile.) Then, decide as a class which of the rectangles would be most suitable for a quilt. The alternative to this is to decide on the finished dimensions yourself and proceed directly to the next problem.

Suppose your class has made 24 quilt blocks and you, or they, have decided that the blocks will be arranged to form a 4 × 6 rectangle. The next problem is to figure out where to put each block. You may have 6 of each character but, more likely, you'll wind up with something like 8 pumpkin blocks, 6 scarecrow blocks, 6 black cats, and 4 apples. How can these arranged to form the most pleasing design?

Session 10 Designing the Quilt Layout (cont.)

This is a great problem to pose to students. Have them start by each cutting a rectangle out of square-inch graph paper to match the dimensions they've planned for the class quilt (or, if you've chosen the dimensions of the quilt yourself, you might want to precut the rectangles for them). Then, with the understanding that red stands for apples, orange for pumpkins, black for cats, and brown for scarecrows (or red for apples, green for fir trees, tan for wood-cutters, and brown for cats), have them count out the needed numbers of each color of construction paper squares and work to create pleasing arrangements on the graph paper.

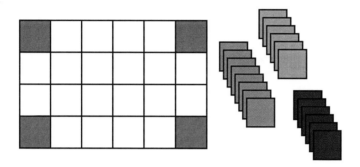

Student Here's my 4 × 6 rectangle. Since we have 4 apples, I'm putting the red squares in each corner, and then I'll figure out where to put the other squares. I think I might put 8 orange squares in the middle for the 8 pumpkins.

The amount of direction you offer as to how to come up with a pleasing design is up to you. We let our students know that quilters often choose to make the four corners of a quilt the same and work from there, and that they usually wind up with a design that has pattern or balance; that the two sides of the quilt usually match each other in some way. (We go as far as to introduce the term *symmetry* and to demonstrate what it means.) Most children will opt for some sort of symmetry or balance in their designs—students who don't are sometimes just overwhelmed by the task. It's fascinating to see how each child responds. Some have such a need to create repeating patterns that they're willing to throw the idea of symmetry out the window.

Once they have designs they like, children can either glue their paper squares onto the graph paper or copy their designs in crayon onto a second graph paper rectangle. The most important thing is that they don't do any gluing or coloring until they've taken the time to come up with a design that pleases them. (There are a few children who will just glue their colored squares to the graph paper at random, no matter what you say or do, either because they don't understand the task or because it's too much for them. For now, it's probably best to accept this. There will be many more opportunities to explore the ideas of balance, design, pattern, and symmetry over the next few months.)

Session 10 Designing the Quilt Layout (cont.)

Set the completed quilt layout designs, labeled with their creators' names, aside to dry. You'll need them for Session 11.

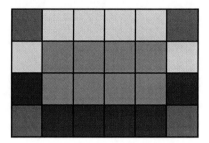

 WORK PLACE NOTES

Send your students out to Work Places with their folders as they finish their quilt layout designs. Some of them probably won't get to Work Places today, but there will be lots of time next session.

Session 11

PROBLEMS & INVESTIGATIONS

Fall/Winter Character Quilt Choosing the Quilt Layout Design

HOME
CONNECTIONS

Overview

Children's quilt layout designs from Session 10 are all admired and then placed in a pile on the floor, face down. One is chosen at random from the pile and used as a blueprint for laying out the actual quilt blocks. Another is then chosen from the pile and the blocks are reconfigured to match the new design. After several repeats with different designs, the layouts are posted on the wall and children vote for their favorite. The blocks are then glued onto butcher paper backing to match the winning layout design.

You'll need

★ the fall character quilt blocks created by your class during Session 9, sorted by type (pumpkins in one pile, cats in another, etc.)

★ students' quilt layout designs from Session 10

★ small sticky notes

★ butcher paper to use as backing for the finished quilt

★ glue

★ Home Connections Blacklines HC 9.1–9.3

Skills

★ exploring symmetry, balance, and pattern

★ exploring scale model—using a small design to lay out the actual quilt

Gather your children into a discussion circle. Open the session by complimenting them on their many creative and beautiful quilt design ideas. You might even want to hold up each layout design to be admired before you place them face down on the floor in a pile. Have a student volunteer choose one at random from the pile and turn it face-up. Then ask two or three of your other children to help you lay out the quilt in accordance with the design that's been selected from the pile.

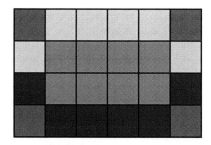

Teacher *This is an interesting design. What does it tell us to do?*

Session 11 Choosing the Quilt Layout Design (cont.)

Ali *There are 4 reds—one in each corner. That means to put an apple in each corner of the quilt.*

David *There are 8 orange squares in the middle, so we need to put the 8 pumpkins in the middle.*

Teacher *What about the scarecrows and the black cats?*

Children *They go around the outside—the 6 scarecrows on the top, and the 6 cats on the bottom.*

Teacher *Sarah, since you created this particular idea, why don't you pick a friend to help you lay out the quilt blocks the way your layout design shows?*

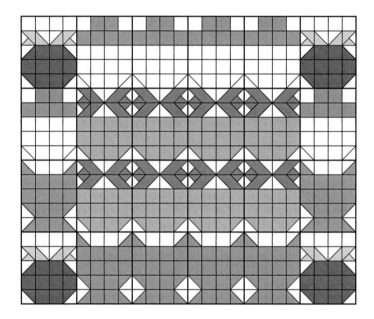

Once the first design has been laid out and admired, take time to choose at least two other layouts from the pile and set up the quilt blocks accordingly each time. It is astonishing to children and adults alike to see how much a quilt can change from layout to layout. You might even want to leave the blocks and designs out and available for students to play with on their own during Work Places or during recess for a day or two. When you feel your class has had adequate time to experiment with various layouts, post all the quilt designs on the wall and ask each child to mark his or her favorite with a small sticky note. (This can be done as children work at other tasks over a morning or afternoon's time.)

When all the votes have been cast, count them up, and glue the quilt blocks onto butcher paper according to the winning design. You can make a nice display of children's work by putting up the finished quilt, all the design ideas, and a poster explaining the activity. The amount of problem solving your students have put into this project should be admired by all!

Session 11 Choosing the Quilt Layout Design (cont.)

WORK PLACE NOTES

The activity above should leave a fair amount of time for Work Places this session. This is an ideal time to revisit any activities that aren't going as smoothly as you'd like. If, for instance, there seem to be children who are still confused about Cats & Mice, you might play the whole-group version using Overhead 3.2 again before they go out to work independently. Bucket O'Bugs Subtraction is another activity that could probably be revisited with the whole group, especially if you are using the graphing mats. As soon as you've done any needed review, send students out with their work folders to choose Work Places.

HOME CONNECTION 9

Activity Make the Sum (Blacklines HC 9.1–9.2, pp. 35–36)
Worksheet Chart the Combinations (Blackline HC 9.3, p. 42)

The homework activity for this week gives children a chance to teach their parents how to play Make the Sum. The worksheet asks them to list some of the addition combinations that come up during the game.

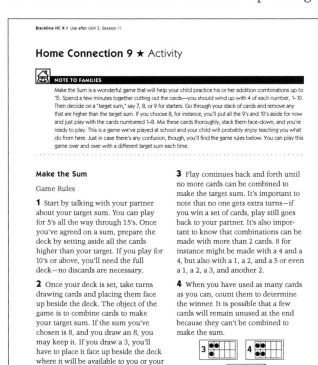

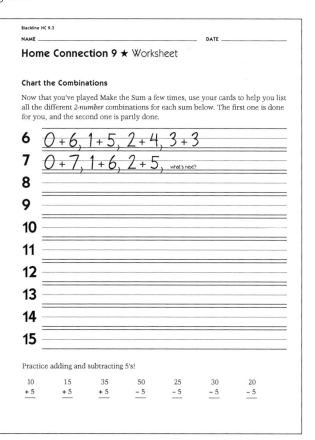

Session 12

PROBLEMS & INVESTIGATIONS

Cover Up, Part 1

Overview

Now that the Fall Character Quilt is complete, it's time to return to addition and subtraction strategies. Cover Up is a game that looks at addition doubles and neighbor numbers in a particularly powerful way, but it takes a bit of introductory work. Today's lesson builds up to the game itself, which you'll play in the whole-group version next session, and return to as an independent activity in Work Places 5.

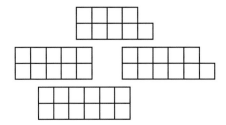

You'll need

★ overhead tile

★ 1" square color tile in baskets, enough for each child or each pair of children to have about 30

★ Building & Recording Doubles & Neighbor Numbers (Blackline 3.22, run a class set)

Skills

★ exploring a visual model for the doubles and neighbor numbers addition combinations to 10

★ exploring a visual model for odd and even numbers

★ searching for visual and number patterns

★ linking number and geometry

To begin the lesson, gather the children into your discussion circle and distribute 1"-square tile so everyone has a supply. Explain that you are going to be building some pictures of addition sentences today. Write the following number sentence on the chalkboard: 3 + 3. More than likely, your group will read it and exclaim that the answer is "6." Tell them that this is correct, of course, and then ask them to build a picture of 3 plus 3 with their tile. You're likely to get a variety of responses, including some of the designs shown below:

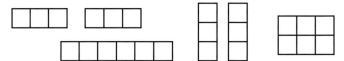

After children have built their renditions of 3 + 3, take a minute to have them share their ideas with neighbors. You might even want to have a child or two share with the entire group. Acknowledge the wonderful variety—there really are many ways to build 3 + 3. Then ask that they all try one particular method and show a 2 × 3 array (or have a child who chose to build it this way demonstrate at the overhead).

Session 12 Cover Up, Part 1 (cont.)

When they've all reshaped their tile to match this design, ask if it's really possible to see 3 + 3. Have children explain where they do see the 2 rows of 3. Tell them that, for now, you'd like them to use this format to show some other addition doubles. (If you did Number Corner lessons with magnetic tile in October, this will probably come fairly easily to your students.)

Post the sentence 5 + 5 on the board and have them build it with tile, using the rectangular method just demonstrated.

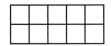

Children *It's 5 plus 5.*
See, it's 5 on top and 5 on the bottom.
I can also see 2 + 2 + 2 + 2 + 2.
Hey! That's five 2's!

Post a couple more addition doubles for the children to build and discuss. Then post the following addition combination: 3 + 4. Ask the children to build this one. Again, you will get a variety of responses. If no one comes up with the design shown below, present it as another possibility and ask that the children try it with their own tile.

Children *It looks like a school bus without wheels.*
Yeah! A bus with the nose sticking out!
It's just like 3 + 3 with 1 more stuck on. But the extra one doesn't have a partner to go with it.
It's an odd number!

After children have built and discussed this combination, explain that people refer to combinations like 3 + 3 as doubles and 3 + 4 as neighbor numbers. Children may want to tell you that this is because 3 + 3 is a double—it doubles itself. The neighbor number combination, they might explain, is like two numbers living right next door: 3 lives next door to 4, and the picture they've built shows it.

Post a few more neighbor combinations on the board for children to build and discuss, using the "school bus" design. You might try 2 + 3, 5 + 6, and 4 + 3. The last one might bring discussion. Is it fair for the bigger number to come first? You may even want to post a counter-example as children work. Is 6 + 8 a neighbor? Why or why not? If it's built in tile, does it have the school bus configuration characteristic of neighbor numbers?

Session 12 Cover Up, Part 1 (cont.)

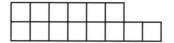

Children The nose is too long for a school bus.
Yeah! It looks crazy! It can't be a neighbor!
Look! If you move one of the ones sticking out, you can level it off into
7 + 7. Then it's a rectangle.

After this initial period of exploration, send the children off to work on their own with the Building & Recording Doubles & Neighbor Numbers worksheets. To complete the sheet, they need to build each addition combination with their tile, using the rectangular and school bus arrangements you just shared. After each number fact is built, they're to color a picture of it in next to the combination on the sheet. The idea is to extend the exploration of doubles and neighbor numbers just a bit further and to look at some of the patterns created by building them in sequence.

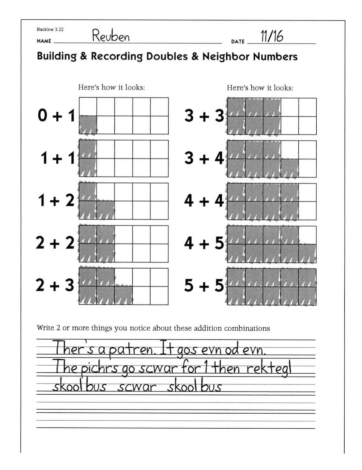

WORK PLACE NOTES

As children finish their worksheets, have them get their folders and choose Work Places.

Session 13

PROBLEMS & INVESTIGATIONS

Cover Up, Part 2

Overview

This game extends the work with addition doubles and neighbor numbers that you started during the last session, reinforcing the useful visual models while offering practice with the facts themselves. All in all, it's a very powerful activity, but also fairly complicated to teach. Because of this, we are suggesting that you present it first at the overhead and then in the form of a team game. It will be featured in the Work Places 5 and will certainly be more enjoyable for children if they've had some exposure first.

· ·

Note This is a long session. You might want to divide it into two parts, one featuring the overhead transparency, and the other featuring the team game.

· ·

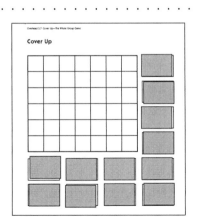

You'll need

★ Cover Up, the Whole-Group Game (Overhead 3.7; before you start the lesson, cover over the game card drawings on the transparency with small sticky notes so there's an element of suspense to the game.)

★ overhead marking pens in several different colors

★ a set of Cover Up cards

★ Cover Up game sheet (Blackline 3.23, run a class set plus a few extra)

★ crayons (each child needs access to at least 8 different colors)

Skills

★ exploring a visual model for the doubles and neighbors

★ practicing doubles and neighbors addition combinations

★ exploring a visual model for odd and even numbers

★ searching for visual and number patterns

★ linking number and geometry

Start by showing the Cover Up transparency. Take a minute or two for observations and then tell the children that you're going to introduce a new game today. The object of the game will be to color in every square on the grid. Explain that the game cards, which are covered for now, will indicate how many squares to color in. Peel a sticky note off one of the card drawings, and ask students how many squares the card indicates should be colored in on

Session 13 Cover Up, Part 2 (cont.)

the grid. Suppose you've uncovered 3 + 3. The children will tell you to color in 6 squares. Tell them that you will, with their help, but that you need to color the 6 squares in to match the formation on the card.

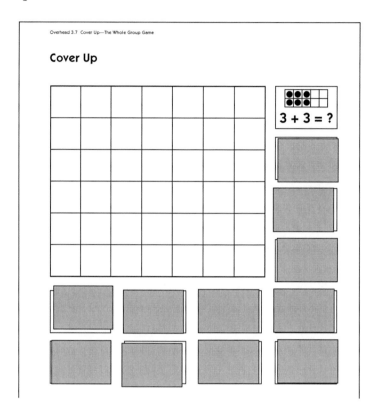

Teacher *I've uncovered a card that reads 3 + 3. How many squares do I get to color in? You're right, it's 6. But I also have to color 2 rows of 3, exactly as shown on the card. I can put my 2 × 3 rectangle anywhere on the grid, though. Can anyone suggest where I could put my rectangle?*

After you get children's suggestions as to where to color in the first 6 boxes, let a volunteer come up to color in the rectangle.

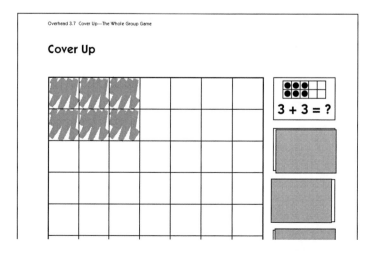

Session 13 Cover Up, Part 2 (cont.)

Then remove the sticky note from another "card." Have a look at it with the children and think about where on the grid to color it in this time. Remind students that you have to color the combination to match the formation on the card, although it's fair to rotate the entire shape when you color it in on the grid (e.g., if the next card you uncover is 2 + 1, you can't color in a row of three on the gameboard; you have to color 2 boxes and then 1 box in the sort of "L" formation shown on the card.) *Be sure to use a different color for each new combination so it's clear where one ends and the next begins.* After 3 or 4 cards have been drawn and colored in, things may start to get interesting.

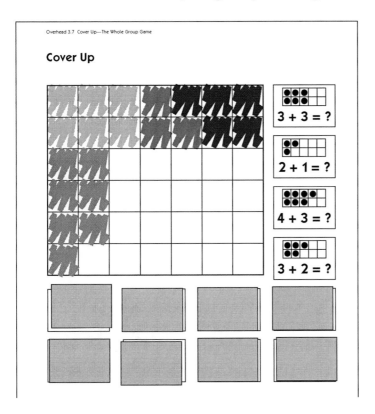

Teacher *Now we've colored in the squares from 4 cards. Do you think we're going to be able to color in all the squares on this grid?*

Children *It's working so far.*
We might get stuck some places. It kind of depends on what cards we get next.
What are we going to do about that one little box by itself on the bottom?

Teacher *That's a good question. I guess we'll have to keep going and see.*

Keep going, removing sticky notes from the cards on the transparency and coloring the grid accordingly. It may be that you have to use a particular card more than once to get out of a fix. In the real game, the cards will be reshuffled and reused if necessary, so it is possible to use a card more than once. Getting in and out of fixes as a whole group may help children begin to see what to do and what to avoid when they play the game on their own.

Session 13 Cover Up, Part 2 (cont.)

. . . .

Note *If you want to break this session into two parts, this is the place to stop and let children go out to Work Places.*

. . . .

Once you've finished coloring in the grid on the transparency, explain to the children that this was just a warm-up. Now you're going to play them a real game of Cover Up. Post two blank Cover Up sheets (Blackline 3.23) on your easel or the board and label one "teacher" and one "students." Shuffle your deck of Cover Up cards, and let students know that they'll be playing as a team against you. Have them each get 8 to 10 different colors out of the crayon baskets, a Cover Up game sheet of their own, and a clipboard if they're going to be working on the floor. Have a volunteer come up, draw a card from the pile, and decide where to color it in on the group's Cover Up sheet. Have everyone copy the formation and placement on their own sheets.

Ciel We got the 4 + 4 card! I've colored it in on the top corner.

Next, draw a card for yourself. Color in the correct formation on your sheet as the children watch. Then have the next student volunteer come up, draw a card from the pile, and color in the combination on the group sheet while everyone copies. *Remind them to use a different color for each new combination so it's clear where one ends and the next begins.* It's okay for children in the group to offer suggestions to the student volunteer each time, but in the end, the child who's drawn the card gets to decide where to color in the combination on the group's sheet.

Continue until one team—you or the students—gets their grid completely filled or until both teams are stuck. If the teams are completely stuck and all the cards have been drawn, reshuffle the deck and start drawing again, with the understanding that some of the cards won't be helpful. If a team draws a card they can't use, they lose that turn. Keep going until one grid is completely filled.

Session 13 Cover Up, Part 2 (cont.)

Don't be too dismayed if some of the children color in the combinations on their own Cover Up sheets differently than what's being demonstrated at the board. Even with yesterday's work, a child may hear that the group has drawn 2 + 2 and color it in on his grid as shown.

 instead of

The fact that some children may color in their grids differently than what's being decided and modeled by the other students may lead to some interesting discussions, and some children may even manage to color in their grids before others in the group. There is no need to be concerned about this. The important thing is that students are representing addition combinations visually; and, we hope, continuing to make some generalizations about doubles and neighbors, as well as odd and even numbers, as they attempt to fit them together. A few days after we'd played this game in one of our second grades, we set up 14, which was the day's date on our magnet board as shown:

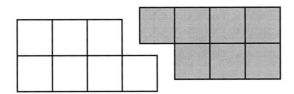

We expected the children to make some observations about 7 plus 7, but we were astonished when one little boy volunteered the theory that *any* two odd numbers would add up to an even number because their noses would fit together. Another child commented that odd numbers worked almost like a lock and a key together.

 WORK PLACE NOTES

If you've chosen to break this session into two smaller parts, children will have time to go to Work Places both days. If, on the other hand, you've decided to do the entire session in one day, there won't be enough time to do Work Places.

Session 14

PROBLEMS & INVESTIGATIONS

Battling Bugs

Overview

With Battling Bugs we return to the idea of differencing as a form of subtraction. The game is very similar to Cats & Mice, but asks the children to do even more in the way using of standard notation. The session today features a whole group introduction to the game, which will reappear in the Work Places 5.

You'll need

★ Battling Bugs gameboard (Overhead 3.8)

★ overhead pens in 2 different colors

Skills

★ learning to record differences as subtraction sentences

★ recording information on a graph

★ adding strings of numbers and comparing the totals

To begin the game, explain that Battling Bugs is very much like Cats & Mice, which children have been playing in Work Places 4. Show the overhead of the game sheet on the screen and divide your students into two teams—the Spiders and the Flies. Have a volunteer from each group come and spin for their team. Record the two numbers by writing them and coloring them in on the ten-strips. Then ask all the children to figure the difference. Record their answer off to the side in the form of a subtraction sentence.

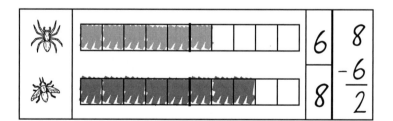

Continue until all three rounds have been played. Then, with the children's help, add all the spiders' points and all the flies' points. Color in the two trains at the bottom to show the point totals. Compare the two quantities visually—which team won? By how much? Finally, record the difference in the form of a subtraction sentence at the very bottom of the sheet. Let children know that they'll see this game again when they start the next round of Work Places.

Session 14 Battling Bugs (cont.)

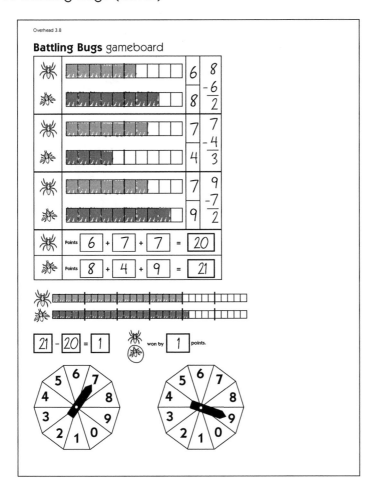

WORK PLACE NOTES

At the end of this activity, send your students out to Work Places with their folders. There are two more sessions after this one before the Work Places change again, which should give most children enough time to finish round 4. If you think your students really haven't had enough time with this set, you might want to schedule an extra day just for Work Places.

At this point, you might also go through the children's work folders and check the papers they've done so far. If you find papers that still need to be finished or discover that some of the children haven't done all of the Work Places, you may want to circle those activities on their planning sheets as a reminder.

Session 15

PROBLEMS & INVESTIGATIONS

Kids in the House

Overview

The teacher demonstrates how to do a work sheet that requires children to search for combinations to make certain target numbers. Once they understand the format, children go off on their own to complete 2 of these worksheets and to do Work Places.

You'll need

★ Kids in the House, sheet 1 (Overhead 3.9)

★ Kids in the House, sheets 1–2 (Blacklines 3.24–3.25, run a class set)

★ translucent game markers, 15 per student and 15 to use at the overhead

Skills

★ searching for combinations for numbers 1 through 15

★ practicing addition facts in a problem-solving context

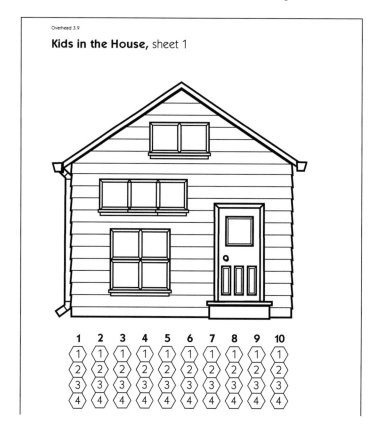

Overhead 3.9

Kids in the House, sheet 1

This activity is similar to Make the Sum in that children search for combinations to make certain target numbers. The difference is that there is more than one target number on a sheet. To start, show the transparency of Kids in

Session 15 Kids in the House (cont.)

the House, sheet 1, and take a few minutes for children to share their observations before you move on.

Once your students have told you what they notice, explain that this is an activity to help them practice their addition facts in an especially interesting and fun way. If you've given them a minute to study the picture, they've undoubtedly noticed the windows, which are somewhat unusual in that each window has a different number of panes. Tell them that lots of children live in this house and they like to look out the windows, but the rule is that no child can look out a window unless there's enough children to fill every pane in that window. (If someone asks why, just tell them it's house rules. Perhaps their mother feels that there's safety in numbers!)

Given the house rules, is it possible for just 1 child to look out a window? Have a volunteer come up to place 1 of the clear counting disks in the correct window. If he places the face in one of the windows with multiple panes, remind him of the rule that every pane in the window has to be used. There is one possibility, though, and that is the window with only 1 pane. Tell the children that you want to keep a record of their experiments, and that you'll mark the fact that one child can look out the window in this house by putting a check mark above the 1 in the columns of numbers at the bottom of the sheet and coloring in the 1 below it

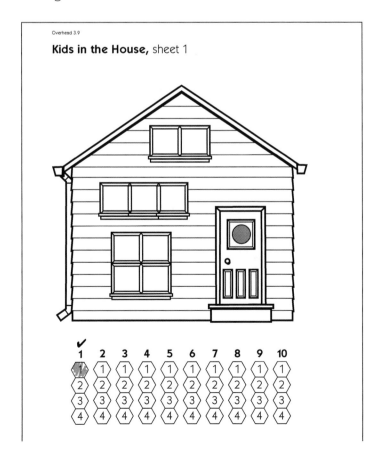

Overhead 3.9

Kids in the House, sheet 1

Session 15 Kids in the House (cont.)

Is it possible for 2 children to look out the windows of the house? Sure—2 children can look out the window that has 2 panes. What about 3 children? That's easy. There's a window with 3 panes, or you might use the 1-pane and 2-pane windows. Your record-keeping on the transparency will show what the volunteers have done so far.

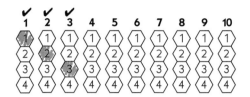

Continue in this fashion with your students. Four kid faces can be placed in the window with 4 panes or in the 1- and 3-pane windows. Five can be placed in the windows with 1 pane and 4 panes or in the 2- and 3-pane windows. Six can be placed in the windows with 2 panes and 4 panes, but also in the 1-pane, 2-pane, and 3-pane windows. Be sure to let children know that there may be more than one solution for some of the numbers, and that it's all right to use more than 2 windows.

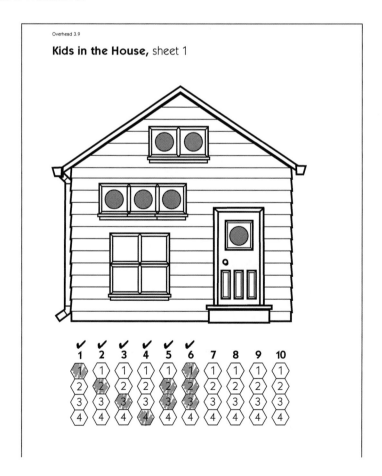

When you've gotten about this far through the sheet with your students, give them their own copies, along with the plastic counting disks and let them go

Session 15 Kids in the House (cont.)

to work. Most of them will understand what to do, although you might want to offer children the option of staying with you if they don't yet feel secure with the activity. As it turns out, there's a way to make every combination on this sheet.

Explain to students that when they finish sheet 1, they're to tackle sheet 2. Sheet 2 works the same way as sheet 1, except the windows have different numbers of panes in them and the sums involve larger numbers. This activity will show up in the next round of Work Places with six different sheets to try. Each sheet is a bit more challenging, and some children will really enjoy working their way through the entire set.

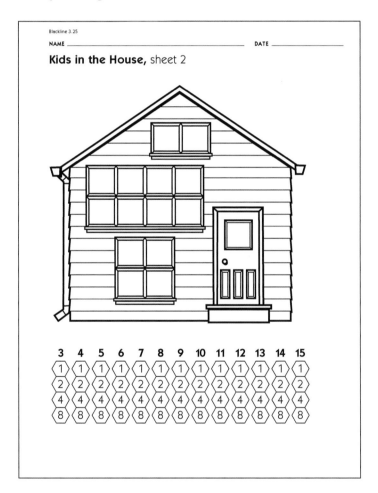

Blackline 3.25

NAME _____ DATE _____

Kids in the House, sheet 2

WORK PLACE NOTES

When the children have finished both sheets, have them get their folders and go out to Work Places. Remind them again that they have today and tomorrow to get around to all the activities in Work Places 4, if they haven't already done so. Be sure to call their attention to any marks you might have made on their planners to indicate things they need to do, finish, or correct.

Session 16

PROBLEMS & INVESTIGATIONS

HOME CONNECTIONS

Crossing the Pond

Overview

Crossing the Pond is a game that provides an opportunity to practice subtraction facts while exploring probability. As the game is played, students keep track of the differences that come up on a double spinner because the information affects their ability to win the game. This game will be featured in the Work Places 5, so children can continue to collect data and perfect their strategies over several days. For now, however, we present the whole-group version of Crossing the Pond.

You'll need
★ Crossing the Pond gameboard (Overhead 3.10)

★ 16 translucent game markers, 8 red and 8 blue, to represent the Blue Frogs and the Red Frogs

★ Crossing the Pond record sheets (Blackline 3.30, run a class set)

★ pencils

★ clipboards, if children are working on the floor

★ Home Connection Blacklines HC 10.1–10.5

Skills
★ practicing subtraction facts

★ collecting data and recording it on a graph

★ making decisions based on collected information

★ exploring probability

To begin the game, show the overhead transparency and take a few minutes to let children make observations. Once students have had a chance to offer any observations they might have about the gameboard, divide them into two teams, the Red and the Blue, and tell them a bit about the game. They don't have to understand everything to play the first time around, but they should know that there is a hungry fox lurking around the near side of the pond. The object of the game is to be the first team to get all 8 frogs across the pond to the safety of the plants on the other side. Frogs are hopped across by spinning the double spinner and subtracting the number on the second spinner from the number on the first. If one of the teams spins 10 – 2, for instance, and happens to have one of its frogs waiting on lily pad 8, that frog may be moved across to the plants on the other side of the pond.

The teams should be allowed to talk among themselves for a minute about where they want to place their frogs to begin the game, and then individuals from each team can take turns placing the red and blue markers, represent-

Session 16 Crossing the Pond (cont.)

ing frogs. Needless to say, there won't be perfect agreement among the 10 to 15 individuals on each team, but the majority of children on both teams will probably favor either a fairly even distribution or some kind of placement revolving around their favorite or "lucky" numbers. Be sure to let them know that they can place more than one frog on a particular lily pad if they want. The first time around, it really doesn't matter. After students have played the game for a little while, they may begin to modify their ideas about where to place their frogs.

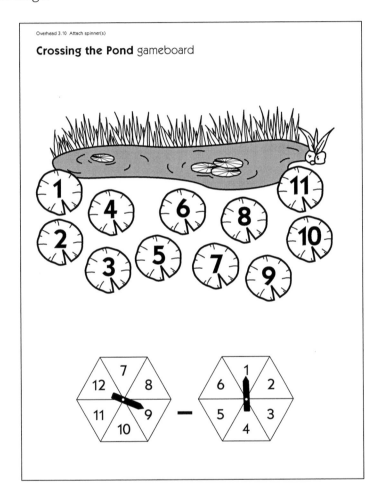

Overhead 3.10 Attach spinner(s)

Crossing the Pond gameboard

Once the "frogs" have been placed, you're ready to begin. Distribute copies of the record sheets and explain that both teams will find it useful to keep track of the differences that are being spun each time. That way, the next time they play the game, they'll know better where to place their "frogs." Have children from each team take turns spinning the double spinners at the top of the overhead and moving their frogs across the pond when the appropriate differences are spun. There will be plenty of times when a team can't move a frog, either because they didn't place a frog on that number to begin with or because all the frogs on that number have already been moved. If a team can't make a move, play simply reverts back to the other team—no one gets an extra turn in this game.

Session 16 Crossing the Pond (cont.)

Each time a spin is made for either team, have everyone mark it on his or her record sheet. The idea of keeping the record sheets is to help children have a better idea of where they want to place their markers on the gameboard the next time around. If the difference of 7 comes up many times during the first game, and the difference of 2 is only spun once or twice, students may think twice about placing any of their markers on 2 next time.

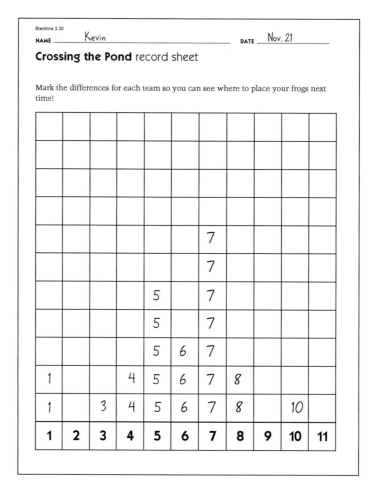

Kevin *Man! Next time we play, I'm not putting any of my frogs on 2!*

Kaitlin *I'm going to put all of mine on 7!*

Ciel *I'm going to put half of mine on 5 and half on 7.*

Peter *I still think we should have put all of our markers on the middle numbers. They always fill up first!*

About halfway through the game, when one of the teams has managed to get 3 or 4 of its frogs across, offer both teams a chance to reposition their remaining "frogs." Children may be very heavily influenced by the data in terms of where they choose to relocate. Their reactions will probably be quite literal too. If 7 happened to come up as a difference lots of times during the first

Session 16 Crossing the Pond (cont.)

part of the game, they may put lots of "frogs" on 7 and tend to ignore the surrounding numbers. After their markers are repositioned, have them continue playing back and forth until one of the teams has moved all its frogs to the far side of the pond. Have them continue to collect data on their record sheets during the second half of the game; the information they collect now might influence their ability to win the game when they play it independently during Work Places.

We're not expecting any mastery of probability here. For some students this game will just provide an opportunity to practice subtraction facts. Others may really begin to base decisions about placing their frogs on the data they collect. A few students may even begin to figure out why they're spinning differences of 6 more often than differences of 1 or 11. If you examine the chart below, you'll see why for yourself.

–	7	8	9	10	11	12
1	**6**	7	8	9	10	11
2	5	**6**	7	8	9	10
3	4	5	**6**	7	8	9
4	3	4	5	**6**	7	8
5	2	3	4	5	**6**	7
6	1	2	3	4	5	**6**

WORK PLACE NOTES

Unless you feel you need an extra day with the Work Places, this is the last day with Work Places 4. Children need to finish their work and mark their planners to indicate what they've completed. Given that all but one of the Work Places required a record sheet this time around, accountability will be nearly one hundred percent. When we go through children's folders to check their work, we circle any mistakes on their papers and ask them to go back and fix them. It may be that some of your students will spend time today working with the materials to finish or correct sheets. If a child has somehow slipped through the cracks and completed an activity with little or no apparent understanding and/or accuracy, we work with him or her during this time or ask another student to help.

Session 16 Crossing the Pond (cont.)

In preparation for the next round of Work Places, we remove the planner from the front of each work folder and staple it at the front of any record sheets the child has completed. We usually mark each sheet in some way—with a star, a happy face, or a comment of some sort—so children and parents will know how much we value the work. Then we send these packets home with our students.

HOME CONNECTION 10

Activity Cats & Mice (Blacklines HC 10.1–10.3, pp. 39–41)
Worksheet Number Sentences Tell the Story! (Blacklines HC 10.4–10.5, pp. 42–43)

The homework activity for this week gives children a chance to teach their parents how to play Cats & Mice. The worksheet asks them to solve some story problems that involve cats and mice.

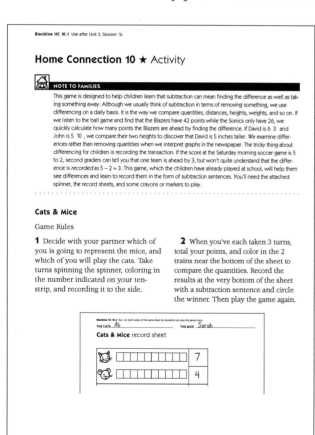

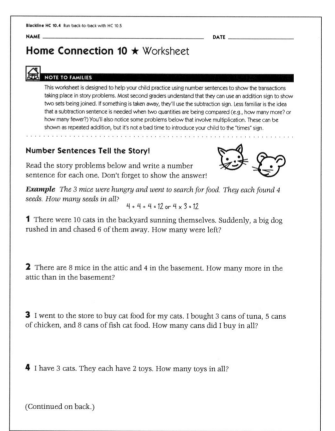

Session 17

 PROBLEMS & INVESTIGATIONS

Scout Them Out 1 Adding & Subtracting 0's & 1's

Overview

Before introducing the new set of Work Places, the teacher conducts a brief discussion with students about adding and subtracting 0's and 1's. The children then do a worksheet to practice finding and solving +0's, +1's, −0's, and −1's. This is the first of a set of sessions that will look specifically at related addition and subtraction strategies. Future sessions will examine the effects of adding or subtracting 2 and 10; adding or subtracting a number to or from itself (4 + 4 or 4 − 4); subtracting half the amount (8 − 4) or subtracting the units digit from a teen number (15 − 5 or 18 − 8); and finally adding and subtracting neighboring numbers (6 + 5 or 6 − 5). In each case, children will develop strategies for solving these combinations efficiently.

You'll need

★ chalk and chalkboard *or* felt marker and chart paper

★ Scout Them Out 1 (Overhead 3.11)

★ 3 overhead pens, 1 blue, 1 red, and 1 black

★ Scout Them Out 1 (Blackline 3.31, run a class set)

★ blue and red crayons or colored pencils

★ regular pencils

Skills

★ analyzing addition and subtraction strategies

★ practicing adding and subtracting 0's and 1's

Before the lesson starts, prepare a quick chart on the chalkboard or on a piece of chart paper similar to the one shown below:

7	5	0	13	17
+0	+0	+9	+0	+0
7	8	5	14	18
−0	−0	−0	−0	−0
8	1	9	1	19
+1	+6	+1	+16	+1
8	9	6	15	13
−1	−1	−1	−1	−1

Spend a few minutes going through each line of examples with your students,

Session 17 Scout Them Out 1 (cont.)

getting the answers and then talking about the facts themselves. What is it that makes adding 0's so easy? (We do understand that for some second graders, there's nothing easy or obvious about adding 1's or even 0's, but many children do find these facts easy and have helpful ways of thinking about them.) What you want to do is help children begin to make some generalizations about certain groups of facts.

$$\begin{array}{ccccc} 7 & 5 & 0 & 13 & 17 \\ +0 & +0 & +9 & +0 & +0 \\ \hline 7 & 5 & 9 & 13 & 17 \end{array}$$

Teacher *Wow! You really knew the answers to that line of addition facts fast! What made them so easy for you?*

Ethan *Adding 0's is really simple—it's like adding nothing.*

Hannah *It's like you have the number and you're not adding anything to it, so it just comes out being the same number.*

Teacher *So you'd probably know the answer to a really big example of adding 0's, like 467 + 0.*

Children *Easy! It's 467!*

Teacher *Does it make any difference if the 0 comes first, like 0 + 9?*

Children *No! It's the same thing, just the opposite. It's still like adding nothing.*

Discuss each line on the chart in a similar fashion, encouraging children's thoughts and observations each time. Next, explain to the children that before you introduce the new Work Places today, you have a quick worksheet for them to do that will help them practice these particular addition and subtraction facts. Show the overhead transparency of Scout Them Out 1 (see following page). Read through the first instruction at the top of the page together, which tells the children to find all the +0's, circle them in blue, and do them.

Overhead 3.11

Scout Them Out 1, Addition

1. Circle all the +0's in blue. Then take a pencil and go back and do them.
2. Circle all the +1's in red. Then take a pencil and go back and do them.

$$\begin{array}{ccccccc} 7 & 6 & 9 & 10 & 0 & 1 & 5 \\ +1 & +1 & +0 & +1 & +4 & +8 & +1 \\ \hline \end{array}$$

$$\begin{array}{ccccccc} 1 & 12 & 0 & 17 & 0 & 11 & 1 \\ +3 & +1 & +13 & +0 & +4 & +1 & +1 \\ \hline \end{array}$$

$$\begin{array}{ccccccc} 2 & 14 & 1 & 13 & 1 & 13 & 1 \\ +1 & +0 & +15 & +1 & +4 & +1 & +9 \\ \hline \end{array}$$

Session 17 Scout Them Out 1 (cont.)

Take your blue overhead pen and go through the addition facts one by one. Have children signal which ones they think you should circle and which ones to leave alone by saying "yes" or "no" to each fact. After you've circled all the +0's, go back with your black overhead pen and do them with the students' help.

Then go back to the top and read the second instruction, which tells you to circle all the +1's in red. As before, take your red overhead pen and go through the addition facts one by one as the children signal you whether or not to circle them. Then go back and do them. Work your way through the subtraction portion of the sheet in similar fashion.

Scout Them Out 1, Subtraction

1. Circle all the –0's in blue. Then take a pencil and go back and do them.
2. Circle all the –1's in red. Then take a pencil and go back and do them.

7	5	9	10	12	6	7
– 1	– 1	– 0	– 1	– 0	– 1	– 1

9	4	18	17	14	8	12
– 1	– 0	– 0	– 1	– 1	– 1	– 1

3	15	1	13	6	11	8
– 1	– 1	– 1	– 0	– 0	– 1	– 1

When you've completed the overhead sheet together, pass out copies of the sheet to the children and have them work their way through as you modeled, top to bottom, one row at a time from left to right, searching out facts, circling them, and then doing them in pencil. When they finish their sheets, have children do some other quiet task until their classmates are finished. Normally, they could get their folders and go to Work Places, but today you'll be introducing a new set.

Notes

Session 17 Work Places 5

WORK PLACES

Introduce Work Places 5

Overview

The teacher introduces a new set of Work Places, many of which build on previous lessons. After the activities have been introduced, the children choose a place to begin. This round of Work Places will carry you and your students through the end of Unit 3 and into Unit 4. While Work Places 4 emphasized practice in addition/subtraction processes and notation, as well as some of the most basic strategies for adding and subtracting, including counting on, counting backwards, and finding all the possible sets of addends for a given number, Work Places 5 becomes somewhat more sophisticated, providing practice with addition and subtraction doubles and neighbors (e.g., $6 + 6$, $6 + 7$, $5 - 5$, $5 - 4$), and continued work with finding differences, searching out combinations for particular "target" numbers, and probability.

You'll need

★ Work Place baskets 5A–5F set up as shown

★ a work folder for each child with a copy of the Work Places 5 Planner stapled to the front (Blackline 3.41)

★ the observation checklists you have been keeping on children since the beginning of Work Places 4 (Blackline 3.7)

In preparation for this session, you'll want to read through the descriptions of the Work Places on the next few pages. Each description explains how to play the game or do the activity, and includes some instructional considerations for you to bear in mind as you introduce the Work Places. Set up your Work Place baskets as shown. Staple the new Work Place planners to the children's work folders.

Session 17 Introduce Work Places 5 (cont.)

Work Places 5 Setup

5A Turn Them Over

This work place basket will need

✓ 6 sets of Turn Them Over cards

✓ 3 dice numbered 3–8 and 3 dice numbered 4–9 (Number the sides of wooden cubes to make your dice)

5B Crossing the Pond

This work place basket will need

✓ 3 Crossing the Pond spinners

✓ 6 Crossing the Pond gameboards

✓ Crossing the Pond record sheets (Blackline 3.30, run 30 copies and place in a folder)

✓ math bucket of frogs

5C Battling Bugs

This work place basket will need

✓ 3 Battling Bugs spinners

✓ Battling Bugs record sheets (Blackline 3.42 *or* 3.43—the Getting Started Version; run 30 copies and place in a folder)

✓ crayons or colored pencils

5D Scout Them Out

This work place basket will need

✓ Scout Them Out 6–10 (Blacklines 3.36–3.40, run 15 copies of each and place in folders)

✓ red, blue, green, and purple crayons or colored pencils

5E Cover Up

This work place basket will need

✓ 3 sets of Cover Up cards and 3 sets of Cover Up Challenge cards

✓ Cover Up game sheets (Blackline 3.23, run 30 copies and place in a folder)

✓ green and yellow tile from the base ten pieces, about 30 of each (optional)

✓ crayons

Session 17 Introduce Work Places 5 (cont.)

5F Kids in the House

This work place basket will need

✓ Kids in the House, sheets 1–6 (Blacklines 3.24–3.29, run 30 copies of each and place in pocket folders)

✓ round plastic game markers (Make 6 sets of 20 markers. Place each set in its own ziplock or other container.)

Introduce the six new Work Places one by one. All six activities are new, although your students will have played Battling Bugs, Cover Up, Kids in the House, and Crossing the Pond as a whole group. They will also just have completed one of the Scout Them Out sheets and will be somewhat familiar with the format. You might want to start by showing the Work Place versions of each of these games first, and then model Turn Them Over, which is a relatively simple and very appealing card game. If you move quickly, your students will probably have a little time to start the new Work Places before it's time to clean up.

As children work at these activities, continue your observations and note-taking on individuals, using the observation sheets introduced with the last round of Work Places. In our own classrooms, we try to get through two or three children during a work period. If we get all the way through the group before the end of Work Places 5, we start over again, watching for growing understanding and knowledge of addition and subtraction facts and strategies.

Session 17 Work Places 5 (cont.)

WORK PLACE 5A

Turn Them Over

This Work Place basket will need

★ 6 sets of Turn Them Over cards

★ 3 dice numbered 3–8

★ 3 dice numbered 4–9

· ·

Note To make these dice, number the sides of wooden cubes with a black permanent fine felt-tip marker.

· ·

Skills

★ practicing addition combinations for the numbers 7–17

★ searching for combinations to equal certain target numbers

★ figuring out strategies to win a game

This is an interesting strategy game in which children search for combinations for certain target numbers. The game has been very popular with many of our second graders over the past few years.

To Work

1. You and your partner will each need a set of number cards. When you're ready to start, lay your number cards face up in front of you, in order from 1 to 10. Have your partner do the same.

2. Take turns. When it's your turn, roll the dice. Add the two numbers that come up. Then figure out how you could turn over some of your number cards to equal that same sum. Here's an example: Suppose you roll a 4 and a 9. Your total is 13. You could turn over your 4 card and your 9 card, or you could turn over a different combination of cards that equals 13, such as 7 and 6, or 5 and 8, or even 2, 7, and 4. The object of the game is to be the first to turn all your number cards face down. *You can turn more than two cards face down with each turn.*

3. There may come a point in the game where you or your partner is stuck. For instance, suppose you have only your 7, 8, and 9 cards left face up and you roll an 8 and a 4 on the dice.

Session 17 Work Places 5 (cont.)

Your total is 12, and there's no way you can make that total with your remaining cards. You are now stuck. In one version of the game, each partner simply stops playing at the point he or she gets stuck. If one of the players gets stuck before the other, she stops while the other continues to play until she also gets stuck. Partners then add the numbers they're stuck with and the person with the lowest total wins.

Another version is to keep playing until all your cards have been turned over. In this version, if you get stuck, you simply let the other person roll the dice. You keep passing the dice back and forth, rolling each time, until one of you is able to turn over all of her cards. Many second graders seem to favor the second version of this game. In any event, it's good fun, and after they've played a few times, children begin developing strategies like trying to use up their larger numbers first and saving their smaller numbers for last.

WORK PLACE 5B

Crossing the Pond

This Work Place basket will need

★ 3 Crossing the Pond spinners

★ 6 Crossing the Pond gameboards

★ Crossing the Pond record sheets (Blackline 3.30, run 30 copies and place in a folder)

★ math bucket of frogs

Skills

★ practicing subtraction facts

★ graphing data

★ making decisions based on collected data

★ exploring probability

To Work

1. Find a partner. You will each need your own gameboard, 8 frogs, a record sheet, and a pencil. You will also need 1 double spinner to share.

2. Before you begin the game, place your frogs on the lily pads you want them to start on. You can put more than 1 frog on a particular lily pad, and you'll probably want to take the information you got during Session 16 into consideration. Did differences of 1, 2, or 3 come up very often? Which differences did come up the most? If you can remember, you'll want to place your frogs on some of the numbers that seemed to come up most frequently.

Session 17 Work Places 5 (cont.)

John *I put two of my frogs on lily pad 5 and two on 7 because we kept spinning 5's and 7's yesterday. But I still want to spread them out a bit, just in case we get some other numbers, like 4 and 6. And I put one frog on 10 because it's my lucky number.*

Andrea *Not me! I put half my frogs on 5 and half on 7 because that's mostly what we got. I'm not going to waste my frogs anywhere else!*

3. Take turns spinning. If you spin and the difference between the two numbers matches one of the numbers where you have a frog, you can move him across the pond to safety on the other side. You can only move 1 frog at a time, though. If you have 2 or 3 frogs on a particular number, you have to wait until you spin that difference again to move one of the others.

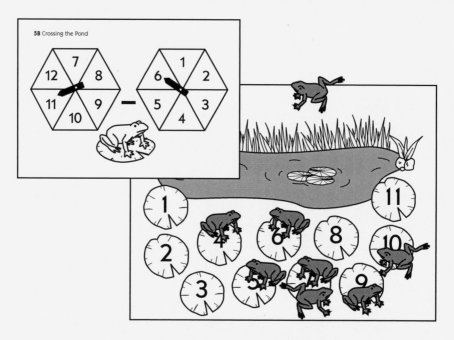

John *Hey, look! I got 11 – 6. That's 5! I get to move one of my frogs across the pond already. I knew we'd get more 5's today!*

Session 17 Work Places 5 (cont.)

4. As you and your partner spin, keep track of the differences both of you get on the record sheet. Keeping track may help you make better and better decisions about where to place your frogs.

5. *When you get about halfway through the game—to the point where either you or your partner has moved 4 frogs across the pond—you can relocate your remaining frogs.* This is where your record sheet will come in handy. What differences seem to have come up frequently? Are there any that haven't come up at all?

6. Once you've repositioned your frogs, keep playing until one of you has moved them all across the pond. The first to do so is the winner.

Instructional Considerations for Crossing the Pond

When you introduce this game as a Work Place, be sure to remind students that they have the option of repositioning their frogs halfway through. Being able to change midway through motivates children to graph the differences as the game proceeds, and to consider their data carefully. Most will continue to respond to the data they collect in a very concrete manner for some time to come, choosing to station most of their frogs at the one or two differences that come up most frequently. It will be the rare child who distributes his or her frogs evenly among the middle numbers, understanding that in the long run, 6 and 8 are at least as likely to be spun as 5 and 7, even if they haven't come up yet. Again, this game is intended to give children an opportunity to base decisions on experimental data—to begin to explore the realm of probability—while practicing basic subtraction facts.

Session 17 Work Places 5 (cont.)

WORK PLACE 5C

Battling Bugs

This Work Place basket will need

★ 3 Battling Bugs spinners

★ Battling Bugs record sheets (Blackline 3.42 *or* Blackline 3.43, the Getting Started Version. Read the Instructional Considerations before you decide which blackline to use. In either case, run 30 copies and place in a folder)

★ crayons or colored pencils

Skills

★ learning to record differences as subtraction sentences

★ practicing subtraction facts to 10

★ recording information on a graph

★ adding strings of numbers and comparing the totals

To Work

1. Decide with your partner which of you is going to represent the spiders team and which of you will represent the flies. Take turns spinning the spinner, coloring in the numbers indicated on your ten-strips, recording them to the side, and then writing the subtraction sentence to reflect the difference each time. *Work on the same sheet together, coloring in your own ten-strips and recording your own scores. Take turns writing the subtraction sentences.*

2. When you've each taken three turns, help each other total the points for each team. Color in these totals on the ten-strip trains at the bottom of your sheet. Figure the difference by comparing the two trains and then record it in the form of a number sentence in the boxes at the very bottom of the sheet.

3. When you're finished, play the whole game through again and use a second record sheet. That way, you and your partner will both have sheets to put in your folders. (We've had better luck working this way than having children try to keep each other's records on their own sheets.)

Session 17 Work Places 5 (cont.)

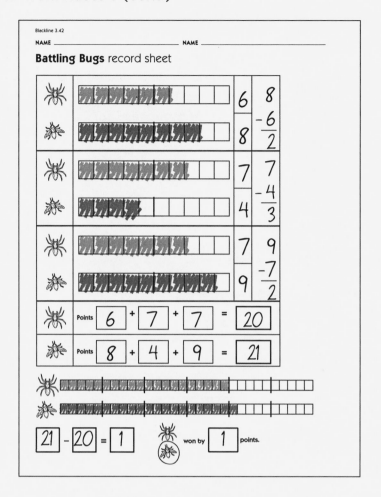

Blackline 3.42

NAME _____   NAME _____

Battling Bugs record sheet

Instructional Considerations for Battling Bugs

Like Cats & Mice, this game is quite challenging for many second graders. They're fine spinning, coloring in the ten-strips, recording the scores, and *seeing* the differences each time. The difficulty comes in writing the differences in the form of subtraction sentences. For some children, all will be well as long as the spider score is greater than the fly score. Looking at the second round on the sheet above, they'd be able to tell you that the score is 7 to 4, the spiders are ahead by 3, and the subtraction sentence to show the difference is 7 – 4 = 3.

When the fly score exceeds the spider score on a particular round, though, the fragility of their understanding shows through. On the first round shown above, they'd tell you that the score is 6 to 8, the flies won by 2, and the subtraction sentence to show the difference is 6 – 8 = 2. They do understand that the difference is 2; it's just that the finer point of writing the larger of the two numbers first escapes them. When we find children in our classes who are writing "upside down" subtraction sentences, we chat with them to make sure they understand the idea of subtraction as finding differences, and then we help them write their subtraction sentences correctly, knowing that it may take a long time before they can do so independently.

Session 17 Work Places 5 (cont.)

If this version of the game seems impossibly hard for some of your children, you might want to introduce it at a slightly easier level, using Blackline 3.43 instead of Blackline 3.42. This Getting Started Version of the game shown below asks children to spin, record the scores on ten-strips, and write the scores and the differences, *without having to show the differences as subtraction sentences.*

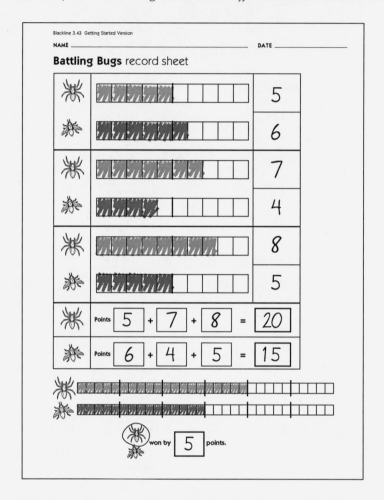

If, after a week or so of play, you feel that your children are becoming confident with the game at this easier level, you can then introduce the form that requires them to record the differences with subtraction sentences.

Session 17 Work Places 5 (cont.)

WORK PLACE 5D

Scout Them Out

This Work Place basket will need

★ Scout Them Out 6–10 (Blacklines 3.36–3.40, run 15 copies of each and place in pocket folders)

★ red, blue, green, and purple crayons or colored pencils

Skills

★ practicing various addition and sub- traction strategies, including adding and subtracting 0's, 1's, 2's, 9's, 10's, doubles, and neighbors

★ looking for relationships between various combinations

★ looking for relationships between addition and subtraction

To Work

1. Look through the folder and find a sheet that you want to do. Read the in- structions and get the colors you'll need to circle facts, as well as a regular pencil.

2. Following the instructions on your particular sheet, circle the first set of facts with the required color. Then go back and do them in pencil. Then go through a second time, following the second instruction. Some of the sheets even ask you to go back a third time, searching for different types of facts. Be sure to follow the instructions carefully.

Scout Them Out 9, Subtraction
1. Circle all the Take Away 10's in blue. Then take a pencil and go back and do them.
2. Circle all the Run Away 1's in red. Then take a pencil and go back and do them.

16	17	10	12	12	13	13
– 10	– 7	– 10	– 2	– 10	– 3	– 10

11	11	18	18	15	15	17
– 10	– 1	– 10	– 8	– 5	– 10	– 10

14	16	12	20	19	11	16
– 4	– 6	– 2	– 10	– 9	– 1	– 6

Instructional Considerations for Scout Them Out

Do you want your students to complete more than one sheet per visit? If you want them to try more than one of these sheets, you might require that they do two or even three per visit. That way, if they only get around to this Work Place once, they'll have completed several sheets instead of just one. Know, also, that the sheets get more challenging as children move through the set.

Session 17 Work Places 5 (cont.)

WORK PLACE 5E

Cover Up

This Work Place basket will need

★ 3 sets of Cover Up cards and 3 sets Cover Up Challenge cards

★ Cover Up game sheet (Blackline 3.23, run 30 copies and place in a folder)

★ green and yellow tile from the base ten pieces (about 30 of each—these are optional, but may help some children plan their moves)

★ crayons

Skills

★ exploring a visual model for the doubles and neighbors

★ practicing doubles and neighbors addition combinations

★ exploring a visual model for odd and even numbers

★ searching for visual and number patterns

★ linking number and geometry

To Work

1. With your partner, choose the set of regular or challenge cards you plan to use. Each of you will also need a record sheet and 6 to 8 crayons in different colors. Shuffle the deck of cards you've chosen and place it face-down between you.

2. Takes turns. When it's your turn, pick a card, read the combination, and find a place on your record sheet to color in that shape.

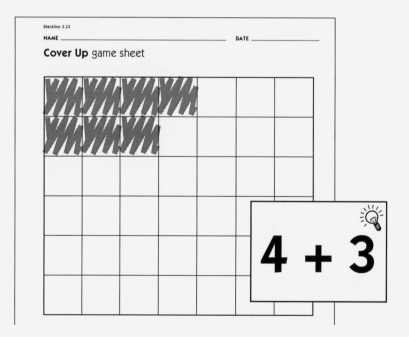

"I picked 4 + 3 and I'm just starting out. I think I'll put it up in the corner. Now if I could get something like 2 + 3, I could fill in the hole at the top and have a nice, smooth rectangle."

Session 17 Work Places 5 (cont.)

3. Continue to play back and forth, each taking cards from the top of the pile and coloring in the appropriate shapes on your own record sheets. If you come to a card you cannot use because your record sheet won't accommodate the shape, put it back at the bottom of the pile and let your partner take his turn. You may find that toward the end, you're missing quite a few turns.

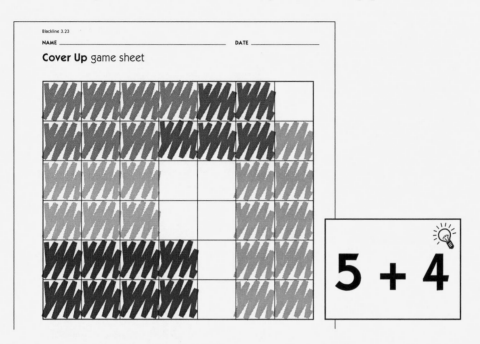

Blackline 3.23
NAME _____ DATE _____

Cover Up game sheet

5 + 4

Student I can't use 5 + 4. All I have room for is 3 + 2 or something smaller, and I really need that 1 + 0 card! I'll have to put this card back in the pile and skip my turn."

4. If you get to the end of the card deck and neither of you has been able to fill your record sheet yet, shuffle the deck, place it face-down between you and continue to draw cards and color in shapes on your sheets until someone wins. Reuse the deck as many times as necessary until one of you fills your record sheet completely. (If this seems too tedious, you or your students might develop an alternative ending, such as declaring the game over if either player draws more than 5 cards in a row that can't be used. In this case, the player with the fewest boxes left to color on his or her sheet would win.)

Instructional Considerations for Cover Up

By the time you introduce this round of Work Places, your students will have played this game as a whole-group activity. You may want to review briefly by having them build some of the doubles and neighbors combinations in the form of rectangles and "school buses" with 1" square tile.

Session 17 Work Places 5 (cont.)

"Here's how you build 3 + 3. It's a 2 × 3 rectangle."

"And here's the shape for 2 + 3. It really does look like a school bus with that nose sticking out!"

You might also show a few counter-examples:

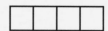

Teacher *Why can't I build 2 + 2 like this?*

Susannah *Because in this game, you have to make rectangles.*

Teacher *But this is a rectangle. It's a 1 × 4.*

Bryce *You have to make your rectangles be 2-by's. That way you can see if it's a neighbor because if it is, it'll have that nose sticking out.*

Once you've reviewed the "acceptable" shapes, you might remind students that the regular cards actually show the shapes of the combinations, whereas the challenge cards just give the numbers. Children who are feeling less secure with the shapes might use the regular cards for awhile before they move to the more challenging set.

Finally, don't be dismayed if some of your students color in the combinations incorrectly for awhile. In the heat of the game, even some of our more able students will color in 2 + 3 as a line of 5, instead of using the "school bus" formation, if they need a long skinny shape to complete their sheet. At the very least, children are practicing addition facts and creating visual models of them. Consistent use of 2-by rectangles and school bus arrangements may be a while in coming. This is not the last time children will see these models.

Session 17 Work Places 5 (cont.)

WORK PLACE 5F

Kids in the House

This Work Place basket will need

★ Kids in the House, sheets 1–6 (Black-lines 3.24–3.29, run 30 copies of each and place in folders)

★ round plastic game markers (Make 6 sets of 20. Place each set in its own ziplock or other container.)

Skills

★ searching for combinations for numbers 1 through 15

★ practicing addition facts in a problem-solving context

To Work

1. Choose a sheet to do. You have already done sheet 1, and may also have done sheet 2. If you want to try these sheets again, that's fine, but you'll also need to pick at least one other sheet. In addition to a sheet, you'll need a crayon, a pencil, and some plastic counting disks.

2. Read the first number in the set below the house. Can you place that many counting disks in the windows shown and still follow the rule that if you use one pane in the window, you have to use all of them? If so, put a check above the number and color in the boxes below to show which window(s) you've used to make the number.

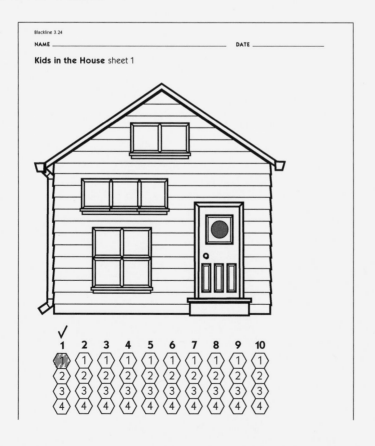

Session 17 Work Places 5 (cont.)

3. Continue in this fashion until you've tried to make all the numbers on the sheet. You'll find that a few of them are impossible on some of the sheets, but don't give up too easily—be sure to use your counting disks and try all kinds of possibilities before you cross anything out.

. . . .

Note *The only combinations that can't be made are the following: Sheet 3 (11), Sheet 4 (5, 12), Sheet 5 (15), Sheet 6 (4, 7, 12, 15).*

. . . .

Instructional Considerations for Kids in the House

Do you want your students to complete more than one sheet per visit? If you want them to try more than one of these sheets, you might require that they do two or even three per visit. That way, if they only get around to this Work Place once, they'll have completed several sheets instead of just one.

Session 18

WORK PLACES

Getting Started with Work Places 5

Overview
The teacher reviews Work Places 5 and sends children out for a long work period.

You'll need
★ work baskets 5A–5F set up for Work Places 5

★ a work folder for each child with a copy of the Work Places 5 Planner stapled to the front (Blackline 3.41)

★ the observation checklists you have been keeping on children since the beginning of Work Places 4 (Blackline 3.7)

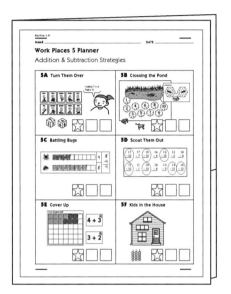

You will almost certainly want to offer your students plenty of time with this new set of Work Places today. Open the session by reviewing any of the activities that didn't go as smoothly as you would have liked yesterday. While you won't want to review all of the games and activities in depth, you might take some time with Turn Them Over, which the children just started to play last session. You might also want to model the Work Place version of Crossing the Pond or Battling Bugs, both of which are fairly complex games. For the most part, though, the activities you choose to review will depend on the how your students responded to the Work Places during Session 17.

Notes

Session 19

PROBLEMS & INVESTIGATIONS

Scout Them Out 2 Adding & Subtracting 2's & 10's

Overview

This is the second in a set of sessions that takes an in-depth look at various addition and subtraction combinations. Comfort and fluency in adding and subtracting 10's is particularly important in that these combinations can become springboards for more difficult facts. For example, children who know that 10 + 4 = 14 are often able to reason that 9 + 4 = 13. Some see that 9 is one less than 10, so the result of adding 9 instead of 10 will be one less. Others imagine taking 1 from the 4 and "giving it to the 9," so that 9 + 4 becomes 10 + 3, which is much easier to solve. Likewise, knowing that 15 − 10 = 5 makes it easier to figure 15 − 9. In this session, students formulate new understandings or share strategies they may already have developed for adding and subtracting 2's and 10's.

Skills

★ generating addition and subtraction strategies

★ practicing adding and subtracting 2's and 10's

You'll need

★ chalk and chalkboard *or* felt marker and chart paper

★ Scout Them Out 2 (Overhead 3.12)

★ 3 overhead pens, 1 blue, 1 red, and 1 black

★ Scout Them Out 2 (Blackline 3.32, run a class set)

★ blue and red crayons or colored pencils

★ regular pencils

7	9	5	2	11	2
+2	+2	+2	+6	+2	+8
7	5	9	8	10	14
−2	−2	−2	−2	−2	−2
10	10	10	10	7	10
+2	+5	+9	+6	+10	+4
14	15	18	13	19	12
−10	−10	−10	−10	−10	−10

Before the lesson starts, prepare a quick chart on the chalkboard or on a piece of chart paper similar to the one shown above.

Spend a few minutes going through each line of examples with your students, soliciting answers, and then talking about the facts themselves. What is it that makes adding and subtracting 2's easy? Some children will tell you that it's just like counting forward (or backward) once, and then once again. If they don't already know the answer, it's pretty fast to count on or count backwards twice. As for the 10's, students may have a variety of observations.

Session 19 Scout Them Out 2 (cont.)

McCall When you add 10's, it's so easy. It's like you just put the other number behind the 10, so 10 + 5 is just 15.

Peter It's kind of like moving the other number into the spot where the 0 is.

Cassie The 10 turns into a teen, like 16.

Ernest It's like the 10 picks up the other number in his backpack and carries it away!

Susannah When you subtract 10's it's easy too. Just the number is left.

Teacher What do you mean?

Susannah Well, on 16 – 10, just the 6 is left.

Jake When you get rid of the 10, just the 1's are left.

After you and the students have worked through the chart, show the overhead transparency of Scout Them Out 2 (see following page).

Model as much of the activity as you feel is necessary; and then send children out to complete their own sheets, searching out facts, circling them, and then doing them in pencil. Have them compare their answers with at least one other child as they finish. Did they circle the same facts in blue? In red? Did they get the same answers? If not, they'll need to work together to correct their work.

Session 19 Scout Them Out 2 (cont.)

Overhead 3.12

Scout Them Out 2, Addition

1. Circle all the +2's in blue. Then take a pencil and go back and do them.
2. Circle all the +10's in red. Then take a pencil and go back and do them.

7	2	9	10	2	2	5
+ 2	+ 6	+ 10	+ 1	+ 4	+ 8	+ 2

10	10	6	10	2	11	2
+ 3	+ 4	+ 10	+ 7	+ 8	+ 2	+ 2

7	10	2	10	3	10	2
+ 2	+ 0	+ 15	+ 8	+ 2	+ 5	+ 9

Scout Them Out 2, Subtraction

1. Circle all the –2's in blue. Then take a pencil and go back and do them.
2. Circle all the –10's in red. Then take a pencil and go back and do them.

7	5	19	14	12	6	9
– 2	– 2	– 10	– 10	– 10	– 2	– 2

11	13	18	17	14	8	16
– 2	– 10	– 10	– 10	– 2	– 2	– 10

3	15	2	20	6	11	8
– 2	– 2	– 2	– 10	– 2	– 10	– 2

WORK PLACE NOTES

As children finish checking their sheets with one another, have them get their folders and go out to Work Places.

Session 20

PROBLEMS & INVESTIGATIONS

Scout Them Out 3 Adding & Subtracting Doubles & Neighbor Number Facts

Overview

This is the third in a set of sessions that takes an in-depth look at various addition and subtraction combinations. Children see how addition doubles, such as 6 + 6, once memorized, become useful in finding the answers to more difficult combinations such as "neighbor number facts" (5 + 6, 6 + 7).

Skills

★ generating addition and subtraction strategies

★ building visual models of addition and subtraction

★ practicing adding and subtracting doubles and neighbors

You'll need

★ the chart shown on the following page, written on paper or the chalkboard

★ tile (Each child in your group should have access to at least 20 tile in a single color and 1 tile in a contrasting color.)

★ overhead tile

★ Scout Them Out 3 (Overhead 3.13)

★ 3 overhead pens, 1 blue, 1 red, and 1 black

★ Scout Them Out 3 (Blackline 3.33, run a class set)

★ blue and red crayons or colored pencils

★ regular pencils

This is the third in a set of sessions that takes an in-depth look at various addition and subtraction combinations. Addition doubles: 1 + 1, 2 + 2, 3 + 3, and so on, are often some of the first combinations children commit to memory. Once memorized, these facts become particularly useful in finding the answers to other, more difficult combinations. The knowledge that 7 + 7 = 14, for instance, can be helpful in figuring out the answer to 7 + 8 or 6 + 7. We refer to these facts as "neighbor numbers" because the numbers "live next door to one another."

Subtraction doubles such as 1 – 1, 2 – 2, 3 – 3, and so on, are obvious to most children. If you have a certain number and subtract that many, the answer will always be 0. Likewise, the subtraction of neighbor numbers is considered easy by many, partly because the answer is always 1, such as 3 – 2 = 1, as does 17 – 16. Although these number relationships may not be readily apparent to every student in your room, the discussion and practice offered in this session may help them begin to develop some strategies other than counting on or counting backwards for dealing with facts they don't yet know.

Session 20 Scout Them Out 3 (cont.)

Before the lesson starts, prepare a quick chart on the chalkboard or on a piece of chart paper similar to the one shown below:

> Make a picture of each addition problem:
>
> | 5 | 5 | 7 | 7 | 6 | 7 |
> |---|---|---|---|---|---|
> | +5 | +6 | +7 | +8 | +6 | +6 |
>
> ---
>
> Which is the neighbor number fact?
>
> 5   or   6
> +4   +4
>
> ---
>
> Name a double for each neighbor number fact and then figure out the answer:
>
> | 8 | 6 | 4 | 8 | 3 | 10 |
> |---|---|---|---|---|---|
> | +9 | +5 | +5 | +7 | +4 | +9 |
>
> ---
>
> Make a picture of each subtraction problem:
>
> | 9 | 9 | 5 | 5 | 8 | 8 |
> |---|---|---|---|---|---|
> | -9 | -8 | -5 | -4 | -8 | -7 |

Distribute tile to your students and explain that you are going to ask them to build models of some addition and subtraction facts today. Have them read the first combination on the chart, 5 + 5, and build it with their tile using just one color. Having played Cover Up recently, many may respond with a 2-by rectangle.

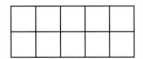

Find a volunteer to build it at the overhead in this form, and ask students to interpret the picture.

Joey Rose *You can see that it's 5 + 5 = 10*

Evan *It's also a 2 × 5 rectangle.*

Ciel *You can tell it's an even number because it doesn't have a nose sticking out.*

Next, ask children to use their single contrasting tile to change their pictures of 5 + 5 into 5 + 6. Be sure to have a volunteer modify the tile at the overhead as well so children can point things out to the entire group as they discuss the new total.

Session 20 Scout Them Out 3 (cont.)

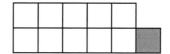

Teacher *If you didn't already know the answer to 5 + 6, how could you see it in your tile?*

Children *Easy—it's 11!*
If you know that 5 + 5 is 10, then you can see that 1 more makes 11!
You can also see that it's an odd number 'cause of that last one sticking out.

Continue in this fashion, having children build and discuss 7 + 7, 7 + 8, 6 + 6, and 7 + 6. There are children in your group who have probably generated a strategy to solve the sum of neighbor numbers already, but for some, it may be a new idea to work from the double to its neighbor number fact. After you've gone through the six examples in the top row, have children consider the question in the second row. The question is, which of the two combinations in the box is an example of a neighbor number fact, and why?

Which is the neighbor number fact?

5		6
+4	or	+4

Sherwin *It's 5 + 4.*

Teacher *Why?*

Sherwin *Because a neighbor is like adding 1 more, and 5 is 1 more than 4.*

Evelyn *I think it's 5 + 4 because 5 and 4 are like next-door neighbors. They come right after each other when you're counting; 6 and 4 are too far apart.*

Next, move to the third row on the chart. Point out to your students that if they can identify a combination as a neighbor number fact and think of a related double, they may be able to use their knowledge of the double to solve the sum of the neighbor numbers.

Name a double for each neighbor number fact and then figure out the answer:

8	6	4	8	3	10
+9	+ 5	+ 5	+ 7	+4	+9

Session 20 Scout Them Out 3 (cont.)

Teacher *Are all of the examples in this row really neighbor numbers?*

Children *Yes—all of those numbers live next door.*

Teacher *Let's go through and name a related double for each neighbor number fact. If we know a related double, we can use it to solve the neighbor.*

Children *The first one is 8 + 8.*

Joey *It could also be also 9 + 9, though. I just go 9 + 9 = 18, and 1 less than that is 17.*

Teacher *Good observation! What are the related doubles for the next example?*

Eloise *6 + 6!*

John *5 + 5!*

Whitney *It could be either, but 5 + 5 is 10, and that's really easy. I just say it's 5 + 5 = 10 and 1 more, which is 11; 6 + 5 = 11.*

Continue working through the examples in this fashion until you have reached the end of the third row. Then move on to the examples of subtracting doubles and neighbors. Here again, you may want to have children build pictures with their tile. Although their inclination will probably be to show the transactions as a process of taking things away, you might also encourage them to use a difference model to illustrate what's going on.

Make a picture of each subtraction problem:

9	9	5	5	8	8
-9	-8	-5	-4	-8	-7

Teacher *How would you show 9 – 9 with your tile?*

Children *Easy—just put out 9 tile and take them all away.*
The answer is 0—subtracting doubles is so easy.
Yeah! The answer is always 0, because you just take them all away!

Teacher *How would you show 9 – 9 with your tile if I told this story: The Blazers had 9 points in the ball game so far. The Knicks also had 9. Which team was winning?*

Children *They're tied—no one's ahead!*

Teacher *Is there a way to show that with tile?*

Session 20 Scout Them Out 3 (cont.)

Andrew How 'bout like this?

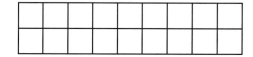

Teacher That's an interesting picture, Andrew. Come build it at the overhead.

Hannah But that looks like 9 + 9!

Teacher Can you explain your picture to the other children?

Andrew It's like a graph. The top row shows the Blazers' points. The bottom shows the Knicks'. You can see that they're even. No one's ahead.

Teacher The difference is 0.

Andrew And if you look at the next one like this, it's easy to see how the difference is 1.

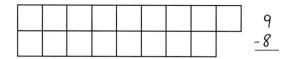

"The difference between 9 and 8 is 1."

Have students use their tile to build the rest of the facts in row 4. The take-away model will make sense to some, while the differencing model demonstrated above may make more sense to others. In any event, encourage your students to make any generalizations they can about subtracting doubles—numbers that are identical—and neighbor numbers—numbers that are one apart.

After you and the students have worked through the entire chart, show the overhead transparency of Scout Them Out 3 (see following page).

Model as much of the activity as you feel is necessary; and then send children out to complete their own sheets, searching out facts, circling them, and then doing them in pencil. Have them compare their answers with at least one other child as they finish. Did they circle the same facts in blue? In red? Did they get the same answers? If not, they'll need to work together to correct their work.

Session 20 Scout Them Out 3 (cont.)

Overhead 3.13

Scout Them Out 3, Addition

1. Circle all the doubles in blue. Then take a pencil and go back and do them.
2. Circle all the neighbor number facts in red. Then take a pencil and go back and do them.

7	6	9	10	3	8	5
+ 7	+ 6	+ 10	+ 9	+ 4	+ 8	+ 5

3	4	6	10	2	3	2
+ 3	+ 4	+ 7	+ 10	+ 2	+ 2	+ 2

7	7	6	9	3	8	8
+ 8	+ 6	+ 5	+ 9	+ 2	+ 7	+ 9

Scout Them Out 3, Subtraction

1. Circle all the doubles in blue. Then take a pencil and go back and do them.
2. Circle all the neighbor number facts in red. Then take a pencil and go back and do them.

7	5	10	14	12	6	9
− 7	− 4	− 10	− 14	− 11	− 6	− 8

11	13	8	10	3	8	16
− 11	− 12	− 8	− 9	− 2	− 7	− 16

6	15	2	20	9	11	7
− 5	− 14	− 2	− 20	− 9	− 11	− 6

WORK PLACE NOTES

As children finish checking their sheets with one another, have them get their folders and go out to Work Places.

Session 21

PROBLEMS & INVESTIGATIONS

HOME
CONNECTIONS

Scout Them Out 4 Adding Doubles & Neighbor Numbers; Subtracting Halves

Overview

In this session, children review the idea of working from doubles to neighbor number facts in addition, and examine a set of related subtraction facts—the halves. Some children in your group may already have developed the halves strategy on their own, and will tell you that they know 8 − 4 is 4 because 4 + 4 = 8. This session will give everyone in your class a chance to consider the idea.

Skills

★ generating addition and subtraction strategies

★ building visual models of addition and subtraction

★ exploring the relationships between addition and subtraction

★ practicing addition and subtraction facts

You'll need

★ the chart shown below written on paper or on the chalkboard

★ tile (Each child in your group should have access to at least 20 tile in a single color.)

★ Scout Them Out 4 (Overhead 3.14)

★ 3 overhead pens, 1 blue, 1 red, and 1 black

★ Scout Them Out 4 (Blackline 3.34, run a class set)

★ blue and red crayons or colored pencils

★ regular pencils

★ Home Connection blacklines HC 11.1–11.5

Before the lesson starts, prepare a quick chart on the chalkboard or on a piece of chart paper similar to the one shown below.

Name a related double for each neighbor number fact and then figure out the answer:

3	5	4	8	1	9
+4	+6	+5	+7	+2	+10

With tile, build and answer the addition and subtraction facts below. How are they related?

3	6	5	10	7	14
+3	−3	+5	−5	+7	−7

2	4	6	12	8	16
+2	−2	+6	−6	+8	−8

Session 21 Scout Them Out 4 (cont.)

Gather your students into a discussion circle and take a few minutes to work through the first line of the chart together. Just as you did in Session 20, have them name a related double for each addition fact and work from the double to complete the sum of the neighbor number fact.

$$\begin{array}{cccccc} 3 & 5 & 4 & 8 & 1 & 9 \\ +4 & +6 & +5 & +7 & +2 & +10 \end{array}$$

Teacher *What do you notice about the facts in the first row of the chart today?*

Children *Some of them are pretty hard.*
1 + 2 is easy—it's 3!
Hey—they're all neighbor number facts. They all live next door.
That's what it says on the chart—"Name a related double for each neighbor number fact."

Teacher *Those things are all true. I did choose these combinations because they're neighbor number facts. These are some of the same facts we worked on yesterday. I'll bet some of you already know the answer to 3 + 4.*

Children *I know that one!*
It's 7!

Teacher *If you didn't happen to know that one by heart, how could you figure it out?*

Jesse *You could count on, like 4—5, 6, 7.*

Teacher *That's true. Can anyone think of another way?*

Ethan *You could say a double, like we did yesterday. You could say, 3 + 3 = 6 and then it's just 1 more, so it's 7.*

Teacher *That's the strategy I'd like you to practice today. Let's go through the whole top line like that, naming the related double first and then adding or subtracting 1. Counting on is definitely a reliable strategy, but the method Ethan just explained helps you practice the doubles and can also be a little faster, especially when you're working with larger numbers, like 8 + 7.*

When you reach the second part of the chart, distribute the tile and have your students build each pair of related addition and subtraction facts. Discuss the results.

Session 21 Scout Them Out 4 (cont.)

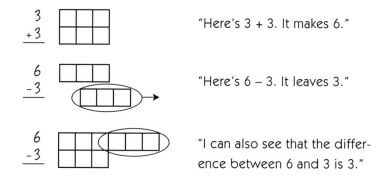

$$\begin{array}{r} 3 \\ +3 \\ \hline \end{array}$$ "Here's 3 + 3. It makes 6."

$$\begin{array}{r} 6 \\ -3 \\ \hline \end{array}$$ "Here's 6 – 3. It leaves 3."

$$\begin{array}{r} 6 \\ -3 \\ \hline \end{array}$$ "I can also see that the difference between 6 and 3 is 3."

Andrew *It's like I've been saying. If you know that 3 + 3 = 6, then you know the answer to 6 – 3. It has to be 3!*

Eloise *The next one works the same; 5 + 5 = 10, so 10 – 5 has to be 5.*

Briana *These are kind of like opposites. It's like you put them together and then take them apart.*

Joseph *Taking away half is really easy if you know the doubles.*

Gavin *I know the doubles up to 7 + 7. After that, it gets harder.*

Teacher *I think it's that way for lots of kids. We'll just keep practicing.*

After you have worked through the entire chart with your students, show the overhead transparency of Scout Them Out 4. Model as much of the sheet as you think is necessary before you send your students out to do their own.

Overhead 3.14

Scout Them Out 4, Addition

1. Circle all the doubles in blue. Then take a pencil and go back and do them.
2. Circle all the neighbor number facts in red. Then take a pencil and go back and do them.

7	9	9	10	3	8	9
+ 7	+ 9	+ 10	+ 9	+ 4	+ 8	+ 8

3	7	6	10	6	5	5
+ 3	+ 8	+ 7	+ 10	+ 6	+ 5	+ 6

5	8	8	2	3	4	9
+ 4	+ 7	+ 9	+ 2	+ 2	+ 4	+ 9

Scout Them Out 4, Subtraction

1. Circle all the halves in blue. Then take a pencil and go back and do them.
2. Circle all the doubles in red. Then take a pencil and go back and do them.

6	6	10	10	12	12	9
– 3	– 6	– 5	– 10	– 6	– 12	– 9

4	4	18	18	8	8	2
– 4	– 2	– 9	– 18	– 4	– 8	– 1

Session 21 Scout Them Out 4 (cont.)

WORK PLACE NOTES

As children finish checking their sheets with one another, have them get their folders and go out to Work Places.

HOME CONNECTION 11

Activity Crossing the Pond (Blacklines HC 11.1–11.3, pp. 45–47)
Worksheet Leapfrog Subtraction (Blacklines HC 11.4–11.5, pp. 48–49)

The homework activity for this week gives children a chance to practice subtraction facts by playing Crossing the Pond with their parents and completing a worksheet titled Leapfrog Subtraction.

Blackline HC 11.1 Use after Unit 3, Session 21.

Home Connection 11 ★ Activity

Crossing the Pond

You'll need 16 beans, buttons, coins, or other small markers in 2 different colors to play this game (e.g., 8 black beans and 8 white beans, or 8 white buttons and 8 brown buttons).

Game Rules

1 After you find something to use for game markers, decide who will play with which set. Then place your "frogs" on the lily pads below the pond. You can place more than 1 frog on a lily pad. The object is to be the first to get all 8 of your frogs across the pond to safety. The way you get them across is to spin both spinners and subtract. If, for instance, you spin a 12 and a 4, you subtract the 4 from the 12 for an answer of 8.

If you have a frog sitting on the number 8 lily pad, you get to move him across the pond. The trick in this game is to know the best places for your frogs at the start of the game.

2 Keep playing back and forth until one player has managed to get 4 of his or her frogs across the pond to safety. At that point, either or both of the players can move their remaining frogs to different lily pads if they want to.

3 Continue taking turns and moving frogs across the pond whenever possible. The first player to get all of his or her frogs across the pond is the winner. Can you use your experiences from this game to place your frogs when you start the next game? Which differences seemed to come up most often on the spinners?

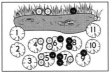

Note You can only move 1 frog at a time. If you have 2 frogs on 8 and spin 10 – 2, you can only move 1 of your frogs.

Child *It landed on 10 – 2. That's 8. I have a "frog" on 8 so I can move it!*

Blackline HC 11.4 Run back-to-back with HC 11.5.

NAME _____

DATE _____

Home Connection 11 ★ Worksheet

Leapfrog Subtraction

See how fast you can leapfrog around this sheet with your crayons and pencil to practice the different subtraction strategies we've learned.

Circle with blue all the Subtract 2's on the sheet. Then take your pencil and go back and do them. (***Example*** *16 – 2*)

Circle with red all the Subtract Halve's on the sheet. Then take your pencil and go back and do them. (***Example*** *12 – 6 or 14 – 7*)

Circle with green all the Takeaway 10's on the sheet. Then take your pencil and go back and do them. (***Example*** *14 – 10 or 19 – 10*)

Circle in purple all the Runaway 1's on the sheet. Then take your pencil and go back and do them. (***Example*** *13 – 3 or 17 – 7*)

And now—see if you can use the ones you've circled and solved to help you figure out the rest!

10	15	14	14	14	13	19
– 2	– 2	– 7	– 6	– 8	– 3	– 9

11	15	16	17	18	17	19
– 2	– 5	– 8	– 8	– 8	– 10	– 2

13	18	14	10	11	18	19
– 2	– 9	– 4	– 5	– 5	– 10	– 10

(Continued on back.)

Session 22

PROBLEMS & INVESTIGATIONS

Scout Them Out 5 Adding 10's & 9's; Subtracting 10's & Run Away 1's

Overview

In this session, students work from two sets of facts they've encountered before—adding and subtracting 10's. Hopefully, the idea that 10 + 5 = 15 has become fairly familiar and comfortable for many children in your group. Students who are able to see this can often jump to adding 9's with relative ease, reasoning that if 10 + 5 = 15, then 9 + 5 will be 14 because it's one less. In many cases, students actually imagine "moving 1 from the 5 to the 9, which would make it 10 + 4, which is 14." In this session, we will present a visual model that makes use of this imagery. By now, too, the idea that 15 – 10 = 5 may have become second nature to some of your students. In this session, we'll ask them to consider what happens when you remove the units instead of the 10.

You'll need

★ Ten-Strips (Overhead 3.16)

★ translucent game markers in blue and red, 10 of each

★ Scout Them Out 5 (Overhead 3.15)

★ 3 overhead pens, 1 blue, 1 red, and 1 black

★ Scout Them Out 5 (Blackline 3.35, run a class set)

★ blue and red crayons or colored pencils

★ regular pencils

Skills

★ generating addition and subtraction strategies

★ building visual models of addition and subtraction

★ exploring the relationships between addition and subtraction

★ practicing addition and subtraction facts

To open the session, display the Ten-Strips transparency on the overhead. Ask children to share any observations they may have with their neighbors and then with the group.

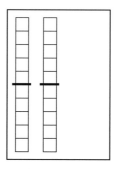

Session 22 Scout Them Out 5 (cont.)

Teacher *We are going to use this picture to help look at some more addition and subtraction facts today. What do you notice about it?*

Hiroki *I see 5 on the top and 5 on the bottom of each row.*

Colby *There are 10 in each row going up and down.*

Teacher *10 in each column?*

Colby *Yes.*

Rob *There are 20 in all. It's like 10 plus 10.*

Whitney *Or it could be like 5 plus 5 plus 5 plus 5. That's 20!*

Once children have had a chance to look over the picture of the ten-strips, start filling in the boxes with game markers to illustrate the operations of adding 10 to a number and then adding nine to the same number (e.g., 10 + 7 and 9 + 7). Ask children to discuss the visuals as you go. Solicit comments and observations about both operations and the relationship between the two.

Teacher *Great observations! What if I put 10 red counters on this side and seven blue counters on the other, like this?*

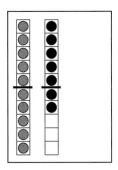

Children *It's 17!*
10 plus 7—17!
5, 10, 15, 16, 17.
The whole thing is 20—if you take away 3 you know there are 17 left.

Teacher *So, I have made a picture of 10 + 7. Do you agree?*

Children *Yes!*

Teacher *What if I changed this picture to show 9 + 7, like this?*

Session 22 Scout Them Out 5 (cont.)

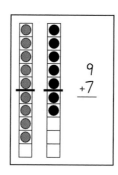

Peter *It would just be 1 less—16!*

Teacher *How do you know?*

Peter *Nine is one less than 10, so the answer has to be 1 less.*

Teacher *Is there anything else about the picture that could help you see that the total is 16 now?*

Susannah *If you move 1 over, it's 10 plus 6.*

Teacher *Can you show us what you mean, Susannah?*

Susannah *Sure.*

If you move 1 over from the 7 to the 9, you have 10 plus 6, and that's easy—it's 16.

Teacher *Oh, I see. So you've changed the problem from one that adds a 9 to one that adds a 10 instead?*

Susannah *Yes. I always do that when I add 9's—it's easier.*

Session 22 Scout Them Out 5 (cont.)

Take time to work through several more examples at the overhead, such as
10 + 4 and then 9 + 4; 10 + 6 and then 9 + 6. While the idea of "moving 1" to
make a 10 when adding 9's won't make sense to every child right now, it's a
great strategy, and one that some of your students have probably developed
on their own. Other children may begin to understand the concept during
this session. For those who don't "get it" right away, the idea will be revisited
many times over in the Number Corner during the months of January and
February.

Once you've worked through several pairs of 10's and 9's, move to subtraction. The idea here is to build a teen number on the ten-strips at the overhead and then to examine what happens when you take away the 10 and
what happens when you take away the 1's.

> **Teacher** *Now that we've had a look at some addition facts, let's
> switch over to subtraction. Who'd like to come up to the overhead and
> build 14 on the ten-strips? Corey?*

> **Corey** *Do you want me to fill one side first? I could do 7 plus 7 instead.*

> **Teacher** *That's true. For now, though, I'd like everyone to see it as a
> 10 and four 1's. Can you set it up that way?*

> **Corey** *Sure.*

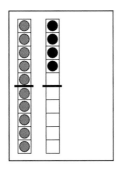

> **Teacher** *What would happen if we took 10 away from the 14 Corey
> has set up?*

> **Children** *Easy! There would be 4 left.*
> *That's easy to see. If you just covered up the red markers, there'd be 4
> blue ones left.*

> **Teacher** *What if we took the four 1's away instead?*

> **Children** *You'd have 10 left.*

> **Teacher** *Let's record what's going on here:*

Session 22 (cont.)

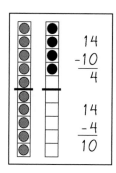

What do you notice?

Children *First you have 4 left and then you have 10 left.*
It's like opposites.
It's kind of like subtracting halves. If you know that 10 + 4 = 14, then
14 – 10 has to be 4.
If you take the 1's away, there's only a 10 left.

With the students' help, explore several more examples of subtracting 10's
and subtracting 1's at the overhead. (The children in one of our classes christened them the Take Away 10's and the Run Away 1's. Perhaps your students
will have their own names for these operations.) Examples might include
17 – 10 and 17 – 7, 15 – 10 and 15 – 5, 12 – 10 and 12 – 2, and so on.

Overhead 3.15

Scout Them Out 5, Addition

1. Circle all the +10's in blue. Then take a pencil and go back and do them.
2. Circle all the +9's in red. Then take a pencil and go back and do them.

10	9	9	10	9	10	9
+ 6	+ 6	+ 10	+ 1	+ 4	+ 7	+ 7

4	9	10	10	9	3	3
+ 10	+ 4	+ 7	+ 10	+ 9	+ 10	+ 9

10	9	10	9	10	9	4
+ 6	+ 5	+ 8	+ 8	+ 2	+ 2	+ 9

Scout Them Out 5, Subtraction

1. Circle all the Take Away 10's in blue. Then take a pencil and go back and do them.
2. Circle all the Run Away 1's in red. Then take a pencil and go back and do them.

16	16	15	15	13	13	9
– 10	– 6	– 10	– 5	– 10	– 3	– 9

11	11	17	17	10	14	16
– 10	– 1	– 10	– 7	– 10	– 10	– 10

15	16	12	20	19	12	19
– 5	– 6	– 2	– 10	– 9	– 10	– 10

Session 22 (cont.)

Finally, show the overhead transparency of Scout Them Out 5 (shown on the previous page), and model as much of the sheet as you feel is necessary before children go out to do their own work.

WORK PLACE NOTES

As children finish checking their sheets with one another, have them get their folders and go out to Work Places.

Sessions 23 & 24

ASSESSMENT

Which Addition & Subtraction Combinations are Easiest for You Now?

Overview

In this session and the next, children retake the 4-minute timed addition and subtraction tests they took at the beginning of this unit. Again, you'll encourage them to find and do the problems that seem easiest first, only going back to the others if they still have time. Analyzing the results and comparing them with the first set of tests may provide you and your students one way to see some of the growth that has taken place over the past 5 weeks.

For Session 23, You'll need

★ Addition Assessment sheets (Blackline 3.1, run a class set)

★ pencils and erasers

★ the Addition Assessments your students took at the beginning of the unit

For Session 24, You'll need

★ Subtraction Assessment sheets (Blackline 3.4, run a class set)

★ pencils and erasers

★ the Subtraction Assessments your students took at the beginning of the unit

Skills

★ practicing addition and subtraction combinations to 20

★ discovering number patterns

★ looking at how addition and subtraction facts relate to one another

★ thinking about which addition and subtraction facts seem easier than others and why

Start the lesson by reminding children about the addition and subtraction tests they took at the beginning of this unit. Now that they've been studying and practicing addition and subtraction facts for several weeks, you're going to ask them to take the tests over—one today and one tomorrow. As before, they'll have four minutes to work on each test, and rather than going from the top to the bottom of the sheets, fact by fact, *they'll need to scan through and do the easiest ones they can find first. If they have more time after that, they can go back and tackle some of the combinations that seem harder.*

Sessions 23 & 24 Which Combinations are Easiest... (cont.)

For each of the two sessions: Distribute the papers, pencils, and erasers and make provisions for children to do their own work. *If the class addition and subtraction charts are still hanging on the wall, don't forget to put them away for now.* Have students put names and dates on their papers and begin at your signal. Let them work for four minutes and then ask them to stop. If you want to give them an opportunity to compare the work they just completed with the tests they took several weeks ago, distribute the papers they completed during Session 3 (or Session 6). Give them a few minutes to compare their "before" and "after" papers. Do they notice any differences?

Second graders are often very concrete, and may want to count up the numbers of facts they were able to complete each time around. You may also want to point out the types of facts on each line. On the addition sheet, they'll find adding 0's, 1's, and 2's on the first two lines; adding 10's and 9's in rows three and four, and adding doubles and neighbor number facts the rest of the way down. On the subtraction paper, they'll see subtracting 0's, 1's, and 2's on the first two lines, doubles and neighbor numbers on the third line, halves and near-halves on the fourth line, 10's and 9's on the fifth line, and Run Away 1's on the sixth line.

Were students able to tackle any new types of combinations the second time around? Were they, for instance, able to add some of the 10's and doubles they didn't get to before? On the subtraction test, were they able to cope more quickly with the halves and 10's? While it's possible that there will be a few children for whom little will have changed on either test, most will be able to see some improvement, especially on the addition assessment. Children who were able to complete all 42 of the facts within four minutes the first time around may realize that things felt easier this time; perhaps they completed their papers even more quickly.

In any event, it's very important for students to realize that they will continue to practice these addition and subtraction facts throughout the rest of the year. The charts will stay up on the wall. Even as you move into units on geometry, money and place value, measuring, statistics, and probability, they'll continue to practice their facts to 20. The Number Corner and the Home Connections assignments will provide opportunities to develop strategies and internalize combinations for months to come. This is only the beginning!

Looking at Children's Work

◀ ASSESSMENT TIPS

Here are some things to consider before you place these pairs of papers in children's work sample files.

1. Which facts have been completed? Do you see changes from the first to the second sheets? Has the child progressed from simply adding or subtracting the 0's, 1's, and 2's to dealing with the 10's, doubles, and some of the neigh-

Sessions 23 & 24 (cont.)

bors as well? Are the children who could add and subtract 10's before able to deal with 9's now?

2. As you look over the second set of sheets, is there any sense that your students have begun to see relationships between some of the combinations? We deliberately set up the sheet to make this possible. 9 + 5, for instance, sits right beside 10 + 5. Children who know the answer to 10 + 5 and see the relationship between the two will often do both. Children who have little or no sense of the relationship between facts may do the 10's and not touch the 9's. On the subtraction sheet, near-halves, such as 12 – 7, are placed beside halves like 12 – 6. Have children done these in pairs? If so, they may be seeing the connection now.

3. How many out of the 42 were completed correctly the first time around? What about the second time around?

 WORK PLACE NOTES

For both sessions: As children finish comparing their "before" and "after" tests, have them get their folders and go out to Work Places. Although these are the last two sessions in Unit 3, you will probably want to keep this round of Work Places going through the first week of Unit 4. After a week or so of geometry instruction, you'll transition into the next set of Work Places.